TIME
REMEMBERED

A Woman's Story of World War II

Gwen Evans Pilkington

GSPH

Published by

GENERAL STORE
PUBLISHING HOUSE

1 Main Street Burnstown, Ontario, Canada K0J 1G0
Telephone (613) 432-7697 or (613) 432-9385

ISBN 0-919431-66-6
Printed and Bound in Canada.

Layout and Design by Gerry Langill

General Store Publishing House gratefully acknowledges the assistance
of the Ontario Arts Council.

Canadian Cataloguing in Publication Data

Pilkington, Gwendoline, 1923-
    Time Remembered: a women's story of World
War II

ISBN 0-919431-66-6

  1. World War, 1939-1945--Women--Biography.
2. Military wives--Canada--Biography. 3. Military
wives--England--Biography. 4. World War,
1939-1945--Personal narratives, Canadian.
I. Title.

D811.5.P45 1993 940.53'15042'0971 C93-090499-0

First Printed September 1993

This book is dedicated to Tony and all the brave young airmen who willingly risked their futures in the cause of freedom. And to the wives, sweethearts, and parents who waited patiently, but too often, in vain.

To Nan, my gratitude for her invaluable input.

TIME REMEMBERED IS GRIEF FORGOTTEN

For winter's rains and ruins are over
And all the seasons of snow and sins;
The days dividing loves and lovers
The light that loses, the night that wins
And time remembered is grief forgotten.

And frosts are slain and flowers begotten,
And in green underwood and cover,
Blossom by blossom,
The spring begins.

From Atlanta in Calydon, a drama written in 1865 by Algernon Charles Swinburne.

CHAPTER I

The haunting train whistle shattered the still winter air and penetrated into the swaying Pullman cars of the Ocean Limited. A few moments earlier the porter rang the bell of the compartment and called out, "Seven o'clock, Miss, we'll be in Halifax in an hour. You'll just have time for breakfast."

Jocelyn knew there was no more time for lying in the comfort of her darkened berth musing over the wonderful prospect that soon she would be with Kit. She rubbed the sleep from her eyes, leaned up on one elbow, raised the blind a few inches and surveyed the white Maritime countryside. It was February 1944, yet the sight of trees and fields clothed in sparkling white snow came as a surprise. When she and her sister, Carol, boarded the train in Montreal the previous day, the city was in the grip of a pre-spring thaw which removed every vestige of snow and reduced the streets to a depressing state of muddy channels of running water mixed with sodden sand—a typical depressing Montreal January scene.

This may be the last time I ever see a white winter, Jocelyn considered ruefully. Kit had told her that snow rarely fell in England and when it did it melted very quickly. Reluctantly, she left the wide picture window, crawled out of the berth, shoved her toes into her slippers and moved unsteadily to the tiny corner sink. As the train jerked along, she managed to have a refreshing sponge-down before getting dressed.

She hoped that the loosely fitting green wool maternity jumper, plus a fur coat, would conceal the fact that it was a mere two and a half months before her baby was due. The rules governing wartime passages to Britain were very specific in stating that no captain could knowingly agree to transport anyone who was more than three months pregnant. One of the reasons for this ruling was that there would not likely be a doctor on board. Ever since receiving news of her passage to England Jocelyn harboured a gnawing fear that when the authorities in Halifax realized her condition they would refuse to allow her to sail.

She forced these depressing thoughts from her mind, pulled back the dark green curtain of Carol's berth and gave her sister a gentle shake. "Wake up, sleepy head. We're nearly there and we won't get any breakfast if we don't get a move on."

A good-natured grumble was her reply. But Carol, too, was soon up and dressed, whisking a brush through her shiny auburn hair. Both girls bore a wholesome, natural prettiness. There was no detectable family resemblance between them.; Jocelyn's dark hair framed a heart-shaped face with high cheek bones which, with her brown eyes, had come from her father, while Carol had inherited their mother's smooth cameo features and oval blue grey eyes. Jocelyn was the younger by eight years, yet it was she who did all the worrying for them, got them places on time, made decisions on what was to be done when and how.

It was only by some strange quirk of fate that they were embarking on this hazardous wartime journey to England together to join their British husbands, both pilots in the Royal Air Force. Jocelyn's husband, Flight Lieutenant Kit Ford, and Carol's husband, Flight Lieutenant Dennis Carter, had spent the past two and a half years in Medicine Hat, Alberta, as flying instructors at No. 34 Service Flying Training School, one of several such establishments set up in Canada to train World War II air crew at a safe distance from the war zone.

Jocelyn and Carol were born and raised in Medicine Hat, a small prairie oasis nestled on either side of the banks of the South Saskatchewan River. The town was founded in 1883 on a huge field of natural gas, a fact which prompted famous visitor, Rudyard Kipling, to say that it had 'all hell for a basement'.

Jocelyn met Kit at an Officer's Mess dance in May of 1941. He was no dashingly handsome Romeo, but his broad white smile, his wavy blond hair, his twinkling blue eyes, his straight shoulders and his slim build reminded Jocelyn of her favourite movie star, Leslie Howard.

Kit claimed that he simply fell in love with Jocelyn the moment he spotted her across the dance floor chatting with one of his fellow officers, and he lost no time in going over to ask for an introduction. From then on they had no time for anyone else. They became engaged in the summer, despite Jocelyn's parents' strong pleas that they should wait until the war was over. After all, Jocelyn's mother argued, Jocelyn was only 18 and Kit only just past his 21st birthday. They could afford to wait a year or two. Besides, Jocelyn was to go to university in the fall.

But they were not to be dissuaded, and they planned a wedding for Christmas day, 1941, so that as many as their friends and Jocelyn's relatives could be present.

A guest at the reception tactlessly commented on the lovely double string of cultured pearls Kit had given Jocelyn for a wedding present. "Pearls are tears, Jocelyn. Aren't you tempting fate?"

She laughed lightly and squeezed the hand of her blond husband more tightly between her fingers. As if Kit would ever make her unhappy. He was the most gentle, considerate person she had ever known. Daft superstition!

It was only after their honeymoon in the Rockies and he had resumed his flying duties that she became obsessed with the notion that they had no time to waste. It trailed her like an insidious shadow and would not be dismissed. It was the only blight on their two happy carefree years spent on the sun-drenched prairies of southern Alberta where the horrors of war were confined to what one read in the newspapers, saw on newsreels, or heard on the radio.

They simply put these realities in the back of their minds and concentrated on making the best of the time they had before Kit would have to return to England for operational duty.

Kit was such a happy, fun-loving person. Like Jocelyn, he loved dancing and they never missed either a Mess party or one of the five formal balls held in the town each year, starting with the Armistice ball in November and ending with the I.O.D.E. ball in the spring.

They enjoyed a busy social life, entertaining other officers and their wives to dinner and cocktail parties, invitations which were reciprocated. Kit was a gifted photographer and spent a great deal of time taking magical pictures of the prairies and the mountains of Alberta in different seasons. He loved his job as an instructor and he was well liked by everyone, and especially by the student pilots he trained who always presented him with a special gift when they received their wings.

Even his batman, a small London cockney called Charlie, was under his spell. He told Jocelyn," 'e's a fine fellow is Flight Lootenant Ford. You're a lucky gel to be getting 'im for a 'usband'." Jocelyn didn't have to be told that. She knew he was the finest of all the officers at 34 S.F.T.S., in fact probably of the whole of the R.A.F.

But their blissful insulation from reality could not last forever, and in July 1943 Kit was posted to Charlottetown, Prince Edward Island, where he was to take a General Reconnaissance Course in preparation for operational duty in Coastal Command. Jocelyn accompanied him to Charlottetown, and there they spent another happy nine weeks while he took his training.

On his days off, weather permitting, they went on picnics to the beautiful P.E.I. beaches; they rented bicycles to discover the interesting sights of the Island, and when Kit was working, Jocelyn would go with another R.A.F. wife to explore the old graveyards which dated back to the earliest days of settlement. Jocelyn's only complaint about their stay there was that it rained too much.

In late September, when Kit graduated, he was posted to the Bahamas where he would be flying the huge Liberator bombers. Unfortunately, Jocelyn was pregnant and, because she had already had one ill-fated pregnancy, they decided that Kit should try to get his posting changed to England where Jocelyn could join him. The doctor had assured her that 'lightning would not likely strike twice in the same place', but just in case it did, she would have Kit's parents to rely on.

After leaving Charlottetown they went to Greenwood, Nova Scotia, where Carol's husband was training on the new light bomber, the Mosquito, prior to his return to Britain.

On the crisp sunny autumn mornings they helped the farmer with whom Carol was boarding to harvest the apple crop, and Kit went off to the Mess with Dennis to have a look at the famous Mosquito bomber. This aircraft was made of wood and was very light and fast. Kit was delighted when Dennis took him up for a trial flight.

After this happy reunion with Carol and Dennis, Kit and Jocelyn travelled to Montreal where Jocelyn stayed with relatives while Kitt went to Ottawa to persuade R.A.F. officials to change his posting from the Bahamas to England. If he was granted his request, Jocelyn could wait in Montreal, staying with a cousin, until her name came up on the passenger list for England.

Kit was successful in his endeavours and in mid-October he left Montreal for the airforce manning depot in Moncton, New Brunswick. Jocelyn travelled from Montreal just to spend a day with him before he left for England. She would never forget the black despair that enveloped her as she bade him good bye on Moncton Station on a rainy October night in 1943. On the station platform Kit did his best to comfort her, trying to persuade her that she would be on her way to join him before she knew where she was. But that awful premonition, no time to waste, inured her to his efforts. She boarded the train and prepared for bed, but she could not stop the tears from streaming down her cheeks. She knew it was silly. Kit was right, of course. She could go to England to join him. But then she would remember that she would likely not be allowed on a ship after her third month of pregnancy and the dark despair would touch off another flood of tears.

Ironically, when Kit arrived in England, he found to his dismay that Air Ministry had mislaid his records. He sat at home in Repton, Derbyshire, where his parents lived, for 16 miserable weeks before his badgering of the authorities in London finally bore fruit. He was then posted to a base in Scotland for training on twin-engined Beaufighters in preparation for operational duty in Coastal Command.

Meanwhile, Jocelyn waited impatiently in Montreal, eventually with Carol, who joined her in late November when Dennis returned to England for operational duty. She prayed for a passage before the expiry of the three month time limit imposed on pregnant wives. Finally, in late February 1944, she admitted defeat and made plans to return to her parents' home to await the birth of the baby, after which she would reapply for a passage.

Two days before she was due to take the train for the West, by some miraculous intervention of fate, or some bureaucratic blunder (she neither knew nor cared which) she received a telephone call advising her that she had a passage to England. She was to report to Halifax the following Friday, the very day she would have left for the West. She was horrified at the thought that she might already have left Montreal before that wonderful call came .

Later that day another call came, this time for Carol, giving her the same instructions. Jocelyn was almost speechless with joy. She had taken the message because Carol was filling in time doing some supply teaching in Montreal while awaiting her passage.

"Oh, how wonderful!" she said to the man relaying the message, adding, "That's my sister, you know."

The man laughed and said, "How nice for you."

Jocelyn hung up the telephone and bounded up the stairs two at a time to tell cousin Margaret, who cautioned her to be careful or she would fall downstairs and lose her baby.

When Carol got home that day, they sat in their cousin's living room, marvelling at their good luck. They had said so often how wonderful it would be if they could go to England together, never dreaming that it would come to pass. Their names had gone on the shipping list at least a month apart, because Kit had returned home that much earlier than Dennis.

That evening, they called their mother and father to tell them the good news. Although they were very disappointed that Jocelyn was not coming home to have their grandchild, they were happy that the two girls would be travelling together.

Their sister, Connie, a Lieutenant in the American Army Nurse Corps was stationed in Pasadena, California, and was awaiting an overseas posting. Later in the evening they put in a call to her. They hoped that she would be coming to England but, unhappily, she told them that she was destined for the far east.

Now on this cold winter morning, which marked the end of their two-day journey from Montreal to Halifax, Jocelyn was sitting on the edge of her berth reading a book while Carol searched for a missing earring and a shoe. The lost having been found, they went out into the draughty corridor to join the long queue for breakfast.

Jocelyn was pretty well over her bouts of morning sickness, but even before they inched their way to the front of the lineup, she had lost all interest in food. When finally seated at a table bedecked with a spotless white table cloth and shining silver flatware, she disappointed the dining car waiter by asking for a pot of tea and a serving of brown toast. Carol, on the other hand, tucked into what she lamented would likely be her last batch of her favourite waffles smothered in butter and Canadian maple syrup.

After breakfast, there was just enough time to gather up their small pieces of luggage before the train slowly drew into Halifax station. It was drab and grimy in the early morning light. Outside, the clean white snow that had brightened the surrounding countryside gave way to a cinder-coated, soot-filled mixture which blended with the decrepit old buildings and heavy slate grey sky.

As they left the train, Jocelyn shivered beneath the folds of her fur coat. Actually, it was Carol's. They had traded in the hope that, since it was more loosely fitting than Jocelyn's, it would better conceal her pregnancy.

"What a miserable place," Jocelyn muttered through her teeth, as she surveyed the cold inhospitable scene. The dampness penetrated right through to her bones.

Other passengers who had also just detrained were jostling one another as they frantically tried to commandeer taxis. Jocelyn urged Carol to get into line while she stood guard over their bags.

Finally, the driver of a battered old Ford urged them to get into the back of his taxi while he stacked their luggage in the trunk and then took off in a series of jerks and bumps in the direction of the Lord Nelson where they intended to stay the night.

Unfortunately, they had not booked a room and the desk clerk told them there were none available. He offered them some names and addresses of people who rented rooms for a night and they took off immediately to try to find something. The first place they visited, a ramshackle unpainted two-storey house owned by an unkempt, obviously tipsy landlady, discouraged them from looking further. She insisted on them giving her a week's rent in advance, assuring them that no convoys left Halifax at weekends. They declined her offer.

On their way back to the Lord Nelson, they wondered aloud how she could have known that they were going on a convoy. They had been warned several times not to advise anyone what their plans were. Jocelyn had not even told Kit that she was coming to England rather than going back home.

Back at the hotel desk they once more asked for a room and when the clerk repeated that there were none available Jocelyn said, "All right, we'll just sleep here in the hotel lounge."

He gave her a withering look, went back to his records, and quite miraculously a room just became available.

Jocelyn spent a very restless night, dreaming alternately of being met at the Halifax docks by an irate captain who would not take her on his ship, and of being held tightly in Kit's arms as he welcomed her to Liverpool. At eight o'clock, she got out of bed, wakened her sister from her untroubled sleep, and urged her to get dressed to go down to breakfast.

The dining room was already filled with service men and women and it was clear from the lineup into the dining room that it would not be politic to linger over their meal. They got through as quickly as possible and returned to their room to pack up and get ready to leave the hotel for the docks.

After checking out, they found a cheerful cab driver who took them to the shipping office, where they met two other service wives who were to travel with them.

It was still bone-chillingly damp outside. Warming her hands before a pot bellied stove in the shipping office Jocelyn said that she preferred to suffer twenty degrees below zero on the prairie than this insidiously clammy, albeit much milder, clime.

When a bespectacled man at the desk advised them sternly not to talk to anyone about their departure, she and Carol exchanged wry looks. He apparently didn't know that the coming and going of convoys was general knowledge among Halifax landladies.

Jocelyn was worried that she had not let Kit know that she wasn't returning home. She decided to ask the R.C.A.F. officer who was there to see that they got aboard safely, "How will our husbands know we are arriving?"

"You needn't worry about that," Flying Officer Brooks replied. "They'll likely be advised by Air Ministry of your arrival so that they can meet you."

Carol said smugly, "I told you something like that would be arranged, didn't I?"

Jocelyn said, "Yes, you did, but I'm still not convinced."

Flying Officer Brooks came back from the steamy window where he had been watching for their transport. He announced, "Your taxi is here. It will take you down to the dock where you'll meet your other fellow passengers. Go right to the customs shed when you arrive and present your embarkation papers to the clerk." He held the door open for them and wished them a safe journey as they left.

They climbed into the cab with the two other wives they had already met. Rose Williams and Bertha Macleod were married to R.A.F. ground crew and had travelled to Halifax together from a small town in Ontario. This was their first excursion from home and they were shy, excited, and apprehensive. On their way to the docks Carol tried to engage them in conversation. They answered her in monosyllables, making it seem as though she were prying, so she quickly gave up.

CHAPTER 2

The mist thickened as they neared the waterfront, and it was several degrees colder when they stepped out of the taxi on to the wharf. Jocelyn was doubly thankful that she was wearing Carol's fur coat. It was an excellent buffer against the cold, and it did conceal her bulge better than her own would have done. Her nightmares in the hotel had made her more anxious than ever that she still might be turned away. She would not rest easily on that score until she was on board and well away from Halifax harbour.

She paid the cab driver while Carol went ahead into the customs shed. When she joined Carol she was surprised to see her talking to a petite blonde girl. They were standing apart from the larger group of people gathered about a small stove at the far end of the room.

As Jocelyn approached them, Carol called excitedly, "Joc, look who's coming with us!"

Jocelyn stared blankly.

Carol said, "Oh, of course, I forgot. You've never met Sheila. Her husband, Simon Barton-Holmes, was on the Mossy course with Dennis. We had some wonderful times together in Greenwood. I was just telling Sheila what an amazing coincidence it is that you and I are travelling together."

"I'm so glad to meet you," Jocelyn said, smiling at Sheila. "I should have recognized you from Carol's tales about your exploits while your husbands were flying but we hardly expected to find you here."

Sheila's broad lips did not part in a smile. She looked intently at Jocelyn and drawled, "It's so nice meeting you, Jocelyn. I've heard a great deal about you, too."

Her voice was soft and very low-pitched. Jocelyn was curious about the distinctly southern drawl. She didn't recall Carol saying that Sheila was an American from the south. In fact, she was certain that she was a Maritimer, born and bred. But she was every bit as attractive as Carol had described her. Her long shining blonde hair cascading over the soft brown fur of her beaver coat, and her wide violet eyes, made her look even younger than her twenty-two years. She has a disingenuous Alice in Wonderland look, Jocelyn decided, and wondered again about the southern accent.

Her musing was interrupted by a peremptory order to everyone to go outside as a tender was expected to arrive momentarily to take them out to their ship.

They trooped out and stood in small clusters on the dock to wait for the transport. While Carol and Sheila chatted about places and people unfamiliar to her, Jocelyn took stock of the other passengers. Two middle thirty-ish American newsmen, their hands dug well inside the pockets of their shabby trench coats, chewed furiously on cigars as they paced silently up and down the wharf. Rose Williams and Bertha Macleod stood chatting with three other wives and a dried up old lady of at least eighty winters. They were clustered around a short fat man in a merchant navy officer's uniform. He was being plied with questions and was relishing the limelight. With his chest puffed out importantly, he looked like a proud pigeon, which was peculiarly apt since his name was Dove.

One of the wives, Lucy Blake, a girl with scarlet lips and a flour-white face, asked him tremulously, "What are we waiting for now, Mr. Dove?"

"Well, m'dear," he answered patronizingly, "we 'ave to 'ave something to git us over to our ship, y'know. There'll be a tender along presently." He cupped his hand behind his elephantine left ear and exclaimed, "By Jove, I think I 'ear it now!"

He was right. A small launch soon emerged out of the mist and edged close to the wharf. The motor chugged quietly as the party, one by one, clambered aboard.

In the shuffle of getting into the tender, Jocelyn became separated from Carol and found herself beside the garrulous Mr. Dove. He was persistent in his efforts to engage her in conversation and wheezed odiously down her neck as he gave her his life history. It seemed he was retiring from the Merchant Navy after forty years service and was returning to Britain to live on his 'bit of a pension'.

Jocelyn listened half attentively, glad that she didn't have to make conversation herself. She was feeling the ill effects of her restless night and the gnawing anxiety that she might still be turned back when she came face to face with the ship's captain.

As Dove chattered on, hugely enjoying the sound of his own voice, the launch glided noisily but cautiously across the misty grey water, bypassing large freighters and heading straight for the Bonaire, the vessel that was to take them to England.

Jocelyn had not expected anything rivalling the dimensions of the Queen Mary, but she gazed upon the Bonaire with astonishment. It was so small! Surely that tiny boat was not meant to withstand the angry winter moods of the Atlantic. It was wartime, of course, and she knew that almost anything that could float was being used to transport desperately needed supplies to Britain. But surely this was more than an act of faith sending them in this tiny tub.

Suddenly, Mr. Dove took hold of her elbow, giving it an irritatingly familiar squeeze. "Well, there she is," he wheezed. "What d'you think of 'er?"

Jocelyn didn't know much about ships but she replied, "It seems a bit small for such a big ocean?"

Dove looked upon her with smug indulgence. "Aye, she is that all right—only three thousand tons. But she's a game little ship. A tropical freighter she was; belonged to the Germans." He put his head so close to Jocelyn's that his dripping sandy mustache almost touched her ear and she instinctively recoiled. He paid no mind but went on, "I've a bit of secret gen about 'er," he whispered hoarsely. "She was running the Caribbean, and the Dutch confiscated 'er at the outbreak of war. In Curacao, it was. Not without a bit of a struggle, mind." He puffed inexpertly on the cigar the American newsman had given him, blowing the odious smoke into Jocelyn's face. Then, he lowered his cockney-accented voice again to a stage whisper which carried his message more effectively than if he had shouted it. "They tell me 'er last crossing was pretty rough indeed. Lost all 'er life boats, she did, and one of 'er crew. Aye, she's been through some rough times, 'as the Bonaire."

The cloak and dagger pose belied the gravity of his information, and Jocelyn had difficulty keeping her face straight. "I sincerely hope we have better luck on this voyage," she said.

"It's not that we'll 'ave to worry about," he replied gravely, shaking his grey-thatched head. "We're to 'ave the commodore of the convoy aboard. Do y'know what that means?"

Jocelyn confessed her ignorance. "Is he something of an ogre?" she asked lamely.

Dove emitted a wheezy chuckle. "That's a good one," he said. "No, m'dear. He's a very nice chap is Admiral Turle. Very nice indeed. What I was meaning was that ours is to be the flagship of the convoy - the prize package so to speak."

He noticed Jocelyn's puzzled expression with smug satisfaction, and puffed again on his cigar. He leaned forward and whispered, "Them Jerry subs will be pretty anxious to get us, by Jove."

His watery blue eyes reflected disappointment when Jocelyn smiled and commented, "But they'll have to find us first, and it looks to me as though it'll be like searching the Atlantic for the owl and the pussy cat in their pea green boat."

He gave her a pitying look and turned his attention to Lucy Blake who continued to listen to him with wide-eyed incredulity.

The tender reached its destination, stopped its engine and bounced gently on the water while waiting for the passengers to disembark. A rope ladder was tossed down by grinning Dutch seamen and everyone was urged to board the Bonaire. When it was her turn, Jocelyn was terrified that she might slip and fall into the icy sea. However. after some puffing, pushing and pulling, and cheering, she found herself safely on deck. She watched nervously as the frail Miss Gillespie successfully made the precarious ascent, followed by the portly Mr. Dove. When the last passenger was aboard, the sailors pulled up the ladder, stored it away, and the tender pulled away, turned around and headed back to the dockside.

They were all directed to the lounge which was below deck. It was a small, poorly lighted, low-ceilinged room with an unpleasant musty odour. A battered piano stood in one corner, most of its keys a dirty yellow colour, and some with no ivory at all. It looked like a wide grinning mouth full of bad teeth. An overstuffed bumpy leather couch stretched along the outer wall, and miscellaneous tables were scattered about the room. Other chairs, as uncomfortable as the couch, were placed at random, and one lone bookcase stood in the corner opposite the piano. It contained about a dozen battered dirty books.

Several ship's officers were in the lounge and they mingled in the crowd, but the only one Jocelyn could distinguish with any certainty was the all-important commodore of the convoy. Admiral Turle was as unmistakably British as the others were unmistakably Dutch. He was at least six feet four, Jocelyn gauged, and was meticulously dressed in his gold-encrusted navy uniform. The Dutch officers were, by comparison, small in stature and were more casually attired, some wearing white scarves instead of regulation black ties.

In the lounge the passengers were registered and assigned cabin mates. They were also given some rules which they must adhere to while aboard. After that they were taken on a tour of the small vessel which didn't take very long. Carol remarked that it was going to be much like living with the old woman in the shoe. The eleven passengers, the ship's officers, the captain, and commodore were to share the tiny lounge, a cramped dining salon, and a very small bathroom. The latter, since it was designated neither ladies nor gentlemen, must be meant for both, Carol correctly assumed.

Later, in the lounge, tea was served and an attempt was made to introduce everyone. A small gnome-like Dutch officer with deep-set twinkling blue eyes and a ruddy lined face strode over and sat down beside Jocelyn on the leather couch. She finally was persuaded that she was now in no danger of being turned back, so she felt no qualms when the officer joined her. However, she was surprised to learn that this unimpressive little man was none other than the skipper of the Bonaire, Captain Joe Maarleveld.

He crossed his short legs and lit a fresh cigar, noting with a sly grin the look of distaste on Jocelyn's face. She hated the smell of cigars and deliberately waved her hand to direct the smoke away from her face.

"Dere iss von ting you pregnant vomen must realize," the captain said pugnaciously. "Dere iss no doctor on dis ship. You haf come at your own risk."

It was such a relief to hear that there must be other pregnant women on board that Jocelyn felt like laughing out loud. Instead, she said defensively, "I'm sure we're all aware of that. I'm just happy to be going to join my husband."

The captain puffed on his cigar for a moment, then turned to her. "I like Canadians, you know. I'fe carried qvuite a few off you vomen, and dere iss von ting dat always puzzles me. Vy vould a Canadian girl vant to marry a damn Englishman, and vy, having committed such folly, she vould vant to follow him back to hiss cold, damp, bombed-out country. Dat chust doessn't make sense to me." He looked at her slyly under his bushy eyebrows, his blue eyes alight with mischief. "Doess it you?"

"Yes, it does," Jocelyn replied solemnly.

He roared lustily. "Vell, I'll do my damn best to get you safely over to your damn English husband den," he promised.

Jocelyn could only feel an enormous sense of relief that all of her fears had been groundless. A surge of happiness went through her whole body like an electric current, and for the first time since receiving the news of her passage she felt secure. She decided to get her coat from the cabin and then join Carol and Sheila, who, she learned from Dove, had already gone out on deck.

As she passed the open doorway of the cabin across the narrow hall from hers and Carol's, she saw Admiral Turle busy unpacking. He looked surprisingly approachable in khaki drill slacks and a faded open-necked shirt. Back in the lounge his gold-encrusted uniform had cloaked him in an aura of lofty dignity and aloofness.

Now, however, he gave her a warm smile and said, "So you are my neigbour. Is your cabin satisfactory?"

"Yes, quite adequate," she replied, returning his smile. She longed to ask him about the voyage. How many days it would take, for example, but she decided that it would be presumptuous. Mr. Dove was quite right though. Admiral Turle was indeed a very nice chap.

* * *

While the Bonaire's passengers familiarized themselves with their ship, the entire convoy of 36 ships was being lined up in formation in the safety of Halifax harbour awaiting orders to put to sea. As far as possible, the convoy would be well protected initially on its flanks and stern by the small but swift Canadian corvettes especially designed for that purpose. As Dove intimated, the commodore of the convoy was entirely responsible for the passage and he was often a senior retired Royal Naval officer who had returned to duty to serve his country in its dire need. His was the flagship of the convoy and had a preferred place in the front of the centre column of ships.

From the earliest days of the war these convoys of allied merchant ships whose deep hulls were laden with desperately needed commodities—food, war materials, and other vital supplies required by Britain—had plied their dangerous paths across the ocean. They represented most of the free western nations, and sailed under the aegis of the White Ensign. In this convoy were ships from Holland, Greece, Norway, and oddly enough, Sweden, a neutral country whose ships should have needed no protection beyond flying their own national flags.

The packs of German U-boats that hunted them down relentlessly in what was known as the Battle of the Atlantic, sent millions of tons of shipping to the bottom of the sea and many lives were lost. In fact, up until the end of 1942 the U-boats sank ships faster than the Allies could build them. Although by 1944, the German U-boat effort had been curtailed, it had not been stopped and crossing the seas was not a venture for faint hearts.

On this frosty foggy morning of February 27, 1944, Halifax harbour had been swept clear of any possible threatening mines, and the submarine gates that guarded the port were now opened to allow the convoy to get under weigh. At exactly ten o'clock, the flagship began plying its plotted path seaward. Following at short and exactly timed intervals, each of the ships in turn took its prescribed place in the line. When all were clear of the harbour, the signal flags from the commodore's ship ordered the long line of ships to break into shorter, more easily protected columns, and the Canadian corvettes assumed their all-important task of guarding the convoy as it plunged eastward across the glassy sea.

CHAPTER 3

The matchbox-size cabin that Jocelyn and Carol shared was overheated and airless, and Jocelyn hurriedly put on her coat and was about to leave. As an afterthought, she leaned over her bunk and struggled with the latch on the porthole until it sprung open admitting a fresh damp breeze which soon chased out the stale atmosphere. Satisfied, she went out on deck to find Carol.

She was standing alone at the ship's railing watching the rugged snow-covered shoreline fade into the mist. She turned to Jocelyn and said, "Do you realize that this is Mom's birthday and my first wedding anniversary?"

"No, it hadn't occurred to me," Jocelyn replied. "But what a nice anniversary present, to be on your way to join Dennis."

Carol leaned on the ship's railing, her chin cupped in her hands. "I was standing here remembering the heavenly honeymoon we had at Mount Temple," she said wistfully. "It was so breathtakingly beautiful in the Rockies. Every day the brilliant sunshine converted the unblemished snow into myriads of tiny diamonds, and a sapphire-blue sky framed the dark brooding peak of Mount Temple. The lodge was set on the mountain's rugged slopes, and in the evening there was always a roaring log fire and we would join the other guests and play silly games and tell jokes until Dennis would wink at me and we'd slip away to our own private world of love and contentment. Just remembering those blissful days makes me ache with longing to be with him. It will never be the same when we're in England. We'll have so little time to be together and there will always be that terrible reality that each time I see him could be the last."

"No doubt we'll be lucky to see much of the boys when we get over there," Jocelyn said. "But at least we'll be close enough for them to have flying visits. That's better than having an ocean separating us." She laughed lightly. "Our honeymoon was a riot. It was 40° below zero in Banff so we couldn't go out and the hotel was so charged with static electricity that every time we touched each other we got a shock - not very romantic but we had a good laugh over it."

Sheila was standing further down the deck in conversation with the Bonaire's First Officer, Willie Van Keekam. She was being prettily coy and was affecting the southern drawl that had puzzled Carol and Jocelyn back in Halifax. Carol decided that she must have acquired the accent when on a recent visit to an aunt in Virginia.

When the First Officer was summoned to duty Sheila came over to Carol's side. She smoothed her small tanned hand over her shining blonde hair and drawled, "Willie's a pet."

Carol grinned. "What sort? Tiger, or tomcat? He's old enough to be your father."

"But I like older men, in fact, I prefer them," Sheila said.

"Prefer them to whom?" Carol asked wryly, munching absent-mindedly on an apple that Dove had given her in the lounge.

Sheila tossed her head and said with a flick of bitterness, "Well, I'd prefer anyone to Simon Barton-Holmes right now." She rested her elbows on the railing, cupped her chin in her small hands and stared moodily out to sea. After a moment, she said, "Do you know what that cad did on our last night together in Canada?"

"No," Carol said. "What did he do?"

"There was I," Sheila went on, her mouth pouting prettily, "stuck all alone in that horrible pokey hotel room in Greenwood, while he went out with the boys and had a good time. Whenever I think of it, I get boiling mad all over again."

"Then why are you bothering to join him in England?" Carol asked dryly.

"First and foremost, I'm going to make him bear some of the burden of this child I'm carrying. He doesn't know about it yet. I didn't know myself until after he left for England. And then I want to meet his wierd family."

Jocelyn listened to Sheila in wonderment thinking what a strange girl she was. Then it suddenly occurred to her that she would soon be meeting Kit's relatives. He didn't have too many, being an only child. He hadn't talked too much about his parents when he was in Canada, and he didn't write many letters to them. Instead, he would send them a cable every few weeks assuring them that he was well and happy. Jocelyn had chastised him once about such callousness, and he blurted out that his most vivid recollection of his childhood was his parents quarrelling over him. The merry twinkle had left his eyes and his lips had set into such a firm line that she was reluctant to bring up the subject again.

His mother's letters to them were effusive in welcoming Jocelyn into the family and assuring her that they were longing to meet her. So, she became convinced that if his parents had not made his childhood a very happy one, they had changed now that he had grown up. She put his cabling idea down to one of his less practical habits such as tossing away his socks when they got a hole in them when they could have easily been mended. She took over the task of writing letters to the Fords and of sending them gifts on their birthdays and at Christmas and hoped that they were pleased with her efforts. Well, she would soon find out. Suddenly, she felt Carol nudging her.

"Jocelyn, wake up," Carol said. "Sheila asked you a question."

"Oh, I'm sorry. I was daydreaming. What was it you asked, Sheila?"

"I was just wondering where Kit is stationed. Simon and Dennis went to the same station when they returned to England."

"Yes, I knew that," Jocelyn replied, noting that Sheila had suddenly dropped the southern drawl. "That'll be convenient for you and Carol. You may be able to join forces as you did in Greenwood. I don't know exactly where Kit is at the moment, to tell the truth. In the last letter I had from him, he said he was being posted to some place in Scotland, heaven knows where. After he went back to England in October, he was home for sixteen weeks, because Air Ministry lost track of him. He finally bugged them sufficiently that they gave him a posting."

"Sixteen weeks!" Sheila exclaimed. "However did he manage that?"

"Manage is hardly the word. He hated every moment of it. He was anxious to get on an ops. station. But when he left Charlottetown he had his posting to the Bahamas changed for one to England and I guess you just don't do things like that where military bureaucracy is concerned."

"Why on earth didn't he want to go to the Bahamas?" Sheila asked.

"Its a long story. But, in short, we discovered that I was pregnant, and I didn't want to go somewhere I would have no family ties. The irony of it all is that now that I'm going to join him, he probably won't get any leave for a coon's age."

"Well, it looks as though we're all in the same boat, literally and figuratively," Sheila replied with no trace of a drawl. "You don't know where Kit is, and we don't know exactly where our husbands are. And despite what old Flying Officer Brooks said, I don't believe for one minute that they'll be advised of our coming."

"But they will," Carol protested. "He was very emphatic about it when Jocelyn asked him They'll be there at the docks, I'm sure."

Jocelyn shared Sheila's doubts. "But if they're not?" she asked worriedly. "What will we do? Where will we go?"

"Oh, I'll go out on a spree," Sheila said mischievously. "Willie told me that Liverpool is quite a place for fun and games."

"Seriously, Sheila, what will you do?" Jocelyn persisted. "Will you go to Simon's parents?"

"Good heavens, no. They're both dead, and his sister, Miggles, and his elder brother, Nicholas, are as mad as March hares from what Simon told me about them. That's one of the reasons I wanted to go to England. To meet them and see for myself."

"But where will you stay?" Jocelyn asked, still curious.

Suddenly Sheila's face assumed a sad, appealing expression, and her dark violet eyes brooded into space. She sighed heavily and drawled, "I don't really know. I expect Simon will dump me in some broken down old pub and forget all about me. In fact, when he learns I'm pregnant, he'll probably disown both me and the baby."

"In that case," Carol interposed, "you can bunk in with Joc and me. Provided we find somewhere to bunk in ourselves. I won't be staying with Dennis's family, that's for sure. His parents died not too long after their lovely old home in Liverpool was demolished in a bombing raid. They simply couldn't get over the shock of losing everything. And Dennis is an only child."

Sheila managed to look very forlorn and vulnerable as she said, "That's sweet of you, Carol."

However, Jocelyn was amazed when, in the next breath, Sheila dropped the 'poor little me' pose and said excitedly, "Say, that's given me a great idea. Why don't we find a place over there to live together. We could have a ball."

Before any discussion could take place on Sheila's 'great idea', a tuneless cowbell summoned them to lunch in the dining salon on the lower deck. Sheila was escorted to the centre one of the three massive round mahogany tables which completely filled the small room. She was delighted to be seated by the First Officer, Willie Van Keekam.

Jocelyn and Carol were placed with Admiral Turle and Captain Maarleveld. Also at their table was one of the American newsmen and Lucy Blake who looked as though she wished herself anywhere but on this boat.

Somewhere between the greasy roast duck and the too sweet fruit compote, Jocelyn begged Carol to trade places with her so that she could avoid watching the watery horizon appear and disappear in the porthole with nauseating regularity. Carol either had successfully attuned her system to roll in rhythm with the sea, or else she was immune to its dizzying effects.

After lunch, the warmth of the distant sun filtered through the mist without dissolving it, tempting many of the passengers out on deck. However, the gentle roll of the ship and the vibration of its engines had a generally soporific effect, and, one by one, they left the railing to stretch out on their narrow cabin bunks.

Carol stayed out until she saw Mr. Dove heading her way with a gleam in his watery blue eyes, at which point she ducked into the nearest doorway.

When he disappeared, she went to her own cabin where Jocelyn was curled up on her bunk with her eyes closed.

"Are you asleep?" Carol asked quietly.

Jocelyn opened one eye. "No, just dozing. What brought you in?"

"I caught sight of Dove winging my way like a hawk after a mouse, so I gave him the slip." She quickly changed out of her suit into green corduroy slacks and a yellow cashmere turtleneck sweater, then flopped on her own bunk.

"Have you seen Sheila?" she asked.

"She popped in a minute ago on her way to the lounge. I've been lying here trying to figure her out. One minute she's as tragic as Joan of Arc and the next she's as bubbly as a campus coed. Just what is she like, really?"

Carol shrugged. "She hasn't decided yet. It depends on whom she is with and where."

"She's like a chameleon," Jocelyn said.

Carol plumped up her pillow and lay back on it, her arms folded behind her head. "She's a good sort, really." Then changing the subject abruptly, she sighed and said, "Golly, it's so wonderful to relax after the hectic last week. I don't think I've slept properly since we heard about our passage, and I'm sure you haven't."

"You're right about that," Jocelyn agreed. "Well, we'll probably get lots of time to rest up on this trip. How long do you suppose it will take us to reach England?"

"Sheila said that Willie mentioned at least two weeks."

"Two weeks!" Jocelyn exclaimed. "Surely not." She felt the strange sense of panic well up within her once more—no time to waste. She swallowed hard to try to quell it. She must not start on that senseless round of introspection again. With some effort, she went on. "Oh, well, we mustn't grumble. At least we're on our way. Tell me more about Sheila. Does she really have such a low opinion of her husband?"

"She's hurt just now, and a bit confused. But I think she really loves him."

"What about Simon? Does he really love her?"

"It's hard to say. He's the type who really loves only one person and that's himself. He was certainly smitten with Sheila when they met, with her glamour and beauty. But he's like the fellow in the song, if he can't have the gal he loves, he'll love the gal who's near."

"What does he look like? I never met him when we visited you in Greenwood."

"He's a kind of blond Lawrence Olivier. Tall, tanned, athletic type, with curly blond hair and an intriguing cleft in his chin. He always wows the gals."

"Is Sheila jealous? Do you think that's part of the problem?"

"Not really. She's a bit of a flirt herself," Carol said.

"How complicated. What makes people mess up their lives like that do you suppose?"

Carol sighed. "We can't understand it because our own lives have always been so straightforward. Our parents have always set us a good example. Sheila's parents parted company when she was quite young and she and her brother were put in boarding schools while their mother and father went their separate ways. As for Simon, I know only what Sheila has told me and she does exaggerate a bit, but his parents seem to have been rather careless about their children's upbringing. Simon went to boarding school when he was eight. Wellington, I think it was. In any case, he has no particular faith and his morals are very elastic. The odd thing is that Sheila would probably be bored bilious with anyone as prosaic as our two loving husbands."

A knock on the cabin door ended this speculation on the Barton-Holmes and someone called in a high pitched sing-song voice, "Teatime please, ladies, teatime."

As Jocelyn opened the door, she caught sight of the tail end of a long white cotton coat disappearing around the corner of the deck. She closed the door and began brushing her hair before the mottled mirror above the tiny sink. "I'm ready for tea," she said. "Up you get, and let's find out where it's being served."

***

That first day aboard the Bonaire passed surprisingly quickly. The grey coastline and grimy buildings of Halifax harbour gradually faded from view and the Bonaire was soon surrounded by the other ships in the convoy. They were on their way at last. Jocelyn could feel only an immense sense of relief after the worrisome days prior to their embarkation. Even her concern that she would immediately be sea sick was quickly allayed. Thus far the sea had remained glassily calm and on deck the ship's movement was barely noticeable.

After their first dinner on board that evening, the small lounge soon filled up with people and smoke. Bertha Macleod and Rose Williams, like Siamese twins, were inseparable. They seemed ill at ease in other company and soon escaped from the lounge down to their cabin.

Sheila's room mate, Rhea Davis, was a pleasant girl if rather affected. She had a very pale complexion and pinky red hair. Her inch-long fingernails were varnished barnyard red, and her eyebrows had been plucked out and replaced by a long thin pencil arch. When she smoked, she did so with painful restraint, using a very long silver cigarette holder. She and Sheila got on very well together. In the lounge that evening they persuaded Willie to play the piano and the two American newsmen danced them around the tiny room, bumping into chairs, tables, and people alternately. Later, the newsmen played cribbage while Miss Gillespie and Mr. Dove scowled at each other over a rummy game, each grimly determined not to let the other win. Lucy Blake, the pasty-faced girl, quickly succumbed to the combined effects of the sea and the rich food, and apparently remained in her cabin.

Jocelyn and Carol were invited to play bridge with Admiral Turle and Captain Maarleveld. The game ended at ten o'clock when both men excused themselves to attend to their duties.

By eleven o'clock, everyone had retired. Only the acrid smell of tobacco smoke lingered, mingling unpleasantly with the musty odour of the lounge. When they awoke the next morning, they were well out to sea.

CHAPTER 4

Life on board the Bonaire quickly settled into a dull routine. Breakfast at 8:30; mid-morning tea served on the deck by the diminutive oriental steward with the sing song call: 'tea time, please, ladies'; lunch at 12:30; afternoon tea at 4:00, again on the deck; dinner at 7:00. All this activity was interspersed with strolls around the deck and rests in the cabins. The evenings followed much the same pattern as the first: Dove and Miss Gillespie fiercely playing rummy; Sheila and Rhea vying for Willie's attention; the two newsmen chewing their cigars and earnestly playing cribbage; and Jocelyn and Carol playing bridge with the captain and the admiral. It was monotonous, but it passed the time.

It was the days that were the most tedious. The routine of circling the small circumference of the deck for exercise was occasionally relieved by lifeboat drill or being able to watch the seamen at gunnery practice. The one activity that everyone joined in enthusiastically was the rumour game. Dove was its instigator. He was always passing on official secrets about the sightings of submarines or enemy aircraft and creating fear in the hearts of his audience, consisting mainly of the more gullible passengers, Miss Gillespie and Lucy Blake.

Because each day brought her that much closer to Kit, Jocelyn didn't mind the tedium of the journey. She still could not imagine how she got this passage when she had official word that her condition disqualified her. Equally miraculous was how Carol had been given a passage on the same boat. It could only have been a miracle, she decided.

Weather permitting, she spent her mornings sitting on a deck bench on the warmer side of the boat, a book or her diary on her lap and a pencil clutched awkwardly in her gloved fingers. At intervals, she would join Carol at the railing and they watched the porpoises flopping about playfully in the grey rolling sea. They usually stayed outside right from after breakfast until the weedy little Chinese steward in his voluminous white coat summoned them to 'tea time, please ladies'.

Jocelyn didn't have Carol's iron clad stomach, but so far she had not been seasick. So many of the other passengers were missing from meal times, but she and Carol were always present. Jocelyn found these intervals the most enjoyable of the trip. True, the food was swimming in grease and the unpleasant cooking odours, especially of cabbage and onions emanating from the galley, were enough to spoil anyone's appetite. But Jocelyn was fascinated by Captain Maarleveld, especially with his ill concealed dislike of the British people in general and of Admiral Turle in particular.

For his part, the Admiral kept his relationship with the wiry little Dutchman scrupulously polite and cool, never revealing by remark or gesture how he was affected by the captain's rudeness. Jocelyn admired his restraint, his impeccable manners, and his dignity. To her, he was like a character from Elizabethan England, a Drake or a Raleigh. Too tall for any of the ship's doorways and almost touching the ceiling of the lounge, he managed to fit his magnificent proportions in amongst that indifferent assemblage with ease and grace. He wore a monocle without the slightest affectation, and his large handsome weathered features betrayed signs of the long and arduous years of duty which his decorations told he must have spent in the Royal Navy. Jocelyn noticed, too, that while on duty he was aloof and constrained, off duty he was charming and courteous to everyone, and especially kind and friendly to herself and Carol. He addressed them both as Sister Sue.

Captain Maarleveld, on the other hand, was in perfect harmony with his ship. He was small, weatherbeaten and crude. His face was saved from being downright ugly by his mischievous cornflower blue eyes and crooked but engaging grin. His table manners were appalling and he flaunted them deliberately. To try to shock the ladies, he told crude stories and smoked his foul cigars at every meal, inconsiderately blowing the smoke into the faces of his table companions. When Jocelyn made a telling gesture by waving her hands in the air to divert the smoke from her face, he would mumble wickedly, "Bah! damn Canadian vomen, spoiled to the core, got no guts!'' And then he would pettily extinguish the offensive weed, only to light up again at the next meal.

By their fourth day at sea, Jocelyn found herself harbouring a strong dislike for him, not only because of his boorishness, but because of his constant goading of Admiral Turle. Nonetheless, his eccentricities did help to alleviate the boredom.

The weather, like the days, varied little. The light mist that marked the start of the journey stayed with them for two days, but suddenly lifted to give them a clear view of their sister ships; then, just as suddenly, the fog returned, enshrouding the convoy and making it seem as though the tiny Bonaire were the lone occupant of the wide expanse of ocean.

On the fifth day out, during lunch, the commodore was interrupted three times by one of his yeomen, who conversed with him in urgent whispers. After the third interruption, he excused himself and left the table.

Any break in the routine, no matter how trivial, was seized upon as fuel for Dove's rumour game, and he was soon reporting submarines half a league off and enemy aircraft hovering within half a mile. He was only slightly dashed when, later that day, the commodore himself announced that he expected a Canadian corvette from the convoy's escort group to come alongside the Bonaire sometime in the afternoon.

Long before corvette arrived, the deck was crowded and curious eyes were strained in all directions in the spaces between the other ships that surrounded the Bonaire. Even though it was a brilliantly sunny afternoon, few actually saw the well camouflaged craft until it was bouncing on the choppy sea parallel to the flagship.

The passengers and crew watched in mesmerized silence as a line was thrown between the Bonaire and the corvette, and a small white cylindrical package was despatched along it from the escort vessel. A British yeoman received it and handed it ceremoniously to the Admiral.

The Canadian sailors manning the corvette were hanging perilously from every part of their craft, seemingly stuck there by some mysterious gravitation. They waved and shouted to the Bonaire's passengers, and each group peered curiously at the other. Then, suddenly, the corvette manoeuvered adroitly around, and, with an amazing spurt of speed, it charged through the waves to rejoin the remainder of the escort group.

That evening even Lucy Blake was lured into the lounge to join in mulling over this event and making wild conjectures about possible contents of the corvette's message. The gravelly voice of Dove could be heard above all others reiterating with great authority, "There's more to it than meets the eye. You mark the words of an old sailor."He emphasized this pronouncement with a twitch of his sandy mustache and a sly look that insinuated that he did indeed know a great deal more than he was prepared to reveal.

On their way to bed that night, Jocelyn and Carol dropped in to see Sheila. She had retired early and was now propped up on her pillow wearing a pair of blue satin pyjamas. Her gleaming blonde hair was pinned up in an alluring upsweep and she was back to her Mona Lisa pose.

"Hi," she drawled. "I was hoping you'd come by. The thick atmosphere in the lounge drove me out."

"You didn't miss anything," Carol said, sitting on the bottom of Sheila's bunk. Jocelyn sat down on Rhea's.

"I was hoping that Willie might come in and give me some inside gen about that message," Sheila said. "Have you heard anything from the captain or the commodore?"

"They'd hardly confide in us," Jocelyn replied. "However, we might have asked that fountain of all knowledge, Mr. Dove."

Carol huffed. "All we'd get from him would be duff gen."

"I'm not so certain about that," Jocelyn said. "When he was talking to me in the lounge earlier, he said something that I don't think he made up."

Sheila quickly dropped her pose and her violet eyes gleamed with curiosity. "Do tell us, Joc. What did he say?"

"He told me that our Canadian escort group has gone back to Canada and, as of now, we have no protection until the British escort group arrives to take over."

"It's likely one of his daft rumours," Carol suggested.

"Perhaps," Jocelyn said, "but I had the oddest sensation when that corvette left this afternoon that we were being abandoned. It was a feeling I got once at the zoo, when I suddenly found myself alone and I couldn't see Mom or Dad, or indeed anyone in the family anywhere."

"Oh, Joc, you're just like Mom, always having ghastly premonitions," Carol said.

"Yes, and they often come to pass," Jocelyn countered. She suddenly was gripped by the terrible presentiment that she and Kit had no time to waste. With effort, she quelled the sensation and was about to suggest that they leave Sheila and go to bed when there was a firm rap on Sheila's door.

"Come in whoever you are; the door's unlocked," Sheila called out.

Captain Maarleveld opened it and stood in the doorway, his arms akimbo. He surveyed them for a moment, then snorted angrily, "Vell, I'll be damned! You damn stupid Canadian vomen! Vat are you doink gettink out off your clothes to go to bed? You know dat iss against the rules. And you two," he added, pointing to Carol and Jocelyn. "Vere iss your life jackets? Such disobedience. Ach!" He pointed his finger at Sheila then and barked, "Before you go to sleep tonight, Mrs. Barton-Holmes, you put on some clothes and lots of dem. You'd look damn silly floating in the ocean in dat outfit."

With that dire warning, he bounded out slamming the door behind him.

Sheila blinked. "Well, what do you suppose he ate for dinner that made him so liverish. He's never made a fuss about clothes before."

"No, he hasn't," Carol agreed, visibly shaken. "Perhaps you're right, Joc, about Dove's information being close to the truth."

"Well, whether or not," Jocelyn replied, "we'd better go to bed, and with our clothes on."

They said good night to Sheila and left.

CHAPTER 5

The night passed uneventfully. Jocelyn awoke the next morning surprised at how well she had slept. Then she realized something else. The familiar drone of the ship's engines had stopped and, except for rocking gently with the swell of the sea, they were not moving. What could be wrong?

By mid-morning, a nervousness as contagious as measles spread through the Bonaire and, until Dove came to the fore with another rumour, no one had even a hint as to what had suddenly brought the entire convoy to a halt. He had found out through devious means that a vessel situated three places behind the flagship, and flying neutral colours, had caused the delay. It was the Swedish ship. She had sailed without an adequate fuel supply, and a tanker had to be sent over to refuel her.

At dinner that evening, there was an obvious air of discord between the commodore and the captain. They snapped at each other with barely concealed irritation, and there was no mention of the bridge game that had become an institution since its first trial. Neither of the men appeared in the lounge all evening.

During the night, the Bonaire's engines chugged madly as she put on a gigantic spurt to make up the lost time. The next morning, however, word spread rapidly that now a fire had broken out in the engine room of the Swedish ship and, once again, the convoy was stalemated.

The Captain's entrance was explosive as he strode into the dining room at lunch time, and flung himself into his seat beside Jocelyn. He choked down his food. Then, with an appalling lack of discretion, he hissed at Admiral Turle, "Dat damn Svedish ship! She iss doink dis on purpose, no? Vat neet had she, a ship from a neutral country, to travel in convoy? I tell you it iss deliberate—vat you damned English say—procrastination. yess, dat iss it." He continued his harangue quite oblivious of the audience. "I told you at the rendezvous in Halifax dat ve should not allow dat ship to join us. But you vould insist!''

The Admiral's reply was low and, as intended, did not reach anyone's ears except the Captain's, who merely grunted "Bah!" and got up and strode out of the room.

By the end of the day, the fire apparently extinguished, the convoy once again regained speed and plunged on its way. The epidemic of nerves, however, was not so easily quelled. No one ventured very far without a life jacket, and both Miss Gillespie and Mr. Dove wore enough extra clothing to make an eskimo look scantily clad.

During the night it was impossible to sleep. Doors opened and closed furtively, footsteps creaked up and down the narrow passageways, and there was the murmur of low voices.

In their cabin, Jocelyn called out softly, "Carol, are you asleep?"

Carol raised herself up on her elbow. "No, I wonder what's happening."

Jocelyn wriggled uncomfortably in her heavy pullover and slacks. The ghastly blue night light lent an eerie glow to the whitewashed walls of the cabin. "I can't imagine, or, at least I prefer not to. In any case, I'll never get to sleep with all this regalia on. One thing is sure, if we do get torpedoed as Dove seems to think we will, we'll sink like a bag of cement under all this weight. On second thought, if something does hit this tiny tub, we'll likely never know what happened."

"A comforting thought," Carol said glumly. "Do you really think anything will happen?"

"It will for sure. That darned idiot Dove has wished it on us," Jocelyn said, trying once more to get comfortable in her narrow bunk.

Just then there was a rumbling that was neither a feeling nor a sound, but rather a combination of both, followed immediately by a deafening boom and a violent upheaval of the ship. They clung to their bed railings, waiting for the signal to flee to their assigned lifeboats.

Jocelyn looked at her watch. It was half past three. She was not aware of any feeling of real fear, but more a great encompassing impatience. This would mean a delay of days—precious days that stretched the distance to Kit. Time her aching heart told her they couldn't afford to waste.

How long did one float about the ocean in lifeboats before being rescued? She tried to recall details of the sinking of the Athenia. But her mind went blank. It was queer how the details of the cabin stood out in the eerie blue night light. The small rusted sink, the mottled mirror, the chest with its chipped painted surface and ill-fitting drawers, the porthole closed tightly, Carol's bunk across from hers, and Carol clinging to the side, her knuckles dead white. Jocelyn could have reached out and touched them, but neither she nor Carol moved a muscle. They scarcely dared breathe.

No shrill warning whistle came to tell them to leave the cabin, but there was another rumbling sound and the Bonaire seemed to be lifted off the sea and then be dropped back with a great dull thump. Then, all was quiet.

Jocelyn pushed away the covers, and swung her legs over the side of her bunk. "We're daft just lying here half paralysed," she said, in a voice that didn't sound like hers at all.

Carol got up too and they helped each other into their life jackets. They no sooner had them on than the rumbling began again, then the explosion. It knocked Jocelyn back on to her bunk. Carol managed to keep her balance but she crawled back into her bunk.

For over two hours, the rumbling followed by the explosions continued. It was as though a super giant were playfully picking up the ship and plopping it back again for his amusement.

Carol was intent on going out on deck to try to find out what was happening, but Jocelyn persuaded her that they should obey orders and remain in their cabin until a warning signal came. But the shrill whistle remained dumb.

At long last, all was calm. In the silence, Jocelyn could hear Carol's breathing, and her own heart was pounding furiously. She jumped nervously when she heard a light tapping on the cabin door.

A voice called out softly, "It's all right now, Sisters Sue, you can go back to sleep."

"It's Admiral Turle," Carol said, hurrying to the door. But when she opened it, the corridor was empty. "Just like a man," she grumbled. "Tells us not worry and doesn't tell us what not to worry about." She sat down on her bunk and looked at Jocelyn whose face was white and her dark eyes were filled with apprehension. "Maybe we should go outside and try to get some information," she suggested.

"A good idea," Jocelyn said. "We'll just slip on our coats over this rig. Come on, let's go."

Frigidly damp air smacked their faces as they stepped out on deck. A slice of dawn lay stretched across the horizon and the deck was coldly silent. Jocelyn leaned over the railing and looked down into the softly undulating grey sea, as though searching for the cause of the disturbance there. The water was deep, changeable, and uninviting—a suitable grave for a ship, for many ships. She peered through the half light towards the visible ships in the convoy. They were like grey silhouettes outlined in the pale dawn. She found herself wanting to count them.

Carol nudged her. "Let's go in. It's freezing out here."

Just as they turned to leave, the captain strode along the deck towards them. He was bleary-eyed and was dressed in his off-duty navy pea jacket and baggy grey pants. "Dere iss no neet to panic," he assured them. "Dere ver submarines, yess, but dey did no damage to us. Vat you heard and felt ver our own depth charges. Now, pleece, go back to your cabin and vash de sleep out off your eyes—and for Gott's sake, comb your hairs!" He was his usual gallant self.

At breakfast that morning, Admiral Turle, appearing relaxed and smiling for the first time in several days, announced to everyone, "You've all been greatly worried, and I'm sure a little frightened, but I'm happy to be able to tell you that the danger is now past. You will be assured of a goodnight's rest tonight. It is true that the convoy was in grave danger of attack, but Captain Walker, who commands our British escort group, has sent word that the pack of enemy U-boats that had located us has been checkmated. In fact, several of them won't be bothering any allied shipping again."

A rude comment from the captain directed at the commodore was drowned out by the cheers that went up at Admiral Turle's welcome announcement.

The convoy was delayed again, briefly, in order to pick up any German U-boat survivors. The newspaper headlines revealed later that Captain F.J. Walker, Britain's most outstanding U-boat killer, was to be decorated once again for recently destroying six U-boats in a single cruise.

For the next two days the convoy zig-zagged slowly through a thick choking fog which again enshrouded the other ships. The effect was stifling and depressing as the monotonous chorus of fog horns called to one another through the dense veil. It made one remember every tear he had ever shed and the reasons why.

But the following day was filled with brilliant sunshine and a gloriously blue sky with every ship in the convoy standing out in relief like chessmen on a rippling board. Like magic, the disagreeable became agreeable, and the grumblers ceased to grumble.

The captain smiled mischievously as he sat at the dining room table and he warned Jocelyn, "Enjoy dis while it lasts. Ve are in the region of the Azores right now, but ve'll soon be headink nort."

It was perfection while it lasted, except at night. When the Bonaire was converted from a banana boat, it was provided with a heating system but, alas, it had only two speeds—stop and go. It was impossible to sleep in the stuffy cabins, and even leaving cabin doors open did little to help. There was no relief from the hissing steam pipes and the hot damp oppressive tropical atmosphere.

After two days of sweltering, Jocelyn begged the captain for the key to the shower.

He scowled at her. "Mein Gott! All dis fuss. Damn spoiled vomen. Vy do you neet a shower? My ship issn't dirty."

"Because I'm hot and sticky," she snapped back.

He shrugged and grinned. "Okay den, after lunch Chiefy vill let you haf de key."

All of a sudden Jocelyn realized that she no longer felt any animosity towards the rugged little man. She mentioned it to Carol while they were relaxing on their bunks after a refreshing shower.

Carol said, "You know you're right. But I still don't like his incessant goading of Admiral Turle or his bad manners."

"Have you thought any more about our arrival in Liverpool?" Jocelyn asked. "I mean what we'll do if the boys are not there to meet us."

"They'll **be** there. After all, Flying Officer Thingamagig assured us that they would be. Have faith."

"I may be a supreme pessimist," Jocelyn retorted, "but you are an incorrigble optimist."

"Might as well be," Carol said, swinging her long shapely legs over the side of her bunk. "Let's not think morbid thoughts. How about going outside and trying to spot some porpoises."

***

Just as the captain predicted, it became much colder as the convoy turned northward. The sun hid itself behind dirty grey clouds, and a cold penetrating fog curled its thin damp arms about the slowly moving vessels. One stroll around the deck was enough to chill to the marrow anyone who, desperate for fresh or exercise, ventured outside the cabins.

Gloom and irritability prevailed once more, and moods were not ameliorated by the notably rougher seas. Seasickness again struck the vulnerable ones, and the dining room was half empty at most meals. In lieu of a qualified doctor on the Bonaire, the first officer, Sheila's friend, Willie, was the appointed medical adviser and keeper of the dispensary keys. He prescribed various potions with reckless abandon.

Jocelyn refused to give in to her queasy stomach, having convinced herself that it was simply a case of mind over matter. At dinner time she solved the problem by having a small glass of port which settled her stomach, but she couldn't do this at breakfast or lunch. With stern resolve, she headed for the dining room, but sometimes got only as far as her chair when she had to make a hasty retreat with her hand clamped firmly over her mouth. The captain would look up under his bushy eyebrows and grunt, "Bah! Weak stomachs. Damn spoiled vomen!"

***

As the convoy approached the Irish Sea, it beat its way doggedly through the roughest weather encountered thus far. The Bonaire shivered and shook as she was rolled, teased, and tossed about like a slipper in the mouth of a playful puppy. Storm railings were put up to save the crockery, and warnings were issued about the danger of going out on deck unaccompanied.

At breakfast one morning, Carol's chair was thrown over backwards by a sudden violent swell, just as she was about to sit down. She was thoroughly surprised to find herself in a heap at the captain's feet. While someone else helped her up and asked if she had been hurt, he sat back and roared with laughter.

The storm did not abate, and after a gruelling day of being bruised and buffeted about, Jocelyn was sadly bemoaning the loss of her sea legs as she tried to brush her hair in front of the mirror. The ship suddenly lurched madly and catapulted her across the cabin. She crashed into Carol's bunk, the sides of which buckled with the impact. The returning pendulum swing eased her and the recumbent Carol to the floor.

"Are you hurt, Joc?" Carol asked anxiously. She hung on to the sink with one hand and helped her sister to her feet.

Jocelyn sat on her bunk rubbing her elbow. "Just my funny bone, and my dignity," she said laughing. "But for one awful moment I thought that Willie might be presiding over the delivery of my first born."

"Are you sure you are okay?" Carol asked, visibly worried.

"Perfectly sure," Jocelyn assured her.

When this unfortunate incident was reported to the captain, he tried to keep the twinkle out of his eyes as he grumbled, "Mein Gott! Dey criticize my food, dey complain about my expensif cigars, dey talk back to me, and now dey try to wreck my damn ship. I vill neffer carry Canadian vomen again!"

CHAPTER 6

It was March 14, 1944, seventeen long days since they boarded the Bonaire at Halifax, and the convoy finally had reached its destination. The Port of Liverpool appeared like a bold pencil sketch on the horizon as the ships awaited the tide, a pilot, and each one its turn to slip into a berth. The first incomparable thrill of sighting land was long past. The Bonaire's passengers now shared only a mutual impatience and a desire to place their feet on firm ground again.

Jocelyn stood before the mirror over the sink in her cabin, humming softly, You'd Be So Nice to Come Home To. She put on what she considered her most flattering pale blue wool maternity dress, and dabbed Kit's favourite scent behind her ears and on her wrists. Her happiness at the prospect of seeing him shone in her eyes, and she couldn't help smiling at herself in the mirror. She checked to ensure that her tiny pearl earrings were firmly in place, and that the clasp on the strand of pearls about her neck was locked securely. She felt satisfied at last that she would meet with Kit's approval. He had a horror of flamboyant costume jewellery, preferring her to wear only the pearls and earrings he had given her as a wedding present. They were her dearest possession and she didn't feel properly dressed without them. She tidied the sink for Carol who was curled up on her bunk waiting her turn. "There you are, hon', I'm finished," she announced, giving her ears one more dab of perfume.

"About time," Carol answered good humouredly. "You'd think you were getting ready for a ball. What should I wear?"

"I hung up your turquoise suit this morning. The creases should have fallen out of it by now. Dennis likes you in that, doesn't he?"

Carol sighed audibly. "You are so disgustingly well organized, Joc. What would I do without you?"

"You'd do very well," Jocelyn replied truthfully.

She began to run water into the rusty sink but stopped when she heard a light tap on the door. Jocelyn answered it and Carol joined her when she heard Admiral Turle's voice.

"I've stopped in to say good bye. My tender leaves very shortly. I do hope your husbands turn up. I'm sure they will."

They shook hands with him and thanked him for bringing them safely to port. He wished them good luck and farewell and then was gone, disappearing from their lives as abruptly as he had entered.

Carol had resumed her toilet when Sheila burst in. She was, as always, beautifully groomed and was wearing a deep mauve wool dress which made her eyes seem more violet than usual. But there was no trace of the silly sophistication in her manner as she reported breathlessly, "Guess what! Rhea, Lucy Blake, and those other two airmen's wives, Bertha and Rose, all have had messages either from husbands, or relatives."

"And there was nothing for us?" Jocelyn asked, her buoyant mood bursting like a bubble.

"Nothing."

Carol hastened to rationalize the situation. "That doesn't mean that we won't get a message later. There'll be another boat along soon and we'll hear then."

"Sorry, there won't be," Sheila said flatly. "Willie said that's the only one coming. But I bet I know what's happened."

"Do tell us," Jocelyn said dispiritedly.

"It's very simple. Those people sent messages to somebody over here before they left Canada, and they somehow learned when we were arriving."

"While we stupidly obeyed the injunction not to tell anyone. Now we'll have to figure out how to get in touch with the boys and also what we are to do when we get off this wretched tugboat," Jocelyn observed miserably.

All Carol said was, "Oh," but her tone of voice clearly bespoke her chagrin.

Jocelyn was silently blaming herself for not letting Kit know that her plans were changed. But it couldn't be remedied now.

Noticing how miserable she looked, Carol tried to cheer her up. "Let's not give up so easily. We could still be met. I'll finish dressing and we'll go out on deck and try to pry some information out of someone. For all we know, they could be waiting for us now."

"Fat chance," Jocelyn muttered gloomily.

Carol again persuaded her to cheer up and join her outside on the deck.

The sun and blue sky were deceptive, and Jocelyn huddled close to her on the bench as the bitter March wind swept over the water and across the deck, twining icy fingers about their silk-clad ankles. In spite of herself, Jocelyn was encouraged by Carol's optimism and still nurtured a small glimmer of hope that Kit would come, or at least send word. Her heart raced madly every time the Bonaire drew near to another pier. But the hours dragged by as they crept laboriously on through the seemingly interminable water lanes.

At one point, a wild excitement surged through Jocelyn as she saw two figures in what looked like airforce blue stride down the wharf and head towards the Bonaire. However, as they came nearer, she realized that they were merely officials of some sort, possibly customs officers. Her heart settled back into its proper place and she chided herself for believing that he might come. She knew now that he had no idea that she had even left Canada.

Trying to sound more cheerful, she nudged Carol and asked, "Do you realize what day this is?"

"No, I haven't the foggiest idea. It could be Christmas, or Easter, or even April Fool's day. Every day of this crossing has seemed endless and dateless. What day is it, pray tell."

"Well, we left on Mom's birthday and your wedding anniversary, and now we've docked on my birthday. How's that for coincidence? I just remembered—I'm the ripe old age of 21 today."

"So you are," Carol said. "Our lives seem to be replete with coincidences these days. Well, happy birthday anyway. I could think of better ways than this of spending one's 21st."

"Wouldn't it be ecstatically wonderful if Kit were to suddenly appear out of the blue," Jocelyn said wistfully. "That would be the best birthday present I could ever have."

But that didn't happen and the Bonaire finally slipped into its allotted berth and the passengers were invited to disembark, this time quite civilly without the use of the precarious rope ladder.

As they walked down the gangplank, darkness was rapidly enveloping the city of Liverpool. Having had neither food nor drink since breakfast, and having spent the entire day waiting for the Bonaire to dock, they were famished, irritable, and close to exhaustion. When they stepped on to firm land at last, they joined the other passengers who were standing around in clusters, silently waiting for someone to direct them further.

There were no welcoming twinkling lights to probe the mysteries of the blackout, and the bleak scene served to deepen Jocelyn and Carol's chagrin. At last, a bus drew up to the pier and, after everyone was seated and their bags were stored away, the bus rumbled off in the direction of Liverpool railway station.

All that could be discerned through the grimy windows of the bus were the shadowy shapes of Liverpudlians hastening home from work.

Fifteen minutes later, the bus drew up in front of the railway station. Their luggage was dumped unceremoniously at the entrance and the bus lumbered off and was soon swallowed up in the total darkness.

Their fellow passengers had all disappeared as relatives or friends arrived to meet them. Carol looked at Jocelyn and Sheila. "Well, what do we do now?" she asked despondently.

"It looks to me as though we've been abandoned," Sheila said unhappily.

Jocelyn was quivering with fatigue and hunger, and they were all chilled to the marrow. It had been a long trying day.

"Well, we can't just stand here doing nothing," Jocelyn suggested. Look, there's a policeman. Perhaps he can advise us what to do."

Together, they marched up to the English bobby who had just come out of the station.

Jocelyn explained their plight to him, and he was very sympathetic. He said that once they got rid of their heavy pieces of luggage, he would take them to the nearest hotel which was within walking distance of the station.

At first the station master refused to store all their trunks and suitcases. The bobby explained their circumstances and finally persuaded him to allow them to leave the larger pieces for at least one day. With bad grace he agreed. Then the policeman guided them through the city's darkened streets, finally depositing them at Liverpool's Adelphi Hotel.

Outside, the building looked shabbily elegant. Inside, it was a relic of Queen Victoria's era—gloomy, cluttered with overstuffed leather couches, heavy end tables and ornate lamps with fringed shades.

When they approached, the desk, the clerk said icily,"You do have a reservation?" She began looking at a book of names in front of her.

They said, no, they hadn't and they explained their situation. She was not impressed. "No reservation, no room," was her rejoinder.

Jocelyn exchanged a knowing look with Carol and they smiled sweetly at the woman. Deploying their Lord Nelson strategy, Jocelyn said, "Well, then, I guess we'll just have to bed down for the night in your foyer."

With that threat, the clerk gave them the same kind of withering look they had received at the Lord Nelson and begrudgingly produced a key for a room which the three of them could share.

The room was on the third floor and faced the street. It was filled with massive pieces of sombre oak furniture, including two large beds and an oversized stuffed sofa. There was a marble-topped table, complete with flowered china water jug, large wash basin and a small cupboard underneath contained a matching chamber pot. Noting that there was no en suite bathroom, Carol observed cheerfully that with a pot so handy, at least they wouldn't have to brave the draughty hallway in their nightgowns in the middle of the night. For that Jocelyn was truly thankful; her bladder was continually working overtime these days.

She sank into one of the chairs, utterly weary from a day unparalleled in its frustration, discomfort, and crowning disappointment—no Kit to meet her, and no message from him. Nothing else had gone right either. After their harangue with the station baggage master and the hotel room clerk, they were obliged to beg the dining room steward to provide them with something to eat (the dining room was closing just as they approached its doors) and then they were forced to beguile a granite-faced clerk into allowing them to send telegrams before she went off duty for the night. Jocelyn was never so thankful to climb into bed and try to drown her sorrows in blessed sleep.

However, the body can be made to lie down, but the mind is something else. Her thoughts were enmeshed in endless knots which she was compelled to unravel. And now, as though in sympathy with her mind, her body resisted rest. The harder she tried to lie in one position and force herself into blankness and relief from the jumbled thoughts and emotions churning within her, the more insistent and disordered they became. She tossed and turned from side to side, trying not to disturb Carol who was sharing the bed with her, while her memory jogged crazily from one happy, exciting, or depressing event to another. From Medicine Hat, to Charlottetown, from her wedding day to the dreadful moment of Kit's departure for England, then skirting over the endless days, weeks, months that followed. And into each topsy turvy scene, happiness, excitement, and morbid fear entangled themselves. She tried to think of something pleasant and her mind went back to when she and Kit became engaged. It was in the summer of 1941. They were driving home from a particularly enjoyable Mess party when Kit suddenly pulled over to the side of the road and stopped the car.

He looked so serious that for a moment Jocelyn was worried. "I must talk to you, darling," he said. "I've been trying for weeks to find the right moment, but it never seemed to arrive. So, here goes. I love you, Jocelyn, and I want to marry you."

"Is that a genuine proposal?" she had asked, suppressing a smile.

"I've never been more serious in my life," he assured her. "So what do you say?"

"I say, I thought you'd never ask." And they both laughed until he leaned over and kissed her.

"I won't be able to afford to buy you a diamond engagement ring," he said. "I don't think you realize how badly paid we Raf types are compared to Canadian officers. And I can't offer you much of a future, at least until this damned war is over. But I can't imagine going through life without you."

"Nor I you," she replied seriously. Then on a lighter note she said,

"A brass ring will do just fine."

"That's settled then," Kit said, starting the car. "I'd better pluck up courage and ask your father for your hand."

The next night he did just that, and after a few days of deliberations, her parents were persuaded, and she and Kit went out happily to buy an engagement ring. They chose a thin gold band with two tiny cultured pearls set in it.

Jocelyn recalled saying some time later, as they sat on a settee in her parents' living room, "You know, I'm sure our meeting was preordained. We've actually known each other for such a short time, and yet I feel as though I've known you all my life."

"It's odd you should say that," he said. "When I finished my instructor training course at Cranwell, I asked to be sent to South Africa to an S.F.T.S., but at the last moment I was put on a contingent of pilots destined for western Canada. How's that for pre-ordination?"

These memories raced through Jocelyn's mind as she lay beside Carol in the hotel bed, trying not to disturb her. She placed the pillow over her head and changed position, but sleep would not come. Now her mind went back to the carefree days they had spent wandering hand in hand across the brown prairie grass which stretched for endless miles beyond the graceful white house where Jocelyn was raised. Kit learned to recognize the playful call of the yellow breasted meadowlark which sang, 'hee, haw, Harry's it'. She showed him the yellow and mauve cactus flower, its large bloom much like the spring crocus but which was so well protected by the plant's long and vicious needles. She persuaded him to taste the deliciously juicy green berries, much the size and shape of a grape, the fruit of another variety of cactus plant which grew close to the ground and bore small mauve flowers. Its needles were not as long as those of the larger plant, but one still had to be careful not to step on them.

Often on days when he was not flying they would gallop on horseback across the bald prairie with the wind blowing their hair and burning their cheeks. Jocelyn always warned Kit to be careful of the network of gopher holes which could so easily trip up a horse. In their daydreams, they would settle down in this cozy western town with its clean widely-spaced and well-kept homes with their gaily coloured rooftops, the neat vegetable gardens and the gaily coloured flowers that bloomed in profusion despite the desert-like climate; the sleepy South Saskaktchewan river that snaked its way through the town, banked by graceful willows and Saskatoon berry bushes; the golden cliffs rising steeply from the river's edge and levelling off at right angles into boundless stretches of prairieland.

Kit loved it as much as Jocelyn and it was an integral part of their future. The only hitch in this perfect scheme was the fact that before it could be implemented, Kit had to return to England for operational duty, and the wretched war had to end. Only then, Jocelyn was sure, would she be able to completely shake off the dread that beset her whenever she had to say good bye to Kit.

She changed position for the umpteenth, and mercifully fell asleep.

CHAPTER 7

When the grey light of a chilly March day filled the room and wakened her the following morning, Jocelyn was sure that she really had not slept at all. However, the realization that she might see Kit today filled her with eager impatience. She must get up and be ready, just in case his parents had received her telegram in time to relay her message to him. He might already be on his way.

Carol and Sheila finally got up too and Jocelyn urged them to hurry so that they could finish breakfast and be back in the room to receive any calls. She had asked the Fords to telephone her at the hotel. Carol and Sheila sent telegrams to relatives with the hope that someone might pass their message on to their husbands.

When they were all dressed they went down to the cavernous dining room which was only marginally warmer than the outside temperature. They were served an austerity breakfast of sawdust sausages and ersatz eggs, a fare even less palatable than the previous evening meal which consisted of pigeon pie. That dish was not enhanced by the fact that they spent their last day on the Bonaire watching hundreds of pigeons flying about or perching on the pier. Carol said she had become quite attached to them and felt like a cannibal.

They decided to forsake their tepid tea and soggy flannel toast and went to the registration desk to enquire whether there were any messages. Since there were none, they returned to their room. To pass the time, they perched on the wide window ledge and watched the early morning traffic bustle up and down what seemed to them the wrong side of the road. They would have to get used to that, Carol remarked.

Liverpool, lightly shrouded in the morning mist, was shabby and drab, and everywhere could be seen ghastly evidence of the devastation wrought by the German blitz. Between buildings yawned great empty gaps where not long before proud edifices had stood; a huge blackened sign on the charred front of a tall skeleton structure was all that remained of a once prosperous department store. They were awed to a horrified silence, but a busy throng of Liverpudlians made their way along the pavement seemingly oblivious to the disastrous mess.

At eleven o'clock the telephone rang. They all made a dash for it, but Jocelyn was there first. She grasped the receiver and called excitedly, "Hello, hello. Who's this? I can't hear you."

Carol nudged her. "Put the other end to your ear, silly," she said.

Jocelyn grinned foolishly and obeyed.

It was the desk clerk. "We have a telegram for Mrs. Ford," she said.

"Yes, this is she," Jocelyn replied.

"It reads, 'Welcome to England, Call Burton-on-Trent 1341' and it is signed C. Ford. Put your call through in the lobby, Mrs. Ford."

Carol recorded the message just as Jocelyn repeated it, so armed with that slip of paper, they returned to the lobby and found the telephone kiosk. Carol and Sheila waited outside while Jocelyn's fingers trembled nervously as she dialled the number. She waited tensely.

After a moment, which seemed like eternity, a male voice said, "Who is this calling?"

"It's Jocelyn, Mr. Ford, Kit's wife."

"Who did you say is calling?"

"It's Jocelyn, Kit's wife," she repeated, raising her voice. She remembered Kit saying that his father was getting a bit deaf.

"What number are you calling?" the voice said irritably.

"Burton-on-Trent 1341. It's Jocelyn. Isn't this Burton-on-Trent?"

"Yes, it is. Are you sure you have the right number? My name is Jones, Alistair Jones."

"Oh, I'm most terribly sorry," Jocelyn said. "I've obviously been given the wrong number."

She hung up the 'phone and reported to Carol and Sheila. They suggested going back to the desk with the piece of paper on which Carol had copied down the message.

Jocelyn handed it to the clerk who began to rummage though a stack of papers on her desk. Finally, she appealed to three other women sitting behind the counter. They parked their cigarettes and searched half-heartedly through the mess on the desk, but failed to produce a copy of the original message.

"It's not 'ere, luv," the woman said. "You likely copied it down wrong." She resumed her smoking and gossiping.

Jocelyn persisted. "But I didn't copy it down wrong. I suppose if you can't find it, I'll have to send another telegram. Will you please give me a form."

She quickly composed another message, asking once again for Mr. Ford to call her at the hotel.

"Surely nothing can go wrong this time," she said, not feeling one bit sure.

It was lunchtime, and after another awful wartime meal of soggy boiled potatoes, tasteless boiled carrots, and stringy mutton, Carol said she would have to go out for some exercise to try to digest the heavy fare. As they passed by the desk on their way out of the hotel, Jocelyn glanced up at a notice board hanging in a prominent place near the desk. At the top of the list of names chalked on the board was her own.

"Look, my name's up there. There must have been another message for me."

She went to the desk and inquired of the clerk on duty. She was assured that there was no message for her. The woman didn't know why Jocelyn's name was on the board. Having said that, she went back to her smoking and gossiping.

Crestfallen, Jocelyn rejoined Carol and Sheila and they started out on their walk. The air was still muggy from the rain that had fallen during the night and the streets were wet and littered with trash. But Carol was intrigued with the odd little shops, the noisy open markets, and what remained of the city's damaged buildings. She was trying to see the city through the eyes of Dennis who had often described his boyhood here. It was difficult to imagine how it had once looked.

Jocelyn hardly noticed anything. She was not convinced that there had been no message for her and she was anxious to return to the hotel—just in case. When a light rain began to fall, she urged Carol and Sheila to turn back.

At the hotel desk a different clerk was on duty and Jocelyn approached her hopefully. "Are there any messages for Mrs. Ford, Mrs. Carter, or Mrs. Barton-Holmes?" she asked.

The woman looked at the file in front of her. "Mrs. Ford, did you say? There was a message for someone by that name. It came in about a half hour ago. But we couldn't locate her."

Jocelyn almost exploded. "I am Mrs. Ford, and I was by this desk less than 15 minutes ago and was told that there were no messages for me." Her cheeks were flushed and her usually warm brown eyes smouldered with anger and frustration. "What was the message?" she asked coldly.

"It was from a Mr. Ford in Burton-on-Trent, and when we couldn't locate you he asked that you call him at Burton-on-Trent 1325."

"Thank you. Will you please let me have the original message with the number on it. Last time I was given a wrong number to call." Jocelyn had to struggle to be polite.

The clerk handed her the message and Jocelyn headed for the kiosk only to learn that there would be an hour's delay. The operator would call her in her room when she had a line.

Back in the room, Jocelyn threw her coat on the bed and sat down on the edge. "There's a conspiracy against us," she said. "We've been here almost two days and we are no nearer to getting in touch with our husbands. They could have walked here from anywhere in the country by now."

"You're probably right," Carol said. "And I had such wonderful visions of myself running down the gangplank into Dennis's arms. It was the one thing that kept me from going completely potty on that awful boat."

Sheila pulled some knitting out of her bag and began to work on it. "I wonder where Simon is," she said idly. "Not that I care, but I would like to get out of this Victorian morgue. Willie must have had rose-coloured glasses when he looked at this town. It's deadly."

Carol looked up from her book. "Dennis said that it was a very pleasant place to live. But the bombing took a terrible toll. I just wish he would turn up so that he could show me round." She added as an afterthought, "I'm beginning to think Joc is right. We are jinxed."

Sheila was bored with her knitting and suggested that they pay another visit to the desk. As they passed two maids in the hall, they heard one of them say to the other, "Them girls, oop and down, oop and down!" They shook their white capped-heads in utter disgust.

For the first time since they arrived, Jocelyn managed to laugh.

Down in the lobby they wandered over to the desk and this time Sheila's name was up on the board. She went to the clerk and asked for the message.

"Oh, yes, madam. It came in just a short while ago." She sorted through a mass of paper on the desk, found the telegram and handed it to Sheila.

It was from Simon's sister, Miggles. It read, 'Welcome to England, Coming, love, Miggles.'

"What on earth does that mean?" she asked, frowning as she read it aloud to Jocelyn and Carol.

"It sounds as though she's coming," Carol suggested.

Sheila replied, "Not very likely. From what I've heard of Miggles she is much too busy living the gay life to be bothered coming to meet me."

They decided to return to the room since it was nearly an hour since Jocelyn had booked her call to Mr. Ford. She sounded utterly dejected as she said, "You know, it frightens me, this business of getting wrong numbers and weird messages. I'm beginning to think we're never going to be rescued from this place."

She was not entirely serious, but as the afternoon wore on and still no word came, she became genuinely concerned. The old nagging ache returned—no time to waste, no time to waste. She lay back on the bed, silent and depressed.

When the telephone did ring, she jumped up as though she had been stabbed with a pin. As she placed the receiver to her ear, she heard a man's voice say clearly, "Hello."

Then the operator cut in with, "Mr. Ford, We have...."

She was cut off as the man on the end of the line shouted, "For Christ's sake. How many more times am I to be called to the 'phone for a wrong number?" With that he hung up, decisively.

Jocelyn didn't say a word. She threw down the receiver and burst into tears.

"What is it?" Carol asked.

"It's that Mr. Jones again," Jocelyn sobbed.

Carol picked up the receiver and listened. Suddenly her face lit up. She shouted joyously. "Joc, it's Kit, it's not Mr. Jones. Here, listen."

Unbelieving, Jocelyn took the 'phone and her heart leapt as she heard the dear familiar voice. "Jocelyn, Jocelyn darling, are you there?"

"Oh, Kit, is it really you?" she breathed.

"Of course it is. What is the matter? Why are you crying?"

"I'm not really," she spluttered. "At least, not any more. I've never been so happy in my life. Where are you? When can you come for me?"

"I'll get there as soon as possible, darling. I only learned this morning that you're here. I still can't believe it. Are you and Rosebud all right?" He always referred to their expected baby as Rosebud, being absolutely certain that it would be a girl, and, in his words, as sweet and beautiful as her mother.

"I'm just fine, and Rosebud weathered the voyage like a trooper. It's just that since we arrived everything has gone wrong. But it doesn't matter now. Where are you?"

"I'm on my way down from Scotland. I expect to be in Liverpool by tonight. I have only a forty-eight, but it's better than nothing, I suppose. I can't wait to see you. I thought...."

Jocelyn interrupted him. "I know; I'll tell you all about that when you get here. Carol is here and she wonders if you could get hold of Dennis and tell him."

"Yes, I'll do that. I was speaking to him two days ago. He was worried that he hadn't heard from Carol."

Sheila was tugging at Jocelyn's sleeve and mouthing a message about Simon.

"Oh, darling. Could you get a message to Simon Barton-Holmes. Sheila is here as well. We've been marooned here since we docked two days ago."

"Yes, I'll ask Dennis to tell Simon. They're on the same station, I gather. Well, I must go now. Cheer up, darling, I'll see you tonight."

After hanging up, Jocelyn sat for moment holding the telephone in her hand, her cheeks flushed with joy. She turned to Carol and said, "Can you believe it, we're to be rescued, we're to be rescued at last."

Jocelyn had never spent such a long day. Later that evening, she answered a light knock on the door, and in seconds she was in Kit's arms, just as she had dreamt she would be that night at the Lord Nelson. She clung to him as though she would never let him go.

They spent a half hour talking to Carol and Sheila telling Kit a little about their trip and then he and Jocelyn retired to the privacy of their own room.

At last they were together after those insufferably long agonizing months. For a few hours they could try to make up for the enforced separation, but Jocelyn knew there would never be enough time. Kit's life belonged to the Royal Air Force and that would prevail until this awful war was over. She would be able to share only snatches of time with him when he could get leave.

Kit crawled into bed beside her and switched out the light. "I can't believe you're really here," he said, for the tenth time. "I just didn't believe father when he rang me up and told me the news."

"I couldn't believe it when they called me in Montreal and told me I had a passage," Jocelyn said.

"We've got a lot of making up to do," he said, enfolding her in his strong and loving arms. "But I guess we'll have to wait until Miss Rosebud arrives to really celebrate."

"Will you mind, Kit?" she asked sleepily. She was so weary from all the harrassment, excitement and joy at being with Kit, that she could hardly keep her eyes open.

He kissed her again tenderly, "Of course, I mind," he teased. But he too had had a long exciting day and after giving her one last kiss, he turned over and went to sleep.

CHAPTER 8

The following morning, with the promise of only forty-eight hours together, Kit and Jocelyn quickly said their farewells to Carol and Sheila, breakfasted on the Adelphi's homely wartime fare, and then hurried off to the railway station to retrieve Jocelyn's luggage. At 10:30 they boarded a train for Burton-on-Trent, the nearest railway depot to the village of Repton where Kit's parents lived.

It was a circuitous journey across England, although not very far in miles. They had to change trains twice and wait for connections, so that it was dark when they reached their destination. Kit managed to procure an obliging taxi driver who agreed to take them the remainder of the journey. In the back seat of the cab they sat close together, Jocelyn's head resting on his shoulder and her hands clasped in his.

"If only time could stand still," she said softly.

Kit kissed the top of her head. "Just what I was thinking. Only yesterday I would have given my wings just to spend one hour with you. Now we have 48 hours and it's not nearly enough. Dennis and Simon were lucky devils to wangle two weeks leave."

"I was envious of them, too. But it's wonderful just to be here and not have that great expanse of ocean separating us. England is so small. You'll be home often, and you'll soon have me living near you, won't you?"

"Just as soon as I possibly can, darling."

There was something in the way he said this which troubled Jocelyn. For a second the old fear welled up—no time to waste.

"You're awfully quiet, Mrs. Ford," he said, tilting her chin and looking into her eyes. "What's going on in that pretty head of yours?"

She was thankful that it was too dark for him to see the foolish tears that had welled up in her eyes. She dare not voice her thoughts. She swallowed hard and said as casually as she could, "I was just wondering how this driver can have the vaguest idea where we are, or even if we are on a road at all. We appear to be driving into oblivion. I had no idea the blackout would be so black."

Kit chuckled. "It only seems that way to the untrained eye. You'll get used to it. This chap could likely drive this road blindfolded, he's been over it so often."

The driver suddenly veered the car off the smooth main highway on to a rougher stretch of road which Jocelyn surmised was a country lane.

"We're nearly at Repton," Kit said. He leaned over and said to the driver, "It's the next turning on the right, about half a mile along."

"I feel quite jittery about meeting your parents now that it's so close at hand," Jocelyn said. "You father must have wondered what was going on in Liverpool. I never did get to speak to him. I kept getting some bad-tempered man called Jones on the line. He got quite annoyed after the second time the operator put me on to him."

"Father **was** in a flap when he called me. I don't know which of us was less coherent. I thought he must be joking when he said you were actually in England."

"I should have cabled you," Jocelyn said regretfully.

"You're here and that's all that matters. Mother thinks you are awfully brave to risk coming over at a time like this."

"A team of wild stallions wouldn't have kept me away once I had that passage. Believe me, the cousins in Montreal thought Carol and I had taken leave of our senses, and did everything they could to dissuade us."

"I still can't quite believe you're here," Kit repeated. He held her more closely and kissed her nose, and her lips. "Still got a cold nose, I see."

"I'll ignore that remark," Jocelyn said. "By the way, how do your parents feel about the baby?" she ventured to ask.

"They're pleased as punch. Father has decided that it will be a boy, but I've assured him that he's wrong. Rosebud it is, and Rosebud it shall be," he said positively.

Jocelyn laughed. "You may be the one who's wrong," she said.

"It won't matter either way," he assured her. "Do you think you can be contented to stay here, darling? I only wish I could stay with you until you really feel at home."

"Will it be long before we can find a place to be together, Kit?"

"Quite awhile, I'm afraid. My ops. course lasts until the end of May and I haven't much chance of getting any decent leave before then. The most I'll be able to wangle will be a day every so often when I can sneak past the Wingco's evil eye. But rest assured, I'll come whenever it's humanly possible."

"Couldn't I come up to Scotland to live?"

"You could," he said hesitantly. "But I'm not allowed to live off base, and you'd be pretty lonely living in digs, not knowing anyone. And we do have little Rosebud to think of."

"I'd almost forgotten," Jocelyn admitted shamefacedly. "However, she must be a pretty rugged little soul the way she weathered that awful crossing."

"Do you think you'll mind living with my folks for a while? I'd feel happier knowing you'll be staying in a comfy home with someone watching over you. Repton is a lovely little village. Did I ever tell you that the film, **Good Bye Mr. Chips**, was filmed there? There's a famous Public School in Repton and it was used for the set of the movie."

"No, I didn't know that," Jocelyn said. She was thinking more of what he had said about having someone to watch over her. She had always been allowed to watch over herself, and she wasn't keen on changing that pattern. However, Kit was probably right. Even though her pregnancy so far had shown no signs of difficulties, she would be better off living with the Fords, at least until after the baby came.

The car slowed down and the driver turned to ask, "Is this the place, Sir?"

"Yes, that's it. You can take us to the gate and then turn around in the driveway, after I've unloaded everything."

When the car stopped Kit got out first, then helped Jocelyn out. As she stepped down on to the gravel driveway, the moon sailed out from behind the clouds giving her a clear view of Haycroft, Kit's boyhood home, and, for the time being, her home.

Haycroft was a square two-storey red brick house, standing alone on top of a small knoll. The grounds were spacious and well tended, and a curved brick path leading to the front door glistened like a silver ribbon in the moon's glow. It was wet from a recent fall of rain. A high, neatly-trimmed hedge ran down one side of the property cutting the house off from the nearest neighbour who occupied a low rambling bungalow at the bottom of the gentle slope. On the other side of the house there were no dwellings, just rolling fields dotted with shrubs and trees and stretching off into the distance.

Jocelyn was suddenly filled with a strange loneliness as she gazed upon her surroundings. She wished that Kit could stay with her, at least for a few days. He paid the driver, unloaded her baggage and escorted her up the path to the solid oak door. No lights were visible because of the blackout.

Kit stood still for a moment and looked down at her. There was a pleading smile on his lips as he said, "Your home, sweet Mrs. Ford—until I can have you near me. I hope you will like it."

Jocelyn squeezed his hand reassuringly. "I will, Kit, if it will like me."

In reply to Kit's knock, a tall stout man of fifty opened the door. His dark hair was thinning on top and he wore horn-rimmed glasses over a rather prominent nose. His chubby rosy cheeks gave him a benign countenance which Jocelyn found appealing. He's a nice man, she thought. Probably just like Kit.

When he saw who it was, he shouted excitedly into the house, "Mother, Mother, they're here!"

"Hello, Father. This is Jocelyn."

Mr. Ford put his arm about her and drew her into the hall.

"Close the door, son, and put on the light so that I can have a good look at this venturesome young woman."

Jocelyn blinked in the brightness of the hall light. She smiled self-consciously as her father-in-law looked her over and proclaimed, "Yes, you'll do."

Kit went back outside to bring in the remainder of her luggage. As he left a tall, slender woman emerged quietly from a door on the right. She didn't look at Jocelyn directly, but gave her husband a reproving glance.

"Now Christopher, where are your manners, keeping this child out in the cold vestibule." She turned then to Jocelyn. "Come in, child. There's a fire in the drawing room. You must be weary after all you've been through."

"I am a bit," Jocelyn admitted, following the ramrod back of Kit's mother into the warmth of the drawing room.

Violet Ford was ten years younger than her husband. She had a clear complexion, a small nose, full lips, and a wide high forehead. Her hair was honey brown, short and naturally curly. She was wearing a straight lined houndstooth check skirt and a long sleeved sweater with a mock turtle neck. It was steel blue, exactly matching the colour of her large round eyes. She was not exactly austere looking, but neither did she seem a warm person, possibly because her eyes were so coldly blue. Jocelyn wasn't sure what to make of her.

A cheery coal fire blazed in the cream-tiled fireplace at one end of the drawing room and beige velvet drapes were drawn right across the leaded bay windows at the opposite end of the large room, toning in tastefully with light peach coloured walls. On the floor was a beige carpet with a darker toned border. The down-filled lounge furniture was covered in brightly hued fabrics with oranges, beiges, browns, and warm yellows blending in harmoniously with the rest of the decor. It was a very pleasant room, Jocelyn felt. Kit helped her off with her coat and she gave him a reassuring smile as he left her to go and hang it up.

Violet bent over the fire and coaxed it with a poker into an even healthier flame. Kit rejoined Jocelyn and they sat, side by side, on a loveseat to the right of the fireplace. Mr. Ford took the armchair opposite them and was occupied for a moment in lighting his pipe. Mrs. Ford stood up, at last content that the fire was going well. She turned to Jocelyn, a wide smile on her pale lips and an inscrutable expression in her large steel blue eyes.

"There," she said, "that will keep you warm for a bit anyway. Kit tells us that life is very different in Canada. We do hope that you'll be happy here, my dear."

"Oh, I'm sure I will be. It's just so marvellous not to be thousands of miles away from Kit."

"Yes, I suppose it is. You know you gave us some very anxious moments this past two days. Christopher and I were quite distressed when you didn't return our messages." She was smiling yet her voice carried a faint note of censure.

"I really do apologize," Jocelyn said. "It was an awful muddle. We were like putty in the hands of some very inefficient and indifferent hotel clerks."

"Of course," Violet replied. She sat on a straight backed chair and picked up some knitting "I know it wasn't your fault. You were in a strange country and didn't know our customs."

Jocelyn was about to say that that had nothing with their problems, but thought better of it. In any case, Mr. Ford came to her rescue. He banged the ashes out of his pipe noisily and said, "Now, Mother, that's all over and done with. Jocelyn is here safe and sound, and it's my bet that these young people would like some tea."

"Jocelyn's always ready for tea," Kit said. "That is one English habit she will not have to acquire. Her folks all came from England originally."

"May I help you get it ready?" Jocelyn asked, rising from her chair.

Mrs. Ford put her knitting down, stood up, and put her chair back in its place. "No thank you, my dear. It's kind of you to offer, but I am used to doing things myself. I won't be a moment."

As she was leaving the room, she plumped up the cushions on the divan, and straightened an ashtray Kit had inadvertently nudged out of place. After a brief glance about the room to ensure that all was in order, she went out to the kitchen.

Kit rose and offered Jocelyn his hands. "Come upstairs with me, darling, and I'll show you our room." He turned to his father. "Will you excuse us, Father? We'll be back in time for the tea."

"Of course, of course. You just do what you want. Jocelyn will want to freshen up a bit, I expect."

The cold air was like a dash of ice water hitting her as they left the warmth of the drawing room, and upstairs was colder than a meat storage locker. Kit led the way and switched on a lamp as he entered their bedroom.

The room was large and almost square. It was furnished with an old-fashioned but beautifully-carved oak suite. Colourful floral drapes were drawn across the windows and the walls were painted a cool mint green. A mountainous brightly hued eiderdown was on the bed, its cover matching the drapes.

Kit left her unpacking her overnight case, returning in a moment with a small electric fire which he plugged into a wall socket.

"There, this will warm the place up a bit for you. I'm used to these frigid temperatures, but I know what a hothouse plant you are. Hopefully, you'll soon get acclimatized."

Jocelyn doubted it, but she smiled gratefully and warmed her hands before the fire. She began to understand why her mother said that she would not like living in England.

"Are you ready to go down now?" Kit asked. "I think I hear Mother going in with the tea, and she hates to be kept waiting."

"I'm ready," Jocelyn said, linking her arm in his as they returned to the drawing room and the promised tea.

She sat through the remainder of the evening in ever growing impatience. She told Kit's parents about Captain Maarleveld and Admiral Turle, about the hair-raising experience with the German U-boats and how Captain Walker had sunk six of them before they had a chance to destroy any of the convoy. When she mentioned that it was a Swedish ship that had delayed the passage and that the Dutch captain had argued at the rendezvous in Halifax against allowing the vessel to join the convoy Kit said, "Do you remember, darling, that a Swedish officer at 34 S.F.T.S., who was posing as Norwegian, was discovered to be a German spy?"

"That's right," Jocelyn said. "I'd forgotten about that."

But there were long days ahead in which she could report at length on her eventful trip. Right now all she wanted was to have Kit to herself. They had so little time left. By this hour tomorrow night, he would be gone and she would be alone; yes, alone, because no matter how much company there might be, she would always be alone without Kit.

At long last, she heard him say, "If you and Father don't mind, I think we'll turn in, Mother. It's been a long day."

In their bedroom, it didn't take Jocelyn long to get out of her clothes and into a warm nightgown, and then to snuggle under the huge eiderdown. Kit unplugged the electric fire before settling in beside her. He held her close until she finally stopped shivering and, in the middle of a sentence describing some of the horrors of the trip, she fell asleep. He lay awake for a long time, wondering how he could be so lucky as to have her here by his side, when just two days ago he envisioned her back to Medicine Hat. It was just too good to be true.

He hoped that she could settle contentedly into his parents' home. He knew there were many pitfalls ahead and somehow he must warn her about some of them. His mother was not an easygoing person and he had learned early in life not to cross her. She had rigid routines, and she didn't like company. Jocelyn's upbringing had been so different from anything his mother had experienced. All he could do at the moment was pray that things would work out.

CHAPTER 9

The following morning, Mrs. Ford wakened them by striding into their room and depositing two cups of tea on the bedside table. She asked Kit where his clothes were so that she could launder them, gave Jocelyn the same wide indefinable smile, and, after picking up Kit's tie from the floor, she left them alone.

Neither of them drank the tea, and after they had dressed, Kit emptied it down the bathroom sink.

"I wouldn't want mother to know we hadn't appreciated her tea," he said with a broad grin. "She'd be upset. Are you ready to go down?"

"Give me a moment," Jocelyn replied. "My hands are still so cold I can hardly hold my brush."

Kit urged her once more to hurry and she found herself saying sharply, "I'm ready. Goodness, darling, it can't be that urgent." she repented immediately and hugged him, as she joined him on the stairs.

Violet and Christopher were seated at the table in the breakfast room where a welcome fire was burning in the hearth of an ugly green tile fireplace. Violet sat very straight and very patient, ready to pour the tea. Kit's father was determinedly jovial.

"Good morning," he greeted them cheerfully. "Did you sleep well?"

"Like the proverbial log," Jocelyn replied, slipping into a char beside Violet. Kit sat down opposite her.

"When do you have to leave, son?" Mr. Ford asked.

"Soon after dinner this evening. The Wingco begrudged giving me even this much time off. The course is very concentrated and two days can mean quite a lot."

"That's a pity. Well, you can rest assured that we'll take good care of Jocelyn, won't we, Mother?"

Mrs. Ford spoke for the first time. "Of course we shall. Kit knows that." She turned her steel blue eyes on Jocelyn. "We hope you will feel right at home, my dear."

Jocelyn's warm brown eyes met the cold blue ones squarely and she said, "It's very kind of you to open your home to me until Kit and I can be together."

"Nonsense!" Mr. Ford exclaimed. "It's only what your parents did for Kit. We've been looking forward to having you, haven't we, Mother?"

Violet had left the table and was tending the fire with her back to them. "Indeed," she answered flatly. "We quite expected you to come and stay with us until the war ends."

This was something that had to be set right immediately, Jocelyn thought. "Oh, I couldn't think of imposing on you indefinitely. As soon as Kit is finished his operational training course and knows where he'll be posted, we'll look for a place nearby."

A look of dismay crossed Violet Ford's face and she exclaimed peremptorily. "But you must not even consider such a move!" She turned to Kit. "You know how difficult life is in England now, Kit. You simply can't think of allowing Jocelyn to travel about with a small infant. Whatever would the people in the village think of me if I allowed such a thing?" She turned back to Jocelyn and added firmly, "No, my dear. You must stay with us."

Jocelyn was stunned to silence. She appealed to Kit with mute distress in her eyes, and he gave her a glance of understanding. He knew better than to argue with his mother, and he simply settled the matter with a casual, "Well, we'll have to wait and see. If you're finished your breakfast, darling, we'll go out for a stroll. It's quite pleasant out this morning."

On their walk through the fields, Jocelyn reproached him. "Kit, you must stand by me in this matter. I won't stay on here indefinitely—infant or no infant."

They stopped near a stile and he lifted her to a seat on top. He took her hands in his. "Have I ever not stood by you?" he demanded reprovingly.

She shook her head. "No, but...."

"Well, I don't intend to start now," he interrupted her. "You know that I want you as close to me as possible. Life has no meaning when you aren't around to share it with me. But Mother's outlook is different from ours. She's practical, probably to a fault, and...well...she just doesn't understand how we feel about each other. She doesn't even realize that I'm grown up and not under her thumb any more. When I returned from Canada, and was home for all those weeks, she was surprised and hurt that I wasn't just thrilled to be back in England, and she didn't have any idea how miserable I was without you. I don't think there has ever been any romance in her life. I think that she and my father were married because their families expected it, not necessarily because they were in love. She had a very rigid upbringing, from what I can gather, and Father has had to simply adjust as best he could to her whims. For instance, you probably wonder why we don't have a telephone in the house."

"I was surprised at how difficult it was to get in touch with them in Liverpool. What was the number that was given to me in the telegram?" Jocelyn asked.

"That's father's office number. Mother argued that we didn't need a 'phone in the house. If he wanted to call anyone, he could call from the office. And it was no use arguing with her. It wasn't because of the expense. Father is very well off. He had a substantial inheritance from my grandfather when he died. But Mother can't help making all kinds of little economies. She got annoyed when Father sent her flowers for her birthday one time. She said we had plenty of flowers in the garden and the greenhouse. He never did it again, needless to say. She didn't like the two of us going anywhere together. But he took me to an airshow in Derby when I graduated from grammar school and it was then that I decided I wanted to become a pilot. Mother thought that it was the war that gave me the silly notion, as she called it. But that only made it easier for me. I joined the Royal Air Force Volunteer Reserve early in 1939, and I got my wish to train as a pilot. When war broke out in September 1939, I was given a commission and posted to Cranwell to finish my training. Mother was very frustrated after that, because it gave me my independence and I didn't have to report my every move to her. It didn't exactly make for a happy home life, but it certainly made my life happier. I told you once that they quarrelled over me constantly when I small. Father always wanted to give me more leeway, and she never thought I was capable of handling freedom of choice sensibly. I don't think you understood why I didn't write to them often when I was in Canada. But you know. it was hard to know what to tell them. Life is so different over there, and Mother wouldn't have had the vaguest idea what I was talking about."

Jocelyn was glad he was telling her these things but it worried her as to how she was going to cope without his steadying influence. She said as much when he was finished explaining his mother's foibles.

"You'll manage," Kit said confidently. "I know you will. Come along and I'll show you where I used to fish when I was the ripe old age of seven."

The hours took wings and sped by. After dinner that evening, Kit glanced unhappily at the clock and begrudgingly said he must leave. He had to travel all night to get back to Scotland.

At eight o'clock he donned his R.A.F. greatcoat, placed his forage cap on his head, and slung his small pack over his shoulder. Jocelyn slipped on her coat and he took her arm as they walked slowly down the path to the gate and to the waiting taxi.

Unshed tears stung her eyes and her heart ached unbearably as he folded her in his arms and kissed her. A lone tear had escaped and dribbled down her face and he tasted the salt as he brushed her cheek with his lips. "Oh, my darling, don't cry, please don't cry."

"I'm sorry, Kit. I'll be alright, really I will," she whispered.

But she was lying. She was beset with fear—fear for the future, fear for how she would face the next few months without him. She knew she didn't have his ability to cope with someone as difficult as his mother appeared to be. He had had years of practice. She was a novice in such things.

Reluctantly, he released her and strode away to the waiting taxi. At the end of the driveway, he turned and saluted, then was inside the cab and lost to her view. She stood for a few moments staring down the empty road, her eyes unseeing, and she wondered again why saying good bye to Kit wounded her so deeply; why it should always leave her feeling utterly bereft, as though her whole heart and soul were trying to break their bonds and follow him. Did other wives feel this same gnawing anxiety? Or could it be that she and Kit were really in a race—a race against time—against death? Horrified that she had put this terrible thought into silent words, she reproached herself sternly aloud. "Jocelyn Ford, you are a silly morbid idiot. You don't deserve the good fortune you are enjoying."

She did her best to shake off the black mood and was at least outwardly composed by the time she reached the house.

CHAPTER 10

Jocelyn knew it was not going to be easy living here without Kit, but she was determined to make the best of everything and to examine all her own motives and reactions squarely and honestly. She didn't have Kit's easy-going nature, and she was less tolerant than he of pettiness. Her own home life had been so free and open. There were differences of opinion and arguments, but they were always dealt with on the spot, and after the shouting was over the air was cleared and all was forgiven and forgotten. She wished that Kit had had more time to talk things out with her, but since they had been denied this opportunity, she must try to make the best of things on her own.

The morning after Kit's departure, she was awakened at seven o'clock when Violet barged into her room, placed the inevitable cup of tea on the bedside table, pulled back the drapes and blackout curtains with a flourish and flung open a window.

"There," she said with what seemed to Jocelyn to be malicious satisfaction, "we'll get some air into this room. Good morning, my dear, did you sleep well?"

"Quite well, thanks," Jocelyn said, snuggling deeper under the covers. The air that Violet admitted was as damp as it was cold.

"Here is your tea," Violet said, handing the cup to Jocelyn. Then she took a sweeping survey of the room, presumably to ensure that it was tidy enough, and left as abruptly as she had entered.

"Well, I suppose this means I must get up," Jocelyn told her reflection in the mirror facing the bed. She looked around for the heater Kit had left for her. It was gone. She had used it to get undressed the night before, so it must have been whisked away after she had fallen asleep. No matter, she must brave the elements and get up. Hadn't Kit said his mother hated anyone to be late for meals? But she didn't have to get dressed with the window wide open. She went over and closed it. When she was ready, she went down to the breakfast room.

Mr. Ford greeted her warmly when she entered the room, but then he went back to his paper, and spoke not another word until he said a cheery, good-bye, as he departed for his office.

Violet had her day's work divided by the clock and it was an inflexible routine. When she finished her own breakfast, she gave Jocelyn a cold empty smile and said, "I hope you will excuse me now, my dear, this is Monday and there are a great many things to attend to."

"Do save something for me to do," Jocelyn said, getting up from the table and clearing away her own dishes.

Mrs. Ford gasped audibly. "Oh, my dear, I couldn't alllow you to do anything at all. What a scandal that would create." She bustled about the table clearing it of the breakfast things.

Jocelyn was puzzled. She must be joking, she thought. "I don't understand," she said. "How could that create a scandal?"

"No, I suppose you wouldn't understand. Kit has told me that it's not the same in Canada. You can't possibly know how people in English villages talk. Why, if anyone knew that I permitted you to do domestic chores, they would all say that I was using Kit's wife as a maid. I can just see Miss Whitcombe, the postmistress, gloating over that bit of gossip."

"How ridiculous!" Jocelyn blurted out without thinking. She regretted it immediately, for although to her Violet's statement was the most arrant nonsense, she realized that it had been spoken in deadly earnest.

There was an awkward silence, then Mrs. Ford said coldly, "I'm the best judge of that, my dear, and you would be wise to allow me to guide you in matters of village life."

"Of course, I will. I didn't mean to be rude. It's just that it is something entirely new to me." She folded her napkin and placed it in the silver ring and left it on the sideboard.

"I'll do the clearing away," Violet said. "You may go up to your room and rest. Or perhaps you have something else to do."

Jocelyn wondered why she needed to rest. She had just got up. However, the gesture and tone precluded discussion, so she left the breakfast room and went dispiritedly up the stairs. She made her bed, tidied the room, and washed out some lingerie in the bathroom, then returned to her room and leaned on the window ledge gazing out across the green fields.

A mist still hovered over the valley and she could hear the frogs croaking their lusty good mornings to one another. It was so completely alien. Even the air had a different quality. It was soft and moist, but heavy with the mustiness of antiquity, and seemed to cry out that this was a land of yesterdays—glorious, but dead, yesterdays. It was so unlike the bold invigorating atmosphere of the Canadian prairies which issued a challenge to youth and progress, and breathed a promise of wonderful tomorrows.

A tiny bird hopped up on the window ledge and Jocelyn was intrigued to see that it had a red breast. Then she recalled Kit saying that English robins were half the size of the Canadian bird which was more like a thrush. It was curious, she thought, how everything was on a much larger scale in the larger country. She must get out her writing case and report to Kit that she had seen an English robin.

On her way downstairs with her writing kit in tow, she met Violet on her way up, carrying the electric cleaner.

"You do seem to have a great deal to do, Mrs. Ford. I wish you would let me do something. I feel so useless."

Mrs. Ford's colourless lips parted in the familiar way that Jocelyn decided was not really a smile, and she said, "It's kind of you to offer. But I'm afraid it's impossible. Besides being very bad form, you aren't familiar with the way things are done, and it would just waste time. I manage quite well since I've had no help. Lunch will be at twelve-thirty. Christopher comes home at twelve."

"Well, if you're sure I can't help, I'll sit in the drawing room and write some letters," Jocelyn said with resignation.

Violet was half way up the stairs, but she turned now and said, "It will be very cold in there. We have fires in that room only occasionally. The breakfast room will be much more suitable."

That was one room in Haycroft that Jocelyn did not care for. It was small, cluttered with heavy furniture, and the sun never seemed to find its way into its gloomy corners. She toyed with the idea of freezing in the cheerier drawing room, but after putting her head inside the door, she quickly changed her mind. It was indeed very cold. So, seated on a bumpy over-stuffed leather chair before the ugly shiny green tiled fireplace in the breakfast room, she wrote first to Kit, then to her parents, and lastly to Carol to whom she related a glowing account of the beauties of Repton and surrounding countryside. She didn't mention the problems she could see looming ahead. No use worrying anyone, especially Kit. She told him simply that so far she was coping. And she told him about the robin, that she loved him to distraction and missed him dreadfully.

Mr. Ford arrived home at noon and Violet came into the breakfast room and turned on the radio. She remained standing as she listened to the grim war news.

The Germans had launched another air attack on London. They had lost three of their aircraft while only two R.A.F. planes were listed as missing. Jocelyn always tuned out when these reports were issued, at lunchtime and at bedtime. She preferred not to know how many R.A.F. planes were lost. It was not a happy thought to go to bed with.

Lunch was placed on the table promptly at twelve thirty and, although Jocelyn chattered gaily throughout the meal, Violet paid scant attention, and Mr. Ford evidently was anxious only to finish his meal and return to his office.

When she had finished eating, Jocelyn said, "I think I'll go out for a walk later on, and post my letters. Would you come with me, Mrs. Ford?"

"Yes, I suppose I could spare some time to go along with you. I don't make a habit of going out on Mondays, but I'll make an exception today to show you where the post office is and some of the shops."

Later in the afternoon, as they strolled along the pretty country lane in bright sunshine towards the village of Repton, Mrs. Ford pointed out the little stone church where Kit was christened and confirmed.

"I always hoped that he would be married there," Violet said, almost wistfully.

Jocelyn suddenly felt a wave of compassion for her. It must have been difficult for them to accept Kit's marriage to a complete stranger and a colonial at that. She suddenly had a brainwave. "We'll have the baby christened there," she said.

If Violet recognized this as a kind of peace offering, she totally ignored it. She strode on, moving along so quickly that Jocelyn had difficulty keeping up. Rosebud's increasing weight and bulk had robbed her of much of her natural agility for the time being.

As they neared the heart of the village, the hedged path gave way to a line of detached ugly red brick council houses set on either side of the narrow walks, their numerous chimney pots jutting from the black slate roofs like giant bobbins of dirty grey thread. Kit had explained that these homes were government built low-cost housing for the poorer sector of communities in Britain.

As they passed by one of the houses, a small child, inadequately clothed for the chilly March day, played with marbles in the doorway of his home. His mother came out, swept him up under her arm, and crossly berated him in a high-pitched midland accent that Jocelyn found difficult to understand. Mrs. Ford looked neither to the right nor left, but marched along purposefully as though wishing to leave this section of the village behind as quickly as possible.

Eventually they came to the town centre where there was a traditional monument in the centre of the village with a large stone cross perched on top. The post office was immediately opposite, located in a tiny vine-covered cottage owned by the Miss Whitcombe that Violet had spoken about earlier. As they entered her home, the tall angular spinster emerged from her kitchen and greeted them warmly.

"How are you, Mrs. Ford? I haven't seen you for some time. I hope you haven't been ill."

"Goodness me, no. It's just that I don't write many letters now that Kit is home, and now we have his wife staying with us. So I am quite busy, and I do a great deal of work for the Red Cross, as you know. By the way, this is Kit's wife, Jocelyn, who has just arrived from Canada."

Miss Whitcombe extended her long veined hand to Jocelyn and said warmly, "Welcome to England, my dear. We've been looking forward to meeting you. I'm very fond of Kit. He used to come in here when he was quite a small boy. Such a fine little chap he was."

"Yes, well, Jocelyn has come for some stamps, Miss Whitcombe. Would you oblige her please?"

"Of course, I mustn't hold you up."

She gave Jocelyn the stamps and blue air letter forms she had requested and Mrs. Ford led the way out of the post office.

Outside on the pathway, she said with a note of irritation, "One has to be very careful in small villages. Miss Whitcombe is pleasant enough, but she does like to keep you talking. My policy is to say as little as possible about my affairs."

And Jocelyn correctly surmised that this was a subtle way of saying that it must be her policy too.

CHAPTER 11

On their way back to Haycroft, they walked at a more leisurely pace, and Mrs. Ford said a curt 'good afternoon' to a few local people they passed on the road. One of these was an older lady, wearing a hip length red suede jacket and a red felt tam on her iron grey hair. She was about to mount her bicycle but seeing Mrs. Ford she stopped as though wishing to chat. But Mrs. Ford wished her a brisk 'good day' and marched on. She explained to Jocelyn that it was the wife of the local doctor and a particularly inquisitive woman who had been constantly prying into Kit's affairs since his return from Canada.

"You'll see," she continued. "It won't be long before she finds an excuse to come to Haycroft to meet you. She has probably heard that you are here."

When they passed the church, she began talking again. "You know, Kit was very strange when he came home from Canada. His father and I simply could not understand him."

"How do you mean?"

"Well, for one thing, he wouldn't associate with any of his old friends. He knew several young men who came from excellent families both in Derby and Burton-on-Trent. And they were often home on leave from their various service posts. But when they tried to meet with him, he turned them down flat. He wouldn't go anywhere—simply sat at home all day, either writing letters, or wanting to talk about you and what he had done in Canada."

Jocelyn wasn't sure how to respond to these comments, or even whether she should. She finally said, "I suppose it did become tiresome."

"Well, I could understand it for a short time, but the longer he remained at home, the worse he became. It was not like him at all. He used to like going about with his friends. He went up to Merrieweathers from the time to time.

That's the doctor's home. He said he was happy there because they were so interested in Canada. When I told him that the villagers were talking and saying how he had changed, why he actually became angry. He said, 'I don't care what other people think'. It was very bad of him.''

Rising to his defence, Jocelyn said "Kit really did take to the Canadian way of life. My mother and father are very fond of him. When we left for Charlottetown last July, Mother cautioned me to take good care of him, rather than telling him to take care of her daughter. We laughed about it afterwards.''

Violet didn't seem to think it was either amusing or interesting. She replied dryly, "Yes, he does seem inordinately fond of your parents. In fact, he wrote to them often which surprised me, since he didn't write many letters to us when he was away in Canada.''

At that point, happily, they arrived back at Haycroft.

Mr. Ford arrived home every night at six and, after a light tea, Violet cleared the table and they spent the evening sitting in front of the fire in the breakfast room, fronts burning and backs freezing. Violet knitted furiously on a balaclava helmet for the Red Cross; Jocelyn, trying to conceal yawns, knitted on a tiny white sweater for Rosebud; and Mr. Ford smoked his pipe while he related a minutely detailed, dreary account of his day at the office. At nine o'clock he listened to the evening news, then switched off the radio, glanced over the top of his glasses at Jocelyn and said, "Well, my dear, it's time to turn in. You've had a busy day, I expect.''

Violet rose promptly. "I'll fill your hot water bottle, and turn your bed down, And, by the way, I'd much rather you didn't make your own bed. I have a special way of doing it which makes it easier to turn down at night.''

"All right,'' Jocelyn replied amiably. There was no point in arguing that it was not necessary to turn her bed down each night. "I do these things mechanically,'' she explained. "At home we always tried to help mother as much as possible.''

"Yes, Kit has told me how even he used to help with dishes and things. That's not done over here you'll find. A wife is expected to take charge of her own household duties.'' She took the steaming kettle from the hearth and filled a stone water bottle. "Now, if you'll come up to bed, my dear, you can be getting undressed while I do my chores."

Jocelyn felt like a small child being led to the nursery. She wondered how she would be able to take this infantile treatment night after night, without breaking her promise to herself and Kit to be patient. She must bear in mind that everything was being done in her best interests. Lord, give me strength, she prayed silently, as she trotted obediently up to bed behind her mother-in-law.

By the end of her first week at Haycroft she was beginning to question how long she could stand the boring routines that were practised by her in-laws. Each day was a dull exacting replica of the first, the only variation being in the kind of household chores Violet engaged in. And that, too, apparently followed a rigid pattern from week to week, month to month, and year to year.

Every morning the unwelcome cup of tea was delivered (and later poured down the sink), the curtains were thrown back and the window opened, rain or shine. The meals were prepared according to an equally rigid schedule. It was mind-destroying for someone like Jocelyn who was raised in a home where routine was almost anathema. Not that her home life was chaotic; far from it. But the idea of doing exactly the same things without variation, of always eating the same meals each day of the week, of never doing anything just for the fun of it, would never have entered either of her parents heads. They rarely went to the same place for vacations each year, whereas the Fords, without fail, went to Llandudno in Wales. They might not like it anywhere else, Kit had explained. She said he must be joking, but he assured her he was not. His parents, at least his mother, didn't like change or variety.

"How dull," Jocelyn replied, and he didn't argue.

After the long enervating days of trying to fill the hours with some type of stimulating activity, came the evenings during which Mr. Ford held forth upon subjects which were of no possible interest to anyone except himself, or perhaps to his partner in his accounting firm. Even Violet didn't listen, or didn't appear to since she reacted neither one way nor another to anything he said. Jocelyn at first tried to show some interest in his monologue but she soon realized that he didn't expect any reaction. He was talking to himself, possibly clarifying some points of business in his own mind. Neither of them went out in the evening and no one came to visit. In Jocelyn's view, they led a totally monotonous and soul-destroying existence.

The brightest spot in her day was waiting for the postman. And finally, ten days after Kit's departure, he whistled when he came up to the door. Jocelyn was sure this was a good omen. She almost knocked a tray from Violet's hands as she rushed to the door to greet him.

Mr. Briggs beamed as he handed her a batch of blue letters. There were nine, all addressed in Kit's beautiful handwriting. She shut the door and looked carefully at each postmark so that she could read them in order. Violet waited quietly at the bottom of the stairs, and Jocelyn, preoccupied as she was, nearly bumped into her again.

"Oh, I am sorry," she apologized. "but look, Mrs. Ford, nine letters from Kit. I wonder what held them up."

"Are there any for me?" Violet asked, stiffly.

"No, I don't think so, but I'm sure there'll be messages in them for you."

"I dare say," Violet said with her odd smile. She turned her back on Jocelyn and went into the kitchen.

Jocelyn took her letters up to her room and scarcely noticed the cold as she sat on her bed reading and re-reading Kit's loving words.

In the most recent letter he wrote: "Darling, I miss you so much, and I've been doing my damnedest to get some time off. And I think I've managed it for next Thursday. It will just be one day. In fact, I'll have to leave the same evening, but it's better than nothing. I can hardly wait to see you. How's little Rosebud? Behaving herself I hope. It won't be long now before she makes her appearance. And every day brings the end of my course nearer. I must go now. We are flying this morning. The weather has been so bad, that we've missed quite a few trips. Until Thursday, I love you with all my heart, Your loving Kit.

Jocelyn hugged the letter to her heart. He's coming! He's coming! I must tell Mrs. Ford.

Suddenly that lady's imperious voice intruded from the bottom of the staircase. "Jocelyn, whatever are you doing up there? Come down at once, before you catch your death of cold."

Jocelyn skipped down the stairs two at a time, and Violet, still standing at the bottom, warned her to be more careful, reminding her of the baby she was carrying.

She waved Kit's letter in the air and shouted excitedly. "He's coming home! He's coming home!"

Violet said flatly, "When?"

"Next Thursday. He thinks he can wangle it."

"Come into the breakfast room," Violet said. "out of the draught. We can't have you catching cold. It would not be good for either you or the baby."

Jocelyn followed her into the cheerless but warmer room. Violet sat down in her favourite straight-backed chair and picked up her knitting.

"Now, tell me, what does Kit have to say? Why have his letters taken so long?"

"It's something to do with censorship," Jocelyn replied. "It has held up all the letters leaving the station. But he has been getting my letters, thank goodness. Isn't it wonderful that he's going to come home?"

"I suppose so," Violet said, the doubt in her tone throwing a damper on Jocelyn's enthusiasm.

But at her next statement, Jocelyn was aghast.

"I do hope he isn't going to be dashing in and out every few days like this," she said, her eyes fixed on her knitting.

Jocelyn couldn't speak for a moment. Finally, she found her voice. "Whatever do you mean? He's been home only once, to bring me here."

The golden head remained bent, intent on two clicking knitting needles. It wasn't raised as she replied, "It's hard for you to understand, I know, but it makes our position very difficult. I've already tried to explain to you how people talked when Kit was home for such a long time. Now, if he keeps turning up every few days, I don't know how I shall explain it."

Jocelyn was utterly bewildered. "I'm afraid I really don't understand. There is no possibility of him doing that. But even if there were, I don't see how anyone could be mean enough to begrudge us the time together."

Violet tightened her lips and the knitting needles clicked furiously. "Well, after all," she said sharply, "Kit was safe in Canada all that time while sons of people here were risking their lives. You and I know that Kit is not one to shirk his duty, but it's what other people think that counts."

Sick anger welled up inside Jocelyn. She wanted to say, 'not in my book it isn't', but she knew that if she spoke now, she would regret it forever. At last, with great effort, she swallowed hard and got up from her chair.

"I suppose I do see things differently. I think I'll go out for a walk before lunch."

She needed the fresh air to clear her mind of the blind rage that consumed her. She took her coat from the hall closet, fumbled into it, and walked out of the house into the bright sunshine. She wanted to run away from here; run to Kit, or to Carol. But she knew she couldn't. She was trapped here and there was no visible means of escape.

She walked as far as the stile where she and Kit had sat together almost two weeks ago. It seemed more like years. Nothing was going as she had hoped, she reflected miserably. She wanted to be able to tell Kit that she was contented to stay here, that she liked his parents. Well, she did like his father, but with each passing day, she found his mother more objectionable. She simply had to find some way to counteract this terrible animosity she felt growing within in her. She was bound to stay here, at least until Rosebud arrived. That being the case, she must return to the house now and face Mrs. Ford as though nothing had happened. Certainly Violet had the capacity of speaking her mind then acting as though nothing had been said. It should be easier for me, Jocelyn thought, because I didn't say what was in my mind.

CHAPTER 12

It was a happy coincidence for Jocelyn that when she returned from her walk there was a visitor at Haycroft. True to Violet's sarcastic prediction, Mrs. Weatherby, the doctor's wife, had arrived.

Oblivious to Mrs. Ford's panicky fluttering about, rearranging chairs and straightening antimacassars, Mrs. Weatherby had settled herself comfortably in an armchair in the corner of the lounge. She still had her coat on and she was studying a wedding photograph of Jocelyn and Kit when Jocelyn entered the front hall.

"Jocelyn dear," Violet called sweetly, for once using her name, "you have a visitor. Here in the drawing room."

Jocelyn hung up her coat, ran a comb through her hair, and then went into the lounge. She was surprised to note that there was none of the usual steely composure about Mrs. Ford as she introduced the guest. She moved nervously about the room for a short while, then retreated to the kitchen. Jocelyn thought she had gone to make some tea.

Joan Weatherby placed the photo back on the table. "You were a lovely bride, my dear, and what a simply beautiful wedding gown. Kit is so proud of you. He used to come to our house often when he was home on leave all those weeks. He seemed to enjoy just talking about the happy times you spent together in Canada. He was so lonely without you. How are you liking it here?"

"England is very beautiful," Jocelyn replied honestly. "Kit hopes to show me more of it when he gets some longer leave."

"Do you plan to leave Repton eventually?"

"As soon as Kit's course in Scotland is finished, and he knows where he will be posted, we intend to find somewhere for me to live nearby."

"That will be nice," Mrs. Weatherby said. "I do hope it all works out for you. You must be rather lonely living in this small village with no other young people to keep you company occasionally."

"The days are rather long, and I do miss Kit so dreadfully. I came over to be with him, but I've seen him only for a few short hours since I arrived."

"That's a shame. Well, I'm sure the future will become brighter."

"Oh, it has in a way," Jocelyn said. "He's coming home next Thursday, but only for a day."

Violet returned then but Jocelyn was wrong about the tea. She was empty-handed.

"I had some things to attend to in the kitchen," she explained lamely.

She sat uneasily in the chair across from Mrs. Weatherby for the remainder of the visit and said very little. Jocelyn knew that she didn't like company. Apparently it upset her routine.

When Mrs. Weatherby at last made a move to leave, Violet in a 'what's your hurry, here's your hat' gesture jumped up and stood by the door. Mrs. Weatherby didn't hurry her exit. She smiled warmly at Jocelyn and said, "You must come over and visit me soon. Why don't you bring Jocelyn over for tea this Friday, Mrs. Ford?"

Violet gave a hollow little laugh. "I'm sure that my daughter-in-law would like to come. She has plenty of time to go out, but I'm afraid these days I'm kept much too busy. But I'll send her along on Friday."

She shut the door firmly behind the departing guest and turned to Jocelyn. "I hope you won't mind going there alone. I suppose she means well, but I simply do not have time to go gadding about."

"No, I don't mind at all," Jocelyn replied truthfully. In fact, she would rather go alone. It would be a break to get away from Haycroft and especially from Violet.

Mr. Ford came home at his usual time, and another long tedious evening passed, its only commendation being that it brought Kit's homecoming that much closer.

Happy events that are so desperately anticipated have an unfortunate way of creeping up slowly, then rushing past so quickly that they seem more like a dream. It seemed to Jocelyn that Kit's visit, to which she had looked forward so eagerly, was over before it had begun. It really was as though she had just dreamed a wonderful dream that he was coming, and then awakened before the visit occurred.

He was at Haycroft only six hours, and in that time they didn't have more than an hour alone. After tea, they escaped to the lounge in the hope of a few precious moments of privacy in which to say good-bye, but Violet was close on their heels. She drew the blackout curtains, switched on the lights, then bent over the fire and poked at the glowing coals.

Without turning her head, she said, "You'll be very tired after this trip, Kit. Do you really think it is worth travelling through most of two nights, losing all that rest, just to spend a few hours here? Father and I are quite concerned about you."

Kit smiled tenderly at Jocelyn and took her hands in his. "Yes, Mother," he said gently, "It's well worth it."

And it was. Yet, parting from Kit was just as heart-wrenching as it had been the first time he had left her at Haycroft. In fact, in some ways it was worse, because she was now knew some of the pitfalls she faced living there. When his taxi pulled away, she asked herself again, would she never reconcile herself to these leave takings. She would have to try some positive thinking, and concentrate on something pleasant—such as the invitation to visit the Weatherbys. Perhaps that would at least get her though the night. She had said nothing to Kit about her problems at Haycroft, and he had purposely not raised the subject, not wanting to spoil the short time they had together.

Friday, the day of the proposed visit to the Weatherbys, was sunny and warm, a perfect day for walking. As soon as she had written her letter to Kit, Jocelyn prepared to leave, armed with instructions from Mr. Ford on how to reach the house which had the intriguing name of Merriweathers.

She had been walking for about a half an hour through the fields in what she thought was the right direction, but there was still no sign of the large brick house with leaded windows and tall chimneys that Mr. Ford described. She sat down on a stile for a moment silently bemoaning her pathetic lack of sense of direction, and wondering which way to go. She had just decided to retrace her steps when a bespectacled gentleman in a brown checked Sherlock Holmes hat, plus fours and matching tweed jacket came striding over the brow of the hill which she had just descended. He approached at a rapid pace, squinting hard at her through his gold-rimmed glasses.

"Good afternoon," he greeted her in an incredibly gruff voice.

"Hello," Jocelyn said. "I wonder if you can help me. I'm trying to find the Weatherbys' house and I seem to have lost my way."

"I believe I could," came the gruff but friendly reply. "I'm heading that way myself, as it happens, so I'll accompany you."

"That's good of you," Jocelyn said and they walked along together, climbing to the top of another steep hill on the left, and there, in a dip on the other side, was the large brick house, with leaded windows and tall chimneys. It had been obstructed from Jocelyn's view by the hill.

"You must be the young lady whom my wife is expecting for tea this afternoon," her companion said.

"Then you must be Dr. Weatherby," Jocelyn replied. " Wasn't I lucky to meet you?"

"I usually go for a stroll after lunch. Some people like to sleep in the afternoon, but I find more relaxation in walking across these green pastures." He looked at Jocelyn and said, "So you are young Kit Ford's wife from Canada. Well, you have a fine lad there. I don't know anyone around these parts who isn't fond of Kit."

It made Jocelyn feel good inside to hear someone speak well of Kit. From the way his mother always alluded to the village people as sitting judgment on his every move, she had begun to think there were no nice people in or around Repton. She was obviously mistaken.

They reached the house and Mrs. Weatherby, in an ancient tweed suit, her short iron-grey hair fluttering in the breeze, came up the path and extended a small work-stained hand to Jocelyn.

"Welcome to Merriweathers, my dear. I see you have already made the acquaintance of Geoffry."

"Yes, your husband rescued me. I was quite lost when we happened to meet."

"That was a stroke of good luck. Do come in. I have the tea all prepared." She turned to her husband and said, "A call came in for you, Geoffry. It's the Bates child again."

"Oh, very well. I'll go along now. I shan't be long. It's a case of measles, I think. I'll drive you home when I return, Jocelyn."

He climbed into his old-fashioned Daimler parked in the laneway and drove off.

Over a delicious tea of home-made scones and gooseberry jam, Joan Weatherby encouraged Jocelyn to talk about Kit, about home, about the fun-loving days they spent together in Alberta. Since these were subjects dearest to her heart, the afternoon flew by and she felt a genuine twinge of regret when the crunching of gravel on the driveway heralded the Doctor's return.

As she was leaving, Jocelyn said sincerely, "I can't tell you how much I've enjoyed this afternoon, Mrs. Weatherby."

"You must come over often," her hostess replied. "It's just as much of a treat for me to have you. Any time you feel like a visit, just pop over. I'm not often out. Perhaps you would like to join the Women's Institute. It would give you something to do and get you out of the house and with other people."

"I'd like that very much indeed," Jocelyn replied. She suspected that Mrs. Weatherby was very aware of the problems she was facing at Haycroft and was trying to do something to help. She was grateful for the gesture.

It was dusk when she left Dr. Weatherby's car and walked up the path to Haycroft. Feeling strangely reluctant, she opened the door slowly and stepped quietly inside. She hung up her coat before Mrs. Ford realized she was home.

"Is that you, Jocelyn?" came the sharp voice from the kitchen.

"Yes, I just got in this minute. Dr. Weatherby drove me home."

She went into the breakfast room, followed by Violet who had her hands full of dishes which she placed on the table.

"You were gone a very long time. I expect Mrs. Weatherby had a great deal of gossip to hand out."

"No, none at all. In fact, we talked of little else but Canada. She and her husband are keen to visit over there."

"They've spent a lot of time and money travelling about the world I believe. But the war fixed that." She sounded as though it were a personal victory. "I suppose their house is very grand?" she questioned, leaning across the table to straighten the cloth.

"It's very nice. Large, but I wouldn't say grand. It has a cozy atmosphere, thanks I expect to Mrs. Weatherby's decorating taste. Have you never been to the house?"

"Goodness no. I'm not one to go about prying into other folk's homes. She has invited me many times, and she has been here once or twice, usually collecting for some charity or other. More out of curiosity, I'm sure."

Jocelyn was sure that Joan Weatherby had better things to do than visit people out of curiosity. "She asked me to join the Women's Institute."

"I thought she would. She's always after people to join. You can please yourself, of course, but it has never been my practice to join any of these women's groups. They're a total waste of time. Just an opportunity for women to sit around gossiping."

Jocelyn did not rise to the bait. "I'll go and wash up for tea," was all she said.

***

The next morning was sunny again, and surprisingly warm. After breakfast, Jocelyn wrote her daily letter to Kit and, after putting her head out of her bedroom window and testing the air, decided that it was a perfect day for a long walk. She could do with the exercise. She returned to her room, changed her precious nylons for ankle socks, put on flat heeled saddle shoes, and a light jacket, and went downstairs. A visit to the pantry yielded an orange, one of a half dozen that Mr. Pike, the green grocer, had sent over for her.

A plan formed in her mind as to what she would do. Kit had told her about some interesting old ruins nearby. She would go to the library first and look up their history, then find the spot and roam about the grounds for a while. The idea was appealing and she was humming as she left the house and went out into the bright sunshine.

Violet was working over a flower bed in the front garden so Jocelyn stopped to tell her where she was going. The steel blue eyes travelled from Jocelyn's feet right up to the scarf tied around her hair and under her chin. The cold smile made her flinch. What have I done now, she wondered.

"You're not going to the village dressed like that?" Violet queried icily.

"I'm only going for a hike, and to the library to ask Miss Jessop about some abbey ruins Kit wanted me to see."

Violet leaned on her garden hoe and said disapprovingly, "It isn't done to wear a scarf on your head. Only gypsies do that. And one doesn't walk about eating food," she added, eyeing the orange Jocelyn was holding. "It's for your own good I tell you these things, and for Kit's sake. The villagers will think you don't know any better."

Jocelyn counted to ten before answering. Then she smiled sweetly and said, "Well, I guess they'll have to think that." And she turned and walked towards the gate keeping her eyes straight ahead.

As she followed the path towards the village, the sure knowledge that this was just round one of the first overt conflict with Violet stole over her like a sinister shadow, and all the enthusiasm for the planned excursion evaporated. She would go as far as the library, but that was all.

At twelve, after a pleasant chat with Miss Jessop, who, like Miss Whitcombe, told her how fond everyone was of Kit, she left the library and with a heart of lead returned to Haycroft.

Violet was silent and forbearing throughout the noonday meal and the rest of the day, which Jocelyn found even less tolerable than the barbed remarks, graced as they always were with the chilly smile.

After the nine o'clock news that evening, Jocelyn was dismissed according to the ritual, and she dutifully followed Violet upstairs to bed. With martyr-like resignation, Violet pulled down the covers and placed a hot water bottle between the cold white sheets. The electric fire which Kit produced on Jocelyn's first night at Haycroft had disappeared never to be seen again.

Violet left the room without speaking, only to return moments later carrying a large cardboard box which she set on the bed. Jocelyn was brushing her hair and she smiled at Violet through the mirror.

"What's that?" she asked curiously.

Violet said nothing but began removing articles from the box and placing them on the bed. Jocelyn turned from the mirror and watched, first in wonderment and then in dismay. Spread out on the bed were all of the Christmas and birthday gifts she had sent from Canada over the past three years.

"I don't know what kind of person you imagined me to be when you sent these things," Violet said, smiling all the while. That smile that seemed to be her way of trying to remove the sting from her reproaches without lessening their effect. She picked up a handwoven paisley scarf as a demonstration and said, "Factory workers wear this kind of thing, my dear. And these stockings are much too fine for country wear. But perhaps you might find them useful. This perfume and bath powder, too, are things I never use. I thought it over today, and decided that the sensible thing to do was for me to return them to you. I'm sure you can find some use for them."

Jocelyn stared silently at the array of articles on the bed, things she had lovingly and carefully chosen over the past three years, hoping that they would give pleasure.

"Well," Violet said, with the satisfaction of a job well done, "I'll be off to bed. I'm sure you must be exhausted after your long walk today. Good night, my dear."

Jocelyn could not even bring herself to say good night. Overwhelmed with disillusionment, and a desperate yearning for Kit, she crept into bed and cried herself to sleep.

CHAPTER 13

While Jocelyn suffered under her mother-in-law's petty tyranny, Carol had been granted her wish that Dennis would remain with her in Liverpool to show her places of interest and particularly ones where he had spent time as a child. He took her to see the ruins of his family home which had taken a direct hit by a bomb.

"Mother and Father never really recovered from the shock," he explained. "They lost all interest in living and seemed almost to will themselves to die. They lasted barely a year after having to move into a small house that they owned on the outskirts of Wigan."

"It's hard for us to imagine how terrible it must have been for the people in Liverpool, Coventry, London," Carol said.

"Well, we mustn't spoil our short time together being morbid," Dennis suggested brusquely. "On a happier note, I intend to take you to see one of my ancient aunts who lives at a place called the Wirral, outside the city."

Carol was perched on the broad window ledge watching Dennis put on a conservative blue tie. Everything about him was neat and clean cut—his long head, fine, rather sharp features, tall, straight, slim physique, long square-tipped fingers; his fresh highly coloured complexion and his natural reserve were typically British. But his clothes never assumed the markedly casual tweedy English style of many of his brother officers. Even in his battle dress uniform he managed to look meticulously neat and tidy.

Now, satisfied that his tie was correct, he brushed his brown wavy hair vigorously, but it refused to flatten.

"It's no use, darling," Carol teased. "You'll lose it soon enough probably, so why fight it. Besides, I like the waves."

He laid his brush down and smiled at her. But then he noticed that she wasn't dressed and his smile vanished. "Carol, don't sit there wasting time. Finish dressing quickly. I want to get to the Wirral before lunch."

She slipped down from the ledge lightly, and threw her dressing gown on to the bed. She kicked her slippers off and, within seconds, was into a plaid skirt and blouse and a stout pair of brown oxfords. Dennis marvelled at how exasperatingly slow she could be and yet, when prodded into action, how startlingly quick.

"There, is that better?" she asked, parading in front of him. "And where is this Wirral place, and how do we get there?"

Dennis picked up her raincoat and helped her into it. "It's a strip of land north of Liverpool facing Ireland. And we are going by taxi, if I can get one willing to take us. So let's be off."

As they descended in the ancient elevator, she gave him a teasing smile and said, "And having made this duty call, then we leave this ancient palace and head for the south of England to find a spot for me to unpack my other suit and our wedding gifts?"

It was a statement rather than a question, and it was a subject he had been trying to avoid even since arriving at the Adelphi. When he didn't answer immediately, Carol said suspiciously, "Or were you thinking of parking me on said aged aunt at the Wirral?"

Outside the elevator he stopped and faced her, taking her hands in his. "Carol, I'll soon be on an active fighting squadron, likely to be moved at any time anywhere. I can't ask you to move about with me like a...a homeless gypsy. I've thought about this a great deal, and I've decided that I should find some place safe and fairly permanent, for you until...."

She had not taken her eyes off his face and now she shook her head slowly.

"But darling," he pleaded earnestly. "Try to see my point of view. You don't know the conditions here. I simply can't have you..."

"Tut, tut," Carol interrupted, putting her finger to his lips. "You're about to repeat yourself. I do see your point of view, but now will you try to see mine? I risked life and limb, to say nothing of my sanity, coming over here on that awful tub, the Bonaire, with its insufferable captain, to be with you.

Not to be parked with some crusty old aunt like a piece of unwanted baggage.''

Dennis knew when he was beaten. He smiled sheepishly, and took her arm leading her to the entrance of the hotel where he managed to commandeer a cab to take them to Aunt Charlotte's home, New Downs.

Dennis's aunt proved to be a vigorous, intelligent lady of 79 with a wry sense of humour, in contrast to the slightly fossilized old lady Carol had envisioned. Her lovely manor house was overflowing with young evacuees and almost as many adults to look after them. More than were necessary, Carol noted happily. Her hands were not needed here, that was certain.

Dennis was subdued to near melancholy by the change the war had wrought on this holiday haven of his boyhood. The lawns were ploughed under and now bore on their rutted breasts unlovely leeks and knobbly brussel sprouts. Flower beds that Aunt Charlotte told them sadly had once been her pride and joy were now home to tomato plants and green beans. She had had to give up her lovely flowers in order to help eke out the rations. "But I'll have flowers again when this war is over," she said firmly.

After lunch Dennis and Carol said thank you and good bye to Aunt Charlotte and then hastened back to the Adelphi in Liverpool. They gathered up their small pieces of luggage and checked out of the hotel before taking off for the railway depot to retrieve Carol's stored pieces of luggage. At three o'clock, the train pulled away from Liverpool station en route to the town of Hunsden in the south of England near which Dennis was now stationed.

When they arrived, Dennis hurried them off in a taxi to a quaint old inn where he had made reservations. There were still three days left of his leave and Carol was delighted to be able to spend some of the time exploring the picturesque area which Dennis saw for the first time through her boundless enthusiasm.

Part of that time they spent in London, an hour's train ride away. To Carol's delight, they visited all the places that had once been only fascinating names to her—Regent's Park Zoo, where, even this early in the season, the paths were lined with exquisite cherry trees in full bloom; the solemn splendour of Westminster Abbey, which had been stripped of much of its grandeur as a precaution against loss in air raids; domed St. Paul's Cathedral, where a black-frocked cleric urged them to visit the whispering gallery for only sixpence.

"He sounds more like a barker at a circus than a priest," Carol said with disgust. "Imagine charging people to go into a church!"

Dennis excused this practice. "They have to make some money to help repair the bomb damage done to the cathedral," he said.

He took her next to famed Trafalgar Square, where Admiral Nelson presided over the daily performance of spoiled fat pigeons; then to St. James Park, where office workers sat on the lawns eating box lunches. They watched youngsters tossing crumbs to greedy ducks, then went to the Mall, and Buckingham Palace which Carol thought looked more like a penitentiary than the home of a gracious king and queen.

They saw St. Martins-in-the-Field, a church that seemed to thrust itself forward in stubborn defiance of the concrete and brick which have crept over its once peaceful rural setting. Dennis guided her to Fleet Street, Threadneedle Street, Cheapside, Waterloo Bridge, Hyde Park, Piccadilly and Oxford Circuses, Grosvenor Square, Kensington Gardens. And everywhere she saw the pitiful devastation wrought by the cruel London blitz. Liverpool was dreadfully battered, but this was worse. And she did not see even half of the damage done to London and environs by the German Luftwaffe.

This exhausting sight seeing tour of London occupied the last day of Dennis's leave. The train taking them back to Hunsden from London rumbled through the dark, damp night. When it came to a halt at the first stop, the three other passengers in their compartment grasped their umbrellas, parcels, and newspapers, and vanished into the black drizzle outside.

The train resumed its speed and Carol turned to Dennis and observed anxiously, "Darling, do you realize that if I were travelling alone in one of these blacked out compartments, I wouldn't have the foggiest idea when to get off. It's bad enough in the day time with all the names of the stations removed, and the Guard may as well be speaking Swahili for all I can make out of his announcements."

"I'll get a railway guide book, and you can study it in your spare time, and familiarize yourself with names and stations. That will help. Then you'll have to train yourself to count the stops or keep track of the time. British trains are pretty much on schedule."

Dear practical Dennis, Carol thought. "You make it sound so easy," she said, picturing him in her position diligently memorizing the railway guide from cover to cover. He was so methodical and he never seemed to tire of trying to change what he considered her scatter-brained ways.

The train stopped again, and when it moved on Dennis stood up and fastened his raincoat. "The next stop is ours. Have you your gloves, and umbrella?"

Carol held them up for inspection. "All ready to disembark, sir," she said with a grin.

The train came to a stop and Dennis lifted the blackout blind and lowered the window by its strap. Then reached through the open window and turned the handle of the door to open it.

As Carol watched him perform this operation, she thought, that's something else I'll have to master. She stepped out on to the platform and put up her umbrella. A light rain was falling. Suddenly, she heard a very familiar voice.

"Carol, hi, fancy meeting you here."

It was Sheila, with Simon. They had been in the next compartment of the train.

"How wonderful to see you, but what are you doing here?" Carol asked.

"We just made the connection from Newmarket by the skin of our teeth," she told Carol. "But Simon managed to grab a taxi at Euston and get us over to Charing Cross just in time to catch this train."

Simon and Dennis saluted each other and launched into station gossip while Sheila, sharing Carol's umbrella, exchanged news with her as they walked quickly towards the centre of the town.

"I thought Simon was leaving you in Newmarket with his sister," Carol said.

"He was, but I persuaded him to bring me down here for a few days. It won't be for long because Simon says that they are moving on to another station soon. What are you up to?"

"Staying at the Gatesman Arms at the moment. Did Simon wire ahead for a room? The place is bursting at the seams."

"We didn't decide that I'd come until the last minute so there wasn't time."

"Well, you may be in luck. It's not a posh place, but it's a port in a storm."

When they reached the inn, Simon went to the desk immediately to try to book a room. Fortunately, someone had just checked out that evening so they were in luck.

Dennis picked up their key and he and Carol left the other two in the lounge sniping at each other over a drink.

Another two weeks passed before the rumoured move of the Intruder Squadron became a reality. Sheila stayed on to keep Carol company and Carol was glad to have her to help fill in the time when Dennis was flying. Together, they browsed through the quaint shops on the High Street, and ventured down narrow lanes where ancient thatched roofs leaned over the road almost touching their neighbours across from them. Carol strained her eyes to try to see through the small leaded windows, and concluded that, although they looked very quaint and romantic from the outside, they must be exceedingly dark and dank on the inside.

When Simon and Dennis finally announced the date of their move to Gravesend, a base on the south east coast, Sheila and Carol had to make a decision where they would go. The coastal areas were out of the question. They were out of bounds to anyone who did not already live there. They had a few days left to think about the future.

Over lunch in the hotel dining room, Sheila said, "Carol, why don't you come back to Newmarket with me? We can share my place. It's quite respectable. It's above an ironmonger's shop—that's a hardware store. And you'll enjoy meeting Miggles. She's as nutty as a fruitcake, but very nice really. We can keep each other company."

Carol hesitated, not wishing to commit herself without consulting Dennis.

"Oh, please say you'll come," Sheila begged. She had forgotten her southern drawl since arriving in England, Carol noticed.

"Well, if Dennis agrees, I'll come."

That evening she wrote to Jocelyn telling her of her plans, and was surprised to receive a reply by return mail. Jocelyn begged her to come to Repton instead. She could go to Sheila later, if she wanted to.

"Aren't I popular?" she said to Dennis having read Jocelyn's letter to him. "I'll have to go to Repton. Joc sounds desperate."

Upon hearing this news, Sheila said despondently, "I suppose you must go to Repton."

"I do think Jocelyn needs some company. She never gets to see Kit. We've been so lucky by comparison."

Sheila was quiet for a minute, then her violet eyes lit up, "You can come to me after you've been to Repton," she suggested.

She was delighted when Carol said, "Okay."

CHAPTER 14

It was ironic that it should have been Mr. Ford who quite unwittingly addressed a problem, the existence of which he was totally unaware. He had not the slightest inkling of the animosity that had grown steadily between his wife and daughter-in-law, or of Jocelyn's misery. Sometimes Jocelyn wondered if he deliberately blinded himself to it. In any case, it was his suggestion that Carol should visit Repton, and he phrased it in such a way that Violet could not argue against it.

It was a week after her coup with the gifts. They had their usual evening snack of bitter cocoa and dry biscuits and, after listening to the news, instead of dismissing Jocelyn as had become habit, Mr. Ford surprised her by saying, "What do you hear from your sister, Jocelyn? You know, Mother and I have always wanted to meet her. Do you think that she would like to come and pay a visit?"

Jocelyn swallowed her astonishment and replied eagerly, "I'm sure she would. And I would give anything to see her."

She stole a glance at Violet and noticed the angry flush that had crept from her neck right up to her high forehead.

Mr. Ford banged the ashes out of his pipe, quite oblivious to his wife's transparent annoyance. "Good, good, that's settled then. It's a fine idea, don't you think so, Mother?"

Violet pursed her lips, then managed to part them in her vacant smile. "Why, yes, I suppose so. You may write to her if you wish. But when you do, don't forget to tell her to bring her ration book. It's difficult enough having company these days."

Strangely enough, it was the following morning that brought Carol's letter saying that Dennis's squadron was being moved to Gravesend and she was going to Newmarket for a while to stay with Sheila. Jocelyn lost no time in getting her letter off persuading her to come to Repton instead. She got Mr. Ford to take the letter into Burton-on-Trent to ensure that Carol would receive it the following day.

Just anticipating Carol's visit and the chance to talk to someone who would understand, who could laugh, and who didn't care a fig about what the neighbours thought gave Jocelyn an entirely new outlook. She had begun to fear that she would never smile again after the past few weeks. All at once she could breathe freely, could smell the freshness of spring in the air, was aware of the birds chattering and singing to one another in the hedges. She noticed with delight the crocuses peeking shyly through the lush spring grass, the daffodils bobbing their heads in the fields beyond the hedges enclosing Haycroft. The transformation of her mood was nothing short of a miracle.

Carol was almost as excited at the prospect of seeing her sister. Sheila was good company, but they were seldom on the same wave length and she tired of listening to the continual carping about Simon's misdemeanours. She had sensed from Jocelyn's letters that all was not serene at Haycroft, and that was another reason she was anxious to go and see for herself what the problem might be.

Sitting in the crowded, smoke-filled carriage en route to Repton, Carol thought about Jocelyn's plight, the fact that she was more or less trapped at Haycroft with in-laws she scarcely knew and with very little opportunity to be with Kit. She said a silent prayer of thanks that she had won the battle with Dennis over his intention to leave her with Aunt Charlotte.

It was a quick direct route from London to Derby, but she had to change to a local train for Burton-on-Trent. The connections were good and she was soon stepping out of the crowded compartment on to the platform and was being hugged affectionately by Jocelyn. She shook hands with the tall austere woman in tweeds whom Jocelyn introduced as Kit's mother. She looks a bit forbidding, she thought. Maybe this is where the trouble lies.

For a second Carol's serene blue eyes met the large steel blue ones of Violet Ford, and as Jocelyn watched the two women appraising each other a chill of foreboding ran through her. It died away quickly, leaving a slight sense of unease as Violet smiled her broad empty smile and said stiffly, "I'm sure we are very glad to have you, my dear. It was remiss of us not to have asked you to come sooner."

"It was kind of you to invite me," Carol said.

Those niceties having been taken care of, they left the busy station, and crossed the street where they boarded a bus which would take them to Repton.

Once out of the city and into the rolling countryside Carol glanced out of the bus window and exclaimed rapturously, "Can you get over the velvety greenness of everything, Joc? It seems impossible that it's only April and yet flowers are blooming everywhere."

"Carol is comparing this to home," Jocelyn explained. "In southern Alberta spring passes us by with barely a nod. We pretty well go from winter to summer most years, and hardly anything dares poke its head out of the ground until June."

"Really," Violet replied flatly, managing to convey her complete lack of interest.

Carol looked at her quickly, then at Jocelyn. There is no love lost between them, she guessed.

"How's Sheila?" Jocelyn asked. "Still grousing about Simon?"

"She's fine, and yes she's still grousing. She was very disappointed that I didn't go back with her, but I promised that I'd go later. The boys are going to be pretty busy from now on and we won't see much of them. And Dennis doesn't want me too near his station now that he's on an operational unit. Says it's bad for morale."

"Kit hinted at much the same thing when I asked him why I couldn't go to Scotland, even though he's still on the ops. training course."

Violet showed no sign of having heard this remark and Jocelyn was happy to see their stop coming up.

The bus came to a halt and she said, "Here we are. Don't forget your bag and brolly."

Carol laughed. "Joc, you're as bad as Dennis."

Violet preceded them and was striding quickly in the direction of Monsom Lane. Carol and Jocelyn had to run to catch up with her.

Mr. Ford left his office early so that he could be home when they arrived at Haycroft. He greeted them at the door and Jocelyn introduced him to Carol. She was relieved to see that there seemed to be an immediate good rapport between them.

"What a splendid view you have across these fields," Carol enthused.

"We think so," Mr. Ford said, evidently pleased that Carol appreciated it. He took her arm and led her inside. "I'll take you for a walk all around when the weather's fine," he promised.

Violet went quickly into the house and was already busy in the kitchen preparing tea. A fire was laid in the drawing room for the first time since Kit's departure, and Mr. Ford quickly put a match to the coals.

With a crackling fire, and the warmth of Mr. Ford's welcome to Carol, Jocelyn was hopeful that the visit would go well, despite Violet's displeasure.

Jocelyn had promised herself that she would not prejudice Carol against Violet. But she found it difficult to acquaint her with the many things which either 'were' or 'were not' done at Haycroft, without making her suspicious. Yet, Carol must be aware of them if the visit were not to terminate disastrously, as silly as some of them were. For example, insisting on them not standing in front of the kitchen window while drying dishes, in case the next door neighbour might see her guests doing this menial chore.

On the first morning of the visit, they decided to explore the old abbey ruins that Kit wanted Jocelyn to see. After talking her out of wearing slacks and socks, Carol turned to her and said, "Just where does one take a course in all these things that are or are not done in Repton?"

Jocelyn chuckled. "You learn by trial and error, and I'd like it if we didn't make any errors while you're here."

She urged Carol to hurry so that they wouldn't be late getting back for lunch.

The postman had been and, as they walked along the path across the fields, they read the letters they had received that day from their husbands.

"Is there any chance of Kit getting home again in the near future?" Carol asked, putting her letter into her pocket.

"No, he's stuck up there until his course is finished. The Wingco is a real slave driver unfortunately."

"A pity he isn't like Wing Commander Dale, Dennis's boss. He's such a pet. The men all call him Daddy Dale. He's very forgetful and is always coming up to Dennis and saying, 'I say Cahtah, who is your pilot?' And Dennis replies, 'I am a pilot, Sir', and Daddy says, "Oh, yes, your wife has just come from Canada, hasn't she? You must have some time off to be with her'."

"Oh, how I envy you," Jocelyn said, laughing heartily at Carol's takeoff of Dennis's Wing Commander. In fact, she laughed more during those few days than she had since she arrived in England.

Each day, in the early April sunshine, they went for long rambles exploring the area around Repton, leaving no spot of beauty or historical interest undiscovered. They poked about the old abbey ruins, examined the crypt in the centuries-old village church, peeked through the gates leading into the playing fields of Repton Public School and laughed at the boys in their old-fashioned uniforms and straw boaters. One afternoon they paid a visit to Merriweathers. Mrs. Weatherby was her usual gracious and kindly self and treated them to some of her delicious scones and tea.

There was no time or need for Jocelyn to unburden her heart to Carol, and she was glad. It would only have blighted this pleasant respite. Violet was agreeable enough on the surface, but her transparent annoyance upon their return from the Weatherbys' made Carol suspect that she might be wearing out her welcome and she decided to leave on the following Saturday. Sheila had written to remind her of her promise to come to Newmarket.

On the Friday, at teatime, Carol raised the subject of her departure. "What time can I get a train to London tomorrow, Mr. Ford?"

He looked at her over the rim of his glasses, an expression of surprise on his face. "You're not leaving us so soon!"

"It's a great temptation to linger on in this lovely part of England," Carol replied. "But I fear that I'm imposing on your generous hospitality."

She looked directly at Violet, but the golden head was turned away.

"Nonsense!" Mr. Ford protested. "That's not so, is it Mother?"

He didn't notice the disapproving look on Violet's face, but Jocelyn did. Her heart sank as Mr. Ford carried on heedlessly persuading Carol not to go.

"It's been a pleasure having you here, and Jocelyn has certainly been happier. I think she's been a bit lonely at times, with only us old folks to keep her company."

Mrs. Ford visibly winced at the term 'old folks'. He might think of himself as old, but she certainly didn't think of herself that way. In fact, at 45 she was not. However, her husband failed to sense that she didn't share his enthusiasm for Carol prolonging her visit. He pressed her further to stay, saying that she must remain, at least until Dennis had found somewhere for her to live.

Jocelyn hoped with all her heart that Carol would not leave, but she didn't dare add her voice. She was vastly relieved when Mr. Ford said, decisively, "We won't take no for an answer. You must stay for another week."

Carol was happy enough to stay; Jocelyn was overjoyed at the prospect; Mr. Ford was pleased. So, everyone was delighted except Violet who could not even manage one of her empty smiles as she began to clear the table of dishes.

Carol got up from the table and said firmly, "Well, if I'm to remain a bit longer, I must start making myself useful. Here, Mrs. Ford, let me take those dishes into the kitchen."

CHAPTER 15

During the next few days Violet went about her tasks with a painful air of martydom speaking only when it was absolutely necessary. Jocelyn sensed that she was angry, very angry. When Mr. Ford came home from the office on Monday, having forgotten to make a purchase she had asked for, she snapped at him, "I didn't think you'd remember."

"I'm very sorry, my dear, but I had a trying day. I think I'll have to go and see Geoffry Weatherby again about this indigestion of mine."

"You smoke too much," Violet snapped.

Hearing this, Jocelyn repressed a smile. Violet was virtually a chain-smoker herself, of cigarettes, but she hated her husband's pipe because she was constantly cleaning up his tobacco crumbs, ashes, and spent matches. Like most pipe smokers, he used more matches than tobacco.

Mr. Ford sighed heavily. "You're probably right. I don't think I'll have any tea tonight, if you don't mind."

Violet decidedly did mind but she didn't voice her objections. She was angry enough at him for encouraging Carol to stay on. He wasn't the one to wait on her hand and foot, catering to her and to Jocelyn's finicky appetites. They didn't eat enough to keep a mouse alive. No indeed, all he had to do was charm them with his generous hospitality. No fool like an old fool. She made a loud 'harumph' sound and set the teapot down with a thump.

"What did you say, my dear?"

"Nothing," she replied. But at that moment she made a decision. That girl was going to leave Haycroft, and not after another week, but as soon as she could get away. She would tell Jocelyn in the morning as soon as her husband left for his office.

The regrettable fact that Jocelyn and Carol were late coming in for tea that day served to strengthen her resolve to carry out her plan. She would put that girl in her place, and it would do Jocelyn no harm to hear a few home truths as well. The audacity of them strutting into her house one half hour late for a meal, and expecting her to accept it just because they apologized. Well, she would smile and be pleasant, for the time being, but tomorrow that girl would leave Haycroft, or her name wasn't Violet Harriet Ford.

Carol may have been deceived by Violet's studied sweetness that evening, but Jocelyn was not. She knew that dangerous outwardly agreeable mood of Violet's too well to be taken in by it. That night, long after Carol was sleeping soundly, she lay awake with a very troubled mind. What will be her revenge this time, she wondered, and she put her hand on Carol's. It was so good to have her here, she thought gratefully. Then she fell into a troubled sleep dreaming all sorts of crazy and disturbing dreams with Violet at the centre making her life even more miserable.

The next morning Jocelyn awakened with a start. Was that really the sun splashing a golden patch on the eiderdown? It was! Whatever time was it? Where was Violet with the inevitable cups of tea? Before she got out of bed, she shook Carol who grunted and rolled over, away from her.

"Carol, wake up! We've overslept!"

"So what? We weren't going to catch a train, were we?" She raised herself from her pillow and rubbed her eyes.

"No, but we're going to catch something else if we don't get up and get downstairs for breakfast. Cone on now, get up and get dressed quickly."

By now she was dressed and ready to go down and face the dragon. They were late for tea the day before, and now they were late for breakfast!

"It's one of these things that aren't done at Haycroft—being late for meals," Jocelyn reminded her.

Her tone was bantering, but Carol realized that she was in deadly earnest. "You're afraid of her, aren't Joc?' she said.

Jocelyn avoided the accusation and told Carol once more to hurry. She could hear Violet banging about in the room below, and a choking feeling of impending calamity overwhelmed her.

When they reached the breakfast room their places were set, their tea and toast were warming on the hearth, but Violet was nowhere to be seen.

"That's odd," Jocelyn remarked. She sat at her place at the table and began unfolding her napkin. "I wonder why she didn't bring up the tea."

"You really are afraid of her, aren't you?" Carol said, studying her sister's strained expression.

Jocelyn continued to spread marmalade on her toast, refusing to look up.

Carol continued. "I shouldn't have listened to Mr. Ford. I must leave here, today."

"Oh, don't say that," Jocelyn pleaded desperately. "She was nice last night, and last week. She'll get over her mad."

"You know I hate to leave you, but I'm not really helping you by staying on if Mrs. Ford doesn't want me here."

"Please don't go, Carol. Stay until Saturday, at least."

It was much against her better judgment, but Carol finally agreed, only because Jocelyn sounded so miserable. She finished her breakfast, then folded her napkin neatly and placed it in the silver ring. She got up and went over to the bay window and stood looking up at the changing sky. "It's clouding over," she reported.

The sun had been chased behind heavy black clouds which were gathering forces to do battle with the good weather. Suddenly, the bright blue coverall that Violet wore to do her gardening appeared around the corner of the summer house and bobbed inside.

"I just caught sight of Mrs. Ford," she said.

"Where was she?"

"Going into the summerhouse."

"Did you see her face?"

"No, just caught sight of her blue smock as she nipped inside." She turned to Jocelyn who was clearing the table of their breakfast dishes. "What shall we do today?"

Jocelyn left her chores and sat on the footstool by the fireplace. "I'm easy. What would you like to do?"

"We might try to curry madam's favour by helping out in the house. I'll go upstairs and make the bed and tidy up the room. You stay here and do up the breakfast things."

"It'll probably just make her angrier," Jocelyn said with a heavy sigh. "but maybe it's worth a try."

Carol closed the door of their bedroom and had begun her chores when Violet entered the breakfast room below. Jocelyn was on her knees before the fire sweeping up some toast crumbs from the hearth. So quietly did Violet come in that Jocelyn didn't hear a sound. Suddenly, sensing another presence, she turned and looked up to see the stern straight figure, arms akimbo, towering above her.

Jocelyn's eyes travelled slowly from the large brown brogues, up the heavy lisle stockings and coarse sky-blue linen smock, and then to Violet's flushed face and into the cold blue eyes. She smiled nervously.

"Good morning. I didn't hear you come."

"I want to have a talk with you," Violet said sternly. " Do get up."

Jocelyn completed her task first then stood up and faced Mrs. Ford who asked icily, "Is your sister up yet?"

"Yes, she is. She just went upstairs to...to...to do something. Do you want to speak with her as well?"

"No, I do not. You can tell her what I have to say later." She hesitated briefly then went on. "I have decided that your sister must leave here, at once. I don't mind being your maid, but I resent having to wait hand and foot on your sister. You Canadian girls have no sense of propriety whatever, no consideration for anyone. Carol is a bad influence on you. I'm sure I don't know what kind of upbringing you've had. Your sister must leave, immediately."

The ultimatum had been delivered. Violet took a deep breath and then gave Jocelyn her meaningless smile. "You may go now and tell your sister."

At the sight of that hypocritical smirk, something snapped inside Jocelyn. All the resentment, humiliation, and frustration that she had bottled up since her arrival suddenly released like a giant coil. An angry light smouldered in her gentle brown eyes and she impelled Violet to meet it. When she spoke, her voice was quiet and withering.

"You are without doubt the most selfish heartless woman I've ever met. I know now why Kit didn't write to you when he was in Canada. No wonder he loved my mother and father so dearly. You've never wasted one ounce of love or affection on anybody but yourself." Tears of anger choked her and she couldn't go on.

Violet turned from ashen white, to crimson, to purple. She spluttered indignantly, "Well, well I never. I was just speaking my mind, simply speaking my mind. That was all, and..."

Jocelyn cut her off. She had managed to quell the maddening tears and she plunged on recklessly. "Speaking your mind, were you. Don't you know that you can't go round speaking your mind to people and trampling on their feelings. How would you like it if everyone spoke their mind to you? Why, if I said even a quarter of the things that have passed through my mind about you...you'd...you'd have shrivelled up long ago!"

Violet's face was now a deep angry red. "Kit will hear about this. After all I have done for you, and you repay me with this insolence, when all I did was speak my mind." She covered her face with her hands and strode out of the room.

Jocelyn heard her go up the stairs, then the bedroom door slammed shut. In a moment, Carol came running down the stairs and into the breakfast room.

"What on earth is the matter?" she demanded, seeing Jocelyn sitting on Mr. Ford's leather chair, the tears now streaming down her face. Carol handed her a handkerchief and sat down on the arm of the chair.

When Jocelyn was sufficiently composed she reported what happened.

"Well, that does it," Carol said. "It's the first time I've ever been thrown out of anywhere," she said with a grin. "There's a train to London around three, and it goes directly from Burton-on-Trent. I don't even have to change trains in Derby. I'll go up and start packing."

Jocelyn followed her upstairs and into their room. While Carol quickly gathered together her things in preparation to leave, Jocelyn sat on the bed and considered every angle of her position, finding nothing to commend it, nothing at all. Again, she was faced with the dilemma—she couldn't leave, yet she didn't see how she could possibly stay, especially after what she said to Violet.

Suddenly, her face lit up and her expression changed to one of calm decision and determination. She left the room, returning in a moment with two suitcases which she set down beside Carol's. Carol looked at her quizzically.

"I'm coming with you," Jocelyn said. "Sheila will have me, too, I'm sure. And we'll look for a house there where we can live together as she suggested on the boat."

"You can't do that, Jocelyn. What about Rosebud? She's due to arrive in a couple of weeks and you're booked into that nursing home in Burton-on-Trent."

"That's why I must go, now. If I wait until after the baby comes, I'll never escape from here. They would have all kinds of good reasons to make me stay. And likely they would have Kit on their side because it would all be so logical and sensible."

"But where will you have the baby? You know how hard it is to get into a hospital or nursing home right now."

"Where is Sheila going to have hers?" Jocelyn insisted.

"She doesn't know yet, but she has until mid-August to find out."

"I don't care. I must go with you today. If I stay here I'll lose my sanity completely without someone normal to talk to and laugh with." She was already taking things out of the drawers and throwing them into one of her cases. "You can't imagine how awful it has been here. I didn't want to say anything to spoil our short time together, and I haven't told Kit. The last thing he needs is to be worrying about me and Rosebud. But I can't stay. I'll go out of my mind."

Carol knelt on her suitcase and snapped it shut. "All right. But we'll have to get cracking if we're to catch that three o'clock train to London."

They completed their packing then hurried off to the village to retrieve their rations books from the grocer. Mr. Bickley showed some surprise when Jocelyn asked for hers.

"You're leaving us, so soon," he asked.

"Yes, I'm just going for a little visit down south with my sister," Jocelyn answered vaguely, taking the book and making a hasty move towards the door of the shop.

They headed for the post office to send telegrams. Carol knew of a small residential hotel in London, the Westway, where she and Dennis stayed on their occasional sightseeing excursions, and she sent one telegram there asking for a reservation. She informed Dennis in her telegram to him that she was going to Newmarket to stay with Sheila and then she sent a message to Sheila to say that both she and Jocelyn were coming.

Jocelyn composed a vaguely worded message to Kit in which she promised to call him. They ordered a taxi, then ate lunch in the Old Lion before returning to Haycroft.

It was one-thirty when they reached the house. There was no sign of Violet anywhere and the house was ominously silent.

Up in their room, they sat restlessly waiting for the taxi, alternately looking at their watches and peering out of the window. Finally, fifteen minutes late, the black cab appeared in the driveway and slowly advanced towards the house.

Carol ran out to ask the driver if he could help them with their luggage which consisted of Jocelyn's steamer trunk as well as the second hand pram that she had purchased in Burton-on-Trent. With some difficulty, the driver got everything strapped on board and they tore off in a swirl of dust and flying gravel in the direction of Burton-on-Trent.

The train was almost ready to depart when they reached the depot. Jocelyn dashed off to buy their tickets while Carol paid the driver and found someone to help get their luggage into the guard's van. By some miracle, the train was a few minutes late leaving and they managed to find an empty carriage. They got in and collapsed on the seat, laughing hysterically as the train slowly drew away from the station.

Soon they were speeding across the midland countryside and Jocelyn watched contentedly as it passed. She could feel nothing but a huge sense of relief to be putting the past few painful weeks behind her. She had no idea what the future would hold but she would have to let it take care of itself. Of one thing she was sure. Nothing ahead could be as bad as the soul-destroying existence she had endured living under the unyielding thumb and insufferable self-imposed martyrdom of Violet Ford.

CHAPTER 16

It was late in the evening when the train drew into St. Pancras Station. But because of Britain's double summer time, there was still an hour or two of daylight left. They checked their cases, the trunk, and the pram, and after procuring one of the ever elusive London taxis were soon honking their way through the city's congested thoroughfares.

They were accustomed to heavy traffic and mad drivers in Montreal, but were quite unprepared for London's larger numbers of single-minded drivers of cars, cabs, delivery vans, and double decker buses. It was every man for himself as the little cockney cabby wove his way skilfully through the narrow streets, finally, by some saintly intervention Carol was sure, safely delivering them to the door of their hotel.

The Westway was an unusual building in that it had been formed out of a whole row of what at one time were several very elegant three-storey Victorian mansions. It could best be described as a tangle of rooms and stairways, and it was as quiet and ultra-respectable as its permanent guests. These were mostly well-to-do elderly ladies who had refused to leave their battered but beloved London and were still sipping their afternoon tea each day in the faded but gracious lounge.

A tiny white-haired clerk behind the front desk smiled sweetly as Carol and Jocelyn approached the counter. "Yes? And what can I do for you?" she asked.

"We, that is I, wired for a room earlier today, for my sister and myself. The name is Carter," Carol replied.

"Oh, yes, we received your message, Mrs. Carter." She tapped her pencil on the desk pad and frowned. "You know," she went on in a cultured English voice, "these days one doesn't simply telegraph for a room in a hotel in London and arrive without confirmation that there is available space." She noticed the frantic exchange of looks between Jocelyn and Carol and hastened to assure them, "But this time, you're in luck. We can accommodate you."

They heaved sighs of relief and smiled at each other, then at the clerk. She summoned an aged porter and asked him to take them to their room which was down some steps and along a narrow dimly lit corridor. He unlocked the door with an enormous skeleton key and led them inside.

"It's not very posh isn't this room," he announced cheerily. "But you'll be quite syfe 'ere if them Jerries decides to pay us a visit."

Neither of them had thought of that possibility, and Carol spoke up, "Is there any chance of there being an air raid?"

"You niver know. But, as I said, you'll be syfe as 'ouses 'ere." He lit a small gas radiant for them and as they thanked him he edged his way to the door and was gone.

The Westway was more accommodating than the Adelphi. Although the dinner hour was over, they were served a light supper in the small dining room on the upper level of the hotel. After they had eaten the delicious thinly sliced bread and butter and some cheese and had the inevitable pot of tea, Jocelyn went immediately to the telephone kiosk to try to call Kit. She was disappointed to be told that there were no circuits available to Scotland.

To pass the time, they joined the elderly guests in the lounge where two very deaf old ladies, each in a wheelchair and watched over from a discreet distance by two uniformed maids, were loudly exchanging the news of the day.

"I see by the paper that they've sent five thousand of our aircraft over Berlin, and dropped four thousand tons of bombs," one of them shouted in a quavering voice.

"You're all muddled up, as usual, Mattie. It was four thousand aircraft and five thousand tons of bombs," her companion insisted.

One of the maids tactfully intervened. "It's time for your game of cards," she said firmly but kindly.

A second maid appeared and they wheeled their two charges into the adjoining small lounge where a card table was set up and the cards were laid out.

At nine-thirty, the incessant argumentative chattering over the cards ceased abruptly as the maids reappeared and wheeled the old ladies off to their rooms for the night.

Carol went off to bed while Jocelyn made a second attempt to call Kit, with same result. No lines available. She decided to wait until morning to try again and returned to the room to get ready for bed.

After two hours of turning and twisting on the lumpy mattress, and reliving the harrowing events of the day, both girls finally dropped off to sleep.

About an hour later, a prolonged, mournful and piercing wail shook Jocelyn into startled consciousness. She leaned up on one elbow, her heart thumping loudly. Carol had not stirred. Jocelyn shook her arm gently and whispered, "Carol, wake up. I think I just heard an air raid siren."

"I am awake, and you did."

Jocelyn looked at her watch. It was twelve o'clock. The wail of the siren became louder and more insistent. Above them, were sounds of running feet, banging doors, and then they heard voices. It sounded as though they came from right outside their door.

Jocelyn sat up, resting her head against the bedstead. "What do you think we should do?" she whispered, not certain why she felt compelled to whisper.

"Stay put, I should imagine. You heard what the porter said—we'll be syfe as 'ouses 'ere," she said, trying to make light of the situation.

Jocelyn got out of bed, switched on the overhead light, and put on her dressing gown. "I suppose he knew what he was talking about. We may as well put something warm on, just in case we get blown out of here on to the street."

"Very funny, " Carol said. "But perhaps we **should** get dressed."

Suddenly, the anti-aircraft guns boomed into action. With every thunderous report, the windows and doors of the ancient hotel rattled and the walls trembled. Jocelyn and Carol slipped back under the bedclothes, covering their ears. Carol's teeth were chattering loudly, which made Jocelyn giggle.

"Don't worry, hon'," she said consolingly. "We can't be worse off then we were on the Bonaire with submarines aiming their torpedoes at us."

"That is n-not v-very m-much c-comfort," Carol stuttered. "B-but s-somehow I d-do f-feel b-better b-being on land."

"So do I. But if we **are** hit, and no one knows we are here, how will anyone know what became of us?"

Above the din they heard someone banging on their door. Jocelyn crawled out of bed to go and answer it. "Who's there?" she called out.

Her voice was drowned out by a deafening explosion accompanied by the sound of falling bricks and mortar. The Westway shook on its ancient foundations and Carol buried herself deeper into the bedclothes. Jocelyn opened the door slightly to see the tiny desk clerk standing outside. Suddenly, all was silent.

"Are you all right?" the clerk asked. "We thought you may be frightened."

"We are, a bit," Jocelyn said in an absurd understatement.

"Well, you are quite safe here," the clerk assured her, shouting over the din of the barrage guns which had started up again. "Just stay in bed where you'll be warm and comfortable. No use going outside to a shelter. I must go now. Good night, and don't worry."

Jocelyn thanked her, said good night, and then crawled back into bed. "She said we'll be safe here," she reported, joining Carol in pulling the covers completely over her head.

Around two o'clock, after what seemed an eternity, the barrage guns were silent, and the blessed All Clear siren announced the end of the raid. London settled back into the peace and quiet of what remained of the night.

To her astonishment, when Jocelyn looked at her watch the next morning, it was nine o'clock. They must have fallen asleep immediately after the All Clear sounded. She nudged Carol who responded, as usual, with a sleepy grunt and turned over on her other side.

Jocelyn dressed quickly, told Carol that she was going upstairs to try again to call Kit, and hurried off.

This time, she was lucky and got through immediately to the Mess. Kit was there. He had begged permission to stay and wait for her call. He was delighted to hear her voice, but was totally shocked to learn that she was in London.

"Whatever are you doing there?" he demanded. "Don't you know that there are still air raids on London?"

"As a matter of fact, I do. We had one last night."

"You **what**! Jocelyn, are you all right? Of course, you are, or I wouldn't be talking to you. What are you doing there? Why have you left Haycroft?"

He sounded so anxious. Jocelyn suddenly felt guilty. "It's a long story, darling, and I haven't time to explain now. But I've left Repton for good."

"What do you mean? You can't have done that. What about Rosebud? Jocelyn, you must return to Repton immediately."

"I'm sorry, Kit. I can't. I've burned my bridges thoroughly, and I'm sure your mother would not have me back. In any case, I don't want to go back. I'm going to Newmarket with Carol, and we're going to try to find some place we can share with Sheila Barton-Holmes. Meanwhile, we'll be staying with her in her flat."

The operator cut in. "You're time is up."

"Oh, damn," Kit swore. He just had time to say, "Call me tonight, darling."

Kit sat in the mess for a few minutes trying to understand why Jocelyn had left Repton. He knew that she might have difficulty coming to terms with his mother's rigidity, but he was puzzled as to what sort of calamity could have prompted her to pack up and leave, especially with her confinement so near at hand. He would have to press her for further details when next he spoke to her.

While Jocelyn was on the 'phone, Carol had received a telegram from Sheila. She was delighted they were both coming and promised to meet them at Newmarket station. Their train was scheduled to leave London at 1:30.

The Westway had suffered very little damage in the raid, but the pictures on the walls were all hanging askew. When Jocelyn and Carol went to the desk to check out, they saw the ancient porter going around with a step ladder straightening them out. As they stepped outside, they saw that across the street squads of men were busy searching through mounds of rubble for the victims of the heartless raid.

"It might have been us they're searching for," Carol said solemnly.

Jocelyn shook her head. "That doesn't bear thinking about," she said.

They hailed a taxi and asked to be taken to St. Pancras station. There they retrieved their checked luggage and then carried on to Euston where they had it put on the train for Newmarket. They found a seat in an empty carriage, and on the dot of 1:30 the train pulled out of the station. They were on the last leg of their escape from Repton.

Jocelyn leaned back on her seat, her eyes closed, and for the first time since leaving Repton she contemplated this insane thing she had done. Kit sounded so worried, and little wonder. She must try to persuade him that it was the only thing she could have done after her terrible scene with his mother. But it wouldn't be easy.

After their disrupted night, she and Carol were both very tired, and it was not long before they were fast asleep. They slept on as the train raced noisily through towns, villages, and suburbs of larger cities, at last bringing them to the small town of Newmarket with its long, covered platform and squatty red brick station. Jocelyn awakened first and wondered for a moment whether they might have passed their stop. She was relieved to find that this wasn't so, and when the train stopped they were delighted to spot Sheila waiting on the platform.

She was wearing a loose fitting camel hair coat, and her thick blonde hair was anchored securely against the stiff April breeze with a brilliant blue kerchief. She ran to greet them. "Hi, I was afraid you might not make it. How was the trip?"

"I wouldn't know," Carol said, laughing. "We were both unconscious for most of it. We've had rather an exciting time."

They found an obliging porter to move their luggage into the baggage room, promising to retrieve it as soon as possible. Sheila then hailed a cab and, en route to her flat, they explained why Jocelyn had come. Sheila found it hilarious and said she wished she could have witnessed Jocelyn's knockout blow to Violet. "Sounds to me as though she deserved a punch in the snoot," she said.

"Well, figuratively speaking, I guess that's what she got," Carol suggested.

Jocelyn was having a private worry of her own as they drove along and finally she asked Sheila, "Do the Potts know about Rosebud's imminent arrival?"

Sheila hesitated a moment before replying. "Well, not exactly. Of course they know about my pregnancy. But Mrs. Potts is a positive old dear. And Rose and Jean, her two daughters, are very nice. They adore Simon and will do anything for him."

This hardly answered Jocelyn's question, but she decided not to pursue it at this time. She would tackle Sheila later, when they were settled in her flat.

The cab inched its way along Newmakret's bustling High Street which was lined on both sides with stalls and tables laden with every imaginable kind of merchandise from pins to corsets to fish. It happened to be Tuesday, the town's market day. The High Street was crowded with shoppers seeking bargains.

In response to Sheila's instructions, the cabby pulled up suddenly on the left hand side of the street and stopped outside an ironmonger's shop. Beside its main entrance was an unobtrusive dark green door bearing a shiny brass plate embossed in black with the name, Surrey House.

"This is it," Sheila said, "Everyone out."

Jocelyn and Carol unloaded their hand luggage and followed Sheila up the long flight of stairs leading to the apartments above the shop owned by Mrs. Potts. After her husband died, she hired someone to run the business and had apartments installed above the shop for herself and her two unmarried daughters. They had rooms at the back of the building, while Sheila's apartment faced the High Street.

Mrs. Potts greeted them in the hallway at the top of the stairs with a wide toothy smile. She was a tiny person with dry wrinkled skin, and her coarse grey hair was cut in a Buster Brown style with bangs almost covering her startlingly blue small eyes. She squinted over the rims of her gold-rimmed spectacles and decided that they were acceptable, but the one who was pregnant must be told that she could not remain here with an infant.

This centre hallway was dark and dismal. It had no windows and the woodwork and furniture were in very dark oak and the floor was covered by a dark brown patterned Axminster rug. However, Jocelyn noticed with relief a telephone sitting on a small table just outside Sheila's lounge. With any luck she could call Kit that night.

Sheila's quarters consisted of a large sparsely furnished sitting room with a fireplace and very large windows overlooking the High Street. There was a small dining table and some old fashioned easy chairs placed around the fireplace. The tiny bedroom situated further back in the house was utterly cheerless. It contained a double bed with an iron bedstead, a small night table with a dilapidated lamp on it and a double dresser over which hung a mirror that was in need of resilvering. The one small window overlooked the parking lot behind the shop. The saving grace of the flat, as Sheila quickly pointed out, was its central location, its indoor plumbing, and the telephone.

Jocelyn was fortunate to get through to Kit that evening. She related the sad story to Kit who said very little. He was pleased when she assured him that Simon's sister could help them find a house, and that she would be able to find a doctor to deliver Rosebud. She also stressed that she was happy here and had no desire to return to his home in Repton. She gave him the Potts' telephone number so that he would be able to keep in touch with her.

He rang off, somewhat relieved but still unsure as to what made her take such drastic action.

After their talk, Jocelyn went off to bed. She had to share a lumpy mattress with Sheila, Carol, and Rosebud who took up more than her share of scarce space. Soon after they settled in for the night, the rickety frame collapsed under their combined weight and they had great difficulty putting it back together because they were laughing so hard. Once back in bed, all Jocelyn could feel was intense relief at being free of Violet. It was like getting a reprieve from prison.

CHAPTER 17

The next morning Jocelyn began to try to make good the promises she had made to Kit. The first line of action was to visit Dovedale, the ramshackle bungalow where Sheila's sisters-in-law, Miggles and Deirdre, lived. Sheila agreed to take her there that afternoon.

The house was located on the outskirts of town, set well back in a grove of trees. When they entered the sitting room, they had to step warily over the clutter of magazines, books, and sundry toys that were scattered about. Jocelyn couldn't help comparing it with the sterile tidiness of Haycroft. She moved a toy fire engine and some crayons from a chair and sat down. Miggles and Deirdre offered them tea and went off to the kitchen to prepare it.

If there were any wariness or reserve in the meeting between Sheila and her in-laws, it would have been on her side, not theirs. Their manners were easy and uninhibited, their outlook unfettered by any conventional moral code, and their life style was totally chaotic. No concern for what the neighbours think here, Jocelyn concluded rightly.

Miggles Oakes, a slim, narrow-hipped, flat-chested woman strode into the room wearing black velvet slacks and a grey-white open-necked satin blouse. Short mousy pigtails stuck out from the sides of her small head, and her small bony hands gripped a pewter tray laden with cups and saucers, sugar, a jug of milk and a teapot. She was Simon's sister.

"Damn!" she swore, kicking aside a teddy bear with her open-toed sandal. She set the tray on a low table before the hearth, then returned to the kitchen.

She came back shortly bearing some dry scones on a plate. After putting them on the table, she sat down, and with a very male gesture pulled up her trouser legs and settled back in the chair and lit a cigarette.

"Where are the brats?" Sheila inquired.

"Our benevolent char has taken them on a picnic, thank God. She adores them, the little wretches, and would rather do that than clean this place. Do you all take milk?"

"Yes, please," Sheila replied. "But no sugar."

"That's good. We don't have much. Tessa wanted to try her hand at making some cakes, and she used up three quarters of our month's ration." She handed round the plate with the sad looking buns on it. "These gawdawful looking things are the result." She bit into one. "God! The're worse than I thought. Don't eat them if you can't. But I'm afraid there's nothing else in the larder."

While they sat drinking tea, struggling with Miggles' twelve year old Tessa's culinary failure, Sheila related an embellished version of Carol and Jocelyn's flight from Repton. This prompted Miggles to tell them about her mad evacuation from Borneo, where she and her army husband had been living until the Japanese took over.

"Bill was whisked off somewhere—God alone knows where; I've never heard from him since," she recounted breezily. "And I got word that the last two ships were waiting to take the wives and children either home or to Australia. There wasn't time to pack, or worry about trifles like household possessions. I was one of the last to be notified, and in a panic I threw some clothes into a valise for me, Tessa, and Randy who was just six months old, stuck him under one arm, the valise under the other, and with Tessa trailing behind hanging on to my skirt dashed down to the pier." She squashed her cigarette in her saucer and then went on with her story. "There, we were the victims of utter confusion and, by that time, total darkness. I lined up in one of the queues, my arms nearly falling off, and finally got on a ship." She stopped to light another cigarette. "I was feeling pretty proud of myself until the next morning when I discovered that I was bound for Australia, not Britain, with very little money and one change of clothing."

"That beats our flight from Repton," Carol said laughing. "At least we got on the right train, with all of our baggage intact."

"More by good luck than good management," Jocelyn added. "What on earth did you do, Miggles?"

"What could I do? I had to go where the ship was going. But I struck it lucky when we got to Sydney. I met up with Archie, and it's thanks to him that we live here."

Deirdre, Simon's elder brother's wife, who had entered quietly a few moments before, tactfully steered the conversation away from Archie. "Miggles has been taking the wrong boats, trains, and buses since she was in frilly pinnies. She can't be trusted with a travel ticket."

Deirdre was a tall, big-boned, broad-shouldered woman with high cheekbones, a ruddy complexion, a small straight nose, long mouse-coloured hair, and pale green eyes. Her slacks were faded red corduroy and her turtleneck sweater a bright blue. She had a grotty ribbon tied around her hair to keep it off her wide high forehead. Jocelyn surmised that she could be very attractive if and when she put her mind to fixing her hair and putting on some decent clothes.

In a surprisingly soft cultured voice, she turned to Miggles and asked, "When will Mrs. Vale be back?"

Miggles emitted a high-pitched squeaky laugh. "Never, I hope. Of course I don't mean that," she said, looking at Jocelyn and Carol as though to assure them she was joking.

Miggles was really quite fond of her two children, and she tolerated Deirdre's rambunctious three little boys because she liked Dee very much. They were two of a kind, well suited to the Bohemian existence that the war allowed them to live. As far as Miggles' husband was concerned, it was a case of out sight, out of mind, especially since Archie was so accommodating. Like Owen Barton-Holmes, Archie was a naval officer and when they were on shore leave, they spent most of their time in London, visiting Dovedale only occasionally.

Tea was over, and Sheila made a move to leave. "We've got to go," she said. "Thanks so much for the tea. We must get back to the flat before five so we can be out of the kitchen before the Potts want in. It's not the greatest thing, this sharing a kitchen, but so far it has worked without me being thrown out on my ear."

"Do you think you can help us find some place to live, Miggles?" Jocelyn asked anxiously. She had not had a chance to raise the subject earlier.

"Don't worry," Miggles assured her. "Something will come up. Archie has lots of contacts and I'll get him on the job right away."

It was a surly day, with a threatening black cloud sitting glumly on the horizon. They walked quickly down the rustic lane which merged gradually into the jostling town traffic. Standing on the curb outside the White Stag, Newmarket's cream stuccoed relatively modern hotel which was directly opposite the Pott's emporium, they waited for an opportune moment to cross the busy street. Some American G.I.s lounging in front of the hotel whistled at them, and Sheila turned and gave them an engaging smile and a wave.

Back in the flat, they made their supper and ate in front of the fire, discussing the housing problem. In addition to it, Jocelyn was anxious to find somewhere for her confinement. Sheila suggested that she speak to Rose Potts about it, so she went into the kitchen to see her.

Rose was preparing supper, but she took time out to speak with Jocelyn.

"Why don't you go to White Lodge Hospital and see Dr. Bailey. He's a good obstetrician, and a very nice man," she assured Jocelyn.

The next morning, in a drizzling rain, but happily optimistic, she set off on the two mile walk to the hospital scarcely noticing the inclement weather as she hurried along. Her thoughts were focused on what she would say to the doctor, and her hopes were pinned on his positive response.

White Lodge Hospital was a long low white stucco building with several outbuildings tacked on at an angle at each end. Jocelyn found a door marked outpatient clinic. She asked at the reception desk where she might find Dr.Bailey and was directed along a poorly lighted passage. Outside his office were two long wooden benches and she was told to wait there until her name was called.

At last it was her turn and a nurse ushered her in. She approached the Doctor's desk uncertainly and waited for him to look up from the papers he was reading. Her composure and confidence were badly shaken when he looked up suddenly and growled, "Well, what do you want?"

As she explained her situation, his eyes turned back to the papers on his desk and he didn't seem to be listening. When she had finished, he looked up, a weariness present in his cold grey eyes, and said, "If you had told me that you were intending to have a child next year at this time, I might have been able to help you. But under the circumstances, I can do nothing."

With that shattering announcement, he went back to his work at hand, the interview apparently terminated.

Jocelyn didn't move from her chair. She refused to be dismissed as though she had merely asked for a couple of non-existent tickets to the opera. She quelled the dismay that had washed over her and said quietly, "Dr. Bailey, I don't think you understand. I have been in England only a few weeks, and in Newmarket a few days. I need your help."

He played with his pencil on the desk but didn't speak.

Jocelyn persisted. "Surely, if you can't help me, you must know someone else who can."

Sounding more tired of the subject than sorry, he replied, "I'm sorry, but I really cannot help you, and I know of no one who can. The hospital is already overcrowded and we cannot accommodate any more maternity cases." He looked up at her through his cold pale grey eyes and asked irritably, "Why did you come to this country anyway?"

Jocelyn stood up, her legs suddenly feeling weak and wobbly. She leaned on his desk for support, and fighting back the insistent tears, she managed to blurt out, "I'm here so that I can be near my husband and so that he can have the joy of seeing his first child. He is risking his life for this country, or he would be here today, beside me, to see that I received help."

Dr. Bailey sighed audibly, took a slip of paper from a pad, and scribbled something on it. He handed it to Jocelyn. "This is the name of a doctor in Bury St. Edmunds. He runs a small private clinic. It's about 14 miles from here. Perhaps he will be able to take you on."

Without thanking him, Jocelyn hurried from the room, down the dimly lit passage, and out into the rain which was now pelting down. Her eyelids were burning from suppressed tears and she was consumed with anger. She had put so much hope in this man, and he hadn't even been civil. What could she tell Kit when he called that evening? She knew without asking that Bury St. Edmunds was too far away from Newmarket to be practical, even if the doctor there would agree to help her. Either she would have to go there to live, or find some alternative arrangement. But there was so little time to begin searching for accommodation in a strange place. Perhaps Rose Potts would be able to make some other suggestion. With that glimmer of hope, she trudged back to Surrey House, arriving there soaking wet and utterly dejected.

Drying out in front of the fire in the sitting room, she told her tale of woe to Carol and Sheila who were appalled at the treatment she had received.

"I've never heard of anything so heartless," Carol fumed.

Sheila was equally incensed, but also very disappointed because she had hoped to enlist Dr. Bailey's services for her own confinement.

Rose was mystified when she heard Jocelyn's report. "He really is a very nice man," she insisted. "I can only think that he had had a bad day, or that he is under some constraints from the authorities that he could not divulge. I do know that White Lodge has been designated a military hospital, and they have to keep a certain number of beds for military casualties."

"Do you have any other suggestions?" Jocelyn asked desperately.

Rose's dark brown eyes lit up. "I do know of someone who will help you. Miss Hatherley, the district nurse, lives just around the corner from here. I know she won't turn you down. Why don't you go over right away and see her?"

CHAPTER 18

Jocelyn quickly put her raincoat back on, a scarf over her head, and started out to find Miss Hatherley's cottage. Since it was now close to supper time, the nurse would likely have finished her rounds for the day, and would be home. She **must** help me, Jocelyn told herself as she walked quickly up the High Street. I 've got to have something positive to report to Kit when he calls tonight.

When she reached the District Nurse's ivy-covered stone cottage, feeling more apprehensive than optimistic, she walked up the brick path and knocked timidly on the blue painted door. Miss Hatherley appeared at the threshold and looked inquiringly at her visitor. She was a wiry little person with a kindly glint in her hazel eyes and a half smile on her thin lips.

"Yes, can I help you?" she asked, in a cultured voice.

She could have been anywhere between thirty and forty-five years old. Her reddish blonde hair was neatly done up in a bun at the nape of her neck, and she was dressed in her dark blue and white midwife's uniform, looking crisp and immaculate. But Jocelyn was most impressed by her kindly demeanour, a distinct and pleasant change from Dr. Bailey.

Noticing Jocelyn's obvious condition, she didn't wait for an explanation of her mission, but invited her into her small parlour where a cheery fire was burning in the grate. She took Jocelyn's damp coat and scarf, hung them on a stand by the door and motioned her to sit by the fire. "Now, tell me what brings you to my door," she asked, settling herself on a chair by the hearth.

Encouraged, Jocelyn poured out the details of her predicament while Miss Hatherley listened intently.

When Jocelyn had finished, she said, "I can understand why Dr. Bailey turned you down. The hospital it is true is overcrowded and they must reserve beds for emergency military personnel. But I do wish that he had not been quite so blunt in his refusal."

"I suppose it was asking too much that he would accept my case on such short notice, but I am desperate. I must find someone who can deliver my baby. It is due in a few weeks."

Miss Hatherley went over to a small desk in the corner of the room and looked at a calendar. Jocelyn looked around the room. The walls were covered with snapshots and formal photographs of babies of all shapes and colour. There was a huge American military establishment just outside of Newmarket housing a great many black servicemen. Obviously some either had married or had relations with English girls. The nurse must be kept very busy, Jocelyn guessed, and also must be well liked if all the mothers of these babies saw fit to present her with pictures of their infants.

Miss Hatherley finished examining her time schedule and turned to Jocelyn with a confident smile. "I'm sure that I'll be able to do something for you," she said. "It's just a matter of fitting you in. We'll have a cup of tea and then talk more about it. Meantime, stop worrying your pretty head. Your baby will be born with a permanent frown on her forehead if you don't."

Jocelyn's chuckled at this absurd suggestion. She had no doubt that she could stop worrying about this problem at least. Miss Hatherley was certainly capable of delivering the baby. All I have to do now, she thought, is find somewhere to live where Rosebud can be brought safely into the world.

After they had taken care of the formalities of booking her in, they chatted over a cup of tea and Jocelyn found to her delight that Miss Hatherley had taken part of her nurses' post graduate training in Canada, at a hospital in Winnipeg. She had great affection for Canadians and for their country and was fascinated when Jocelyn told her about her own maternal grandmother, Sarah Bennett Haimes, who was a midwife in England for many years before emigrating to Canada and whose case book recorded that she had delivered over 1,000 babies during her career.

Jocelyn was enjoying herself so much, she hated to leave but she realized that she was taking up a lot of time of this busy woman. After expressing her deep gratitude, she donned her coat and scarf and hurried back to Surrey House to pass on the good news.

When she spoke to Kit that evening, he was clearly relieved to learn that she had one of her major problems taken care of. But he was still apprehensive about the housing problem. As it transpired, that issue was to be resolved the very next day.

In response to an urgent telephone call from Miggles, received after breakfast the following morning, Jocelyn and Carol and Sheila left the apartment and walked the half mile to a coffee house where they had been asked to meet Simon's sister.

As they entered the shop, Miggles waved them over to the table she had taken, and said good bye to someone she had been chatting with. She was wearing the same scruffy black velvet slacks and crumpled grey-white blouse that had never been graced with an iron. Her pigtails still stuck out from her small head, and a cigarette dangled from one corner of her thin slightly crooked lips.

"I've had the most incredible luck," she bubbled in her high squeaky voice. "I bumped into Mrs. Lee yesterday. Her husband is a colonel in the army and he has been posted somewhere in Scotland. She is going to move out of her house for a while to be near his station, and she'll rent you her place."

"But that's marvellous, Miggles!" Jocelyn exclaimed.

"When can we move in?" Carol asked anxiously.

"Hold on! Nothing has been signed, sealed, and delivered. And there **is** a catch."

Jocelyn's heart sank. "Nothing too serious, I hope."

"That depends on how fussy you are. She has already rented part of the house to a couple with a young daughter. But it's plenty large enough for you as well, as long as you don't mind sharing with someone."

"I'd share with a bull elephant if the house is suitable for me to have the baby," Jocelyn replied.

"What about you, Sheila, and Carol?" Miggles asked.

"It's okay with me," Sheila said readily.

"If she doesn't mind letting us share with these other people, and they don't mind, then it's settled as far as we're concerned," Carol added.

"When will we know for sure, Miggles? Time is running out on me," Jocelyn said.

"Tonight. Archie is going over to see Mrs. Lee. He's an old friend of her husband's. He'll arrange all the formalities for you." Miggles picked up her string bag which served as her handbag, and got up to leave.

"Can't we treat you to a coffee?" Jocelyn asked.

"Thanks awfully, but I have to meet Dee at the Chemist's shop in a few minutes. I had coffee with Betsy Carson before you arrived. So, ta, ta. I'll be in touch." With a wave of her small bony tanned hand, she was away to her next appointment.

They finished their coffee and left the shop, chattering gaily about this wonderful news as they strolled back to Surrey House.

***

A call from Miggles the next morning told them they could go that afternoon to meet the owner of the house.

Queensbury Lodge, Mrs. Lee's home, was an early eighteenth century, two-storey building with a forbidding grey stone front rising directly from the High Street, and with no windows on that front elevation. The outside wall abruptly ceased being part of the house and continued to enclose the grounds as a high thick stone fence at the end of which was a dark green lattice gate leading to the rear of the house. Here were located the stables and gardens, a fragment of the charming rural scene amidst which the Lodge had once stood. The lawns were uncared for now, and wild flowers bloomed in profusion among the weeds.

Mrs. Lee, greeted the three young wives in the garden, apologizing for its sad state. She had not been able to keep a gardener since the war started, she explained with obvious regret as she escorted them inside the Lodge.

The house could easily occupy the full time efforts of at least two maids. One glance at the cavernous dark kitchen and scullery was sufficient evidence that no lady of the house had ever spent a whole morning working there. However, Jocelyn noted with satisfaction that it had a gas cooker in the scullery, and, in the main kitchen, was an Ideal Boiler for heating water. Above it was suspended an extra large clothes rack, or maiden in British lingo, which would be just the thing for drying the babies' diapers and nighties. She pointed this feature out to Sheila.

"That'll be a boon in this soggy climate," Sheila agreed.

The dining room, which was to serve as a combined dining-sitting room, contained a small square mahogany table, six chairs, a small buffet, a love seat, and two easy chairs. The dark oak panelled walls were cluttered with photographs of the owners, their horses, jockeys, and, of all things, a large autographed photo of Fred Astaire, patting a horse's nose and grinning widely. There was a gas radiant instead of a coal grate, so at least they would be able to keep warm easily. And there was a dumb waiter between this room and the kitchen.

The entrance hall was almost as large as the dining room. It boasted a marble fireplace in which no fire had ever been laid, a colossal Japanese silk screen which served no apparent purpose, a formidable array of brass ornaments that pleaded dumbly to be cleaned, and sundry other pieces of memorabilia of the Lees' overseas postings. On one wall was a huge oil painting of a turbulent sea, and on the opposite wall was a water colour of two dead ducks hanging upside down.

What took Jocelyn's eye was the telephone sitting on a small mahogany table in one corner. She could keep in touch with Kit.

The three bedrooms they were allotted were adequately furnished, and the beds seemed to be comfortable, as far as they could tell at a glance. Of course, after what they had been sleeping on in Sheila's flat, anything would have been an improvement. Carol and Jocelyn elected to sleep upstairs. The room Sheila chose was on the main floor at the end of the very long passage which stretched along the street side of the house. The hallway had no natural light but the bedroom had two long windows overlooking the back gardens.

Adjacent to Sheila's room, and right at the end of the passage, was another small room containing a single iron bedstead, a rusty sink, and it had forbidding iron bars on the windows. It was a maid's room, Mrs. Lee explained and was no longer used except for storage.

All in all, they agreed that the Lodge would suit them very well, so they wasted no time in completing the formalities of a lease to rent it for an indefinite period. This allowed them to be free to leave, but it also gave the owner the option of turfing them out at any time. However, beggars could not be choosers. They accepted this arrangement, said good bye to Mrs. Lee, and hurried back to Surrey House to break the good news to the Potts.

CHAPTER 19

By the following Monday, Sheila had beguiled a reluctant taxi driver into moving their heavier pieces of baggage to the Lodge which was located about three blocks from Surrey House. He was also persuaded to make a detour to the railway depot to pick up Jocelyn and Carol's possessions which had been causing strained relations between them and the baggage clerk for the past week.

Since the cab driver would not overload his car, they had to find another way to transport Sheila's various household utensils. They hit on the idea of using Rosebud's pram which they loaded up with sundry pots, pans, and dishes. Attempting to maintain a degree of dignity, Jocelyn pushed the pram while Sheila walked alongside holding on to the pieces that were in constant danger of falling off. As they made their way up the High Street, Jocelyn smiled to herself wondering how poor Violet would have reacted had she seen them.

Carol had gone ahead to meet the cab driver. When he had unloaded all of their possessions on to the pavement in front of the Lodge, he took his fare and was about to get back into his cab. Carol went over to him and put on her most appealing expression. "I don't suppose you would consider taking the trunks into the house?" she asked plaintively.

"Sorry, Miss, that's not in me line of dooty." And with that he got into his cab and drove off.

Carol watched him go, sadly bemoaning the death of chivalry.

Left to their own initiative, by lunch time they managed to transfer everything from the trunks into the front hall, and then moved the now empty trunks into the unused maid's room. Working with beaver-like perseverance, and stopping only to have a hasty snack and some tea, they were almost completely settled into the Lodge by bed time.

That evening, Jocelyn telephoned Kit to tell him that the move had gone very well and had done neither herself nor Rosebud any harm. With Kit mollified, with the assurance that Miss Hatherley would be on hand for her confinement and that she now had a home in which to have her baby, she climbed gratefully into her very own comfortable double bed and slept solidly until morning.

The moving day had been sunny, and the good weather continued, so they were able to make use of the garden at the back of the Lodge for reading and getting some sun. It was much more pleasant than the Potts' domain, and the sharing of quarters proved quite satisfactory. The Doles were a pleasant couple and had only one child, a daughter aged 10. Mrs. Dole, a plump blonde woman with rosy cheeks, a high-pitched girlish voice and dyed blonde Shirley Temple ringlets, did intrude on them occasionally. From time to time, she would put her head through the dumb waiter which opened into their lounge cum-dining room and say, "I say theya, we must get organized." They never did discover just what it was she wanted them to do, but having made the gesture, and received their promise to talk it over with her, she would retreat to her own part of the house evidently feeling completely satisfied that she had done her part to be cooperative.

Not only did they enjoy the garden but they took great pleasure in giving the race horses that were lodged in the stables daily treats of carrots and sugar cubes. Mrs. Lee was very proud of the fact that one of the King's horses was often stabled at the Lodge and that, since the war, the famous Derby was held in Newmarket.

Every Tuesday was racing day at which time the town was crammed to bursting point with the oddest conglomeration of people who came from far and near for the races. The High Street was jammed with a rare assortment of vehicles—horse drawn four-wheeled and two-wheeled carts, buggies, bicycles, motorcycles, anything that ran with little or no scarce petrol and that would transport the racing enthusiasts to the course which was located on the outskirts of the town.

On racing days there was a constant stream of strangers who knocked on the door of the Lodge begging for a place to stay the night. It was finally agreed that on Tuesdays they would bolt the front door securely and retreat to the garden, weather permitting, or if it was raining, simply stay indoors and ignore all callers.

The days and weeks ahead were filled with housekeeping, shopping for rations, and trying to find ways to eke out the food and prepare it to the best advantage. They found a dozen ways to serve dried eggs and to make their small meat rations spin out. And they waited—for letters, for telephone calls, for the too brief flying visits of husbands, and for the expected babies.

Rosebud obliged by not entering the world on May 8th, the prescribed date, which gave Jocelyn the chance to settle in at the Lodge and make all the necessary preparations for the confinement. Miss Hatherley popped in for a visit to ensure that the house was a suitable substitute for a maternity ward, and she gave Jocelyn a list of things she would need for the birth.

Even though their most pressing problems were resolved, that of finding a home and someone to oversee the delivery of Jocelyn's baby, there was an undercurrent of anxiety and fear in the atmosphere. When the telephone rang, or someone came to the door unexpectedly, there was always the chance that it could bring a dreaded message from Air Ministry, 'We regret to inform you....'

But the moment the innocence of the call or message was established, the fearful expressions would vanish and a more relaxed mood would prevail. It was not too difficult to extinguish the outward manifestations of the fear that haunted their lives, but it burned like a steady low flame in their hearts.

Jocelyn now rarely left the Lodge except on warm sunny days when she would sit out in the garden and read, or knit on the small garments for Rosebud. It was on such a day, a little more than two weeks after they had moved, that Carol came flying out of the house waving a letter in the air.

She called to Jocelyn, who was sitting in a sheltered corner reading.

"Joc, Joc, I've got the most wonderful news! I'm going to Blackpool, at least Dennis is, and he wants me to join him. For a whole week!"

"That's marvellous! When do you go?"

Carol's joy suddenly turned to chagrin. "Oh, my gosh. I forgot. You'll be all alone if I dash off, and what if Rosebud should arrive?"

"If I need you desperately, I can always send a smoke signal, and you can come back in a few hours. You can't afford to miss an opportunity like this," Jocelyn insisted.

"You're a brick, hon'. But I feel like a selfish pig getting so excited about this when I see Dennis quite often and you never get to see Kit."

"Our turn will come. Don't you dare spoil your good fortune because of me. Right now, just living here with you and Sheila and being able to speak to Kit every evening is absolute heaven."

"Oh, I almost forgot," Carol said, fishing in the pocket of her jacket. "Here is your daily pick-me-up." She handed Jocelyn three letters.

Jocelyn took them and said, "You tear along and let Dennis know you're ready, willing, and able. I'll spend some time with my beloved, at least in my imagination."

Although Kit telephoned almost every night, he still faithfully wrote to her each day, even if it was only to remind her of his love. Jocelyn sat absorbing his loving words, over and over, her heart surging with longing. It was not often that she had difficulty counting her blessings, or refusing to compare her lot with that of Sheila and Carol. But there were moments when the futility of Kit's and her position—that of being so near and yet so far apart—filled her with bitter despondency. It was so unfair that he could not get down to Newmarket, even for a day. And it wasn't as though they could look forward with any assurance to the situation improving in the near future. In one of his letters that day, he said that there was talk of posting his entire course to the Middle East when their training was finished. It wasn't definite, and he was working against it with all his might. But, in all fairness, he felt he had to warn her.

A black cloud suddenly blotted out the warmth of the sun's rays and a cool breeze sprung up from nowhere causing her to shiver and scattering the thin blue pages of her letters over the grass. She leaned down to retrieve them, and as she placed them on her lap a tear trickled down the side of her nose and dropped on to the page, making an inky blue pool where it fell.

She brushed it away, smudging the ink as she did so. Then, hearing Carol's voice beckoning her in to supper, she dried her eyes, picked up her book and Kit's letters and walked slowly back to the house.

***

It was strange how unobservant one became when engrossed in one's own problems. Jocelyn had been living in close quarters with Sheila these past weeks, and yet it wasn't until Carol went to Blackpool that she discovered what a tangle Sheila and Simon were making of their marriage.

The day after Carol's departure, she was seated in the lounge, the dry penetrating heat of the gas radiant toasting her legs, when Sheila came in with the mail. She handed Jocelyn her letters, then sat down on the footstool, her blonde head resting against the chair, and her small tanned hands toying with the sapphire ring on her finger. She rarely received any letters. Simon never wrote to her.

"You're so lucky, Jocelyn," she said sadly.

Jocelyn looked up quickly. "Me? Lucky? I've always been very unlucky. I never win anything, not even a game of solitaire, and look how little I've seen of Kit since I came here."

"I guess I don't mean lucky exactly. But you're sure of Kit. I've only met him once, for that short time in Liverpool, but it was so obvious that he adores you."

Jocelyn smiled. "He's having a hard time doing that right now. You're the lucky one. Look how often Simon pops home for a day or two. I'd give my eye tooth if Kit could come just for a few hours."

Sheila's said bitterly, "Oh, yes, Simon comes home all right. But how much do I see of him? He whips down to Miggles and Deirdre's as soon as he's dumped his knapsack. He just loves going there and communing with the spooks they conjure up in their silly seances."

"Why don't you go with him?"

Sheila snorted. "And make a fool of myself pretending to commune with spirits. No thanks! If he prefers the company of departed spirits to mine, then he's welcome."

"Is he really serious about spiritualism?"

"I don't know. It's likely just an excuse to leave me behind. He knows I won't go to seances, so it gives him a good chance to escape."

"Escape what?"

"Me. He's ashamed of me at the moment. I had a nice figure, but right now I look like a misshapen old dunnage bag and I'm not much use in bed." Her mouth drooped in a pathetic pout.

Jocelyn suddenly felt sorry for her. She stared into the fire wondering how their marriage could have got off to such a bad start. How they could have so little insight into each other's feelings. Life was complicated enough with this cursed war and its hazards and inhibitions, without deliberately adding to the chaos.

A sideways glance at Sheila's face revealed the helpless pathetic expression that had replaced her more usual carefree pose. She was like a sad, defenceless child, and Jocelyn realized that all her flirting, her capriciousness likely were a front—a buffer between her and the world, or more exactly between her and the callous indifference of Simon.

"Couldn't you have a talk with Simon, and try to make him see how you feel?"

Sheila shook her head in a gesture of hopelessness. "He wouldn't know what I was talking about. He's sweet in lots of ways, and loving, but his standards are his own. He's not stable or dependable like Kit, or Dennis."

"Couldn't you sort of persuade him to be a little more considerate," Jocelyn suggested.

"Not a chance. We didn't get off to a very good start you know."

"What do you mean?"

"Well, I had only known him three weeks, and of course we fell madly in love. At least I did. I'm not so sure about him. We dashed off in a romantic cloud of dust and got married. On the first night of our honeymoon, in the small hotel near Simon's station, I received a visitor. It was the irate father of the girl Simon had been engaged to. My ears are still burning from the fiery insults he flung at me. He wasn't angry at Simon, the louse who had jilted his daughter. Oh, no. All his venom was directed at me, the jezebel who had lured Simon away. Of course, he wouldn't even let me explain that I knew nothing about the engagement."

"I expect you got some sort of explanation from Simon?"

"Not really. He just laughed and shrugged it off. But I know he still gets letters from the girl. He claims he doesn't answer them, but I'm sure he does."

Jocelyn was nonplussed. She didn't know what to say. It was hard to believe that someone as charming and likeable as Simon could be so unprincipled. And yet, she felt instinctively that this was not one of Sheila's flights of fancy. The hurt in her eyes was real.

After a moment Jocelyn said, "Well, if you love him and believe he's worth fighting for, then I'd fight tooth and nail against that scheming female, and Miggles' spooks."

Sheila's face brightened. "You're a real tonic, Joc. No wonder Kit adores you, and Carol thinks you're great."

"They're both somewhat biased. I didn't exactly make a hit with my mother-in-law, did I?" She got up and went to the door. "What do you say we brew up a pot of strong tea and drink to the extermination of all female dragons?"

"A great idea!" Sheila replied, regaining her usual good humour. She saluted Jocelyn and said, "To the galley, Mate, to brew some tannic acid for this excellent toast."

CHAPTER 20

The due date for Jocelyn's confinement, May 8th, 1944, came and went and Jocelyn still waited. In a letter to Kit she said that she now hoped that the baby would be born on May 24th. He asked why and she answered by reciting a jingle popular among Canadian school children—'the 24th of May's the Queen's birthday, if we don't get a holiday, we'll all run away'. And they always did get a holiday and had picnics, fireworks, and bonfires to celebrate the occasion of Queen Victoria's birthday. Kit saw no logic at all in Canadians celebrating the birthday of this long-dead Queen, and Jocelyn argued that it made more sense to pay homage to a monarch who had presided over the building up of the British Empire than to remember a foolish Guy Fawkes who, eons ago, had merely tried to blow up the Parliament Buildings. Neither succeeded in convincing the other.

Jocelyn's main reason for wanting this date was that Rosebud would always be sure of having a holiday on her birthday. However, she was destined to be disappointed because it was two days earlier, on the 22nd of May, that Rosebud finally made her way into the world, aided and abetted by the experienced Miss Hatherley and the very inexperienced Carol.

The doctor whom Miss Hatherley had enlisted to be present came at 1:30 p.m., looked the situation over and pronounced confidently that the baby would not appear until much later in the day. He then hurried off to a prearranged golf game, promising to return later in the afternoon.

The front door of the Lodge had scarcely closed on his departure when Jocelyn went into the final stages of labour and Miss Hatherley, with Carol's assistance, delivered a healthy eight and a half pound baby girl.

When Miss Hatherley cleaned the baby up and handed the tiny bundle to Carol to be placed in the basket, two large round violet eyes peeped out from beneath the blanket with such a comic look of shocked surprise that Carol promptly nicknamed her new niece, Boo.

The doctor, as promised, returned around 5 o'clock and, without any apology, administered some anaesthetic to Jocelyn before putting in the stitches that Boo's arrival had occasioned. As she told Kit later, the pain relief would have been more welcome earlier in the day. Nevertheless, considering the circumstances, everything went well and both mother and child were in good shape. In fact, Jocelyn was in much better shape than she had been for many months.

She was exhausted not only from the excruciating labour pains, but also from the previous night's surprising and chilling air raid. The warning was sounded about midnight, and it was the last thing that anyone expected in this part of England. They learned later that three houses on the High Street just north of the Lodge were hit by a strange kind of missile, the like of which had never been seen before.

Although it was some weeks before it was officially acknowledged, the strange object was one of the Germany's new secret un-manned weapons, the flying bomb, which was to terrorize the inhabitants of the southern counties and take the lives of so many innocent victims. Fortunately, it was a fluke that one had gone off course and had come as far as Newmarket, and they were not bothered by any more such raids.

For a few days the entire household of Queensbury Lodge was at the mercy of Boo's whims and cries, but gradually, under Miss Hatherley's expert guidance and sound common sense, Boo gradually fitted into a routine, and all was serene again.

It was serene perhaps, but not quiet. The week of Jocelyn's confinement saw the beginning of a gigantic movement of war vehicles and military personnel down to the south coast, in preparation for the long-awaited invasion of Europe. Motorcycles, jeeps, trucks, flame throwers, airplane carriers, tanks, every conceivable type of war transport rumbled up the High Street, passing directly under Jocelyn's rattling bedroom window. There was little respite from the roar of the engines as they ground into low gear in order to make the incline sloping past the Lodge. The unbearable racket went on from four in the morning until midnight. Although Jocelyn found it very wearing, the noise had not the slightest effect on Boo who slept peacefully through it all, waking only when she was hungry or needed changing.

The scent of a rainbow assortment of spring flowers permeated Jocelyn's room. They were a pleasure in themselves, but the most wonderful thing about them was the message written on the card enclosed with them. Kit was coming home!

Lying in bed waiting for that day to arrive was a trying test of patience. Jocelyn was so afraid that something might go wrong and he would not be able to come at the last moment. However, the day finally arrived and, when she heard Carol greet him at the door, heard his voice and his wonderful chuckle, then his footsteps on the stairs, she thought her heart would pound right out of her breast.

He opened the bedroom door softly, tip-toed in, and before turning to her, stood silently by the bassinet, gazing with wonderment and pride on the tiny sleeping form of his daughter. Then he turned to Jocelyn, a shy expression on his face. "She's beautiful. Just as I said she would be. Just like her mother."

In fact, with her violet eyes and golden reddish fuzz crowning her head, in looks she was far more Kit's child than Jocelyn's. Kit left the bassinet and went over to her and enfolded her in his arms. Tears of joy glistened on her long dark lashes, and he held her tightly in his arms and kissed them away.

It was only one day, one out of all eternity, and every second of it was made to count to its fullest measure. He had so much to tell her, and she to tell him, but the news that eclipsed all other was that his course was over in a week's time and his posting to a squadron operating in England was assured. Best of all, he was to have nine days leave between leaving Scotland and reporting to 254 Squadron based at North Coates near Grimsby on the east coast. It was only thirty miles, as the crow flew, to Newmarket.

As Kit lay beside her that night, sleeping soundly, with his blond head resting on her arm, a half smile on his lips, a new peace came to Jocelyn—a peace, she thought, recalling the familiar words from the Anglican prayer book, that passeth all understanding. She prayed fervently that it might last.

***

The day Kit returned to Scotland, Carol, who was cook for that week, busied herself in the kitchen, using all her skill and ingenuity to concoct, out of the skimpy rations, a meal that would satisfy another hungry male—and one a great deal harder to fill than Kit who was lean and always ate sparingly. Simon was a blond, handsome, giant of a man, with a giant's appetite.

On the small table in the centre of the room, Carol deftly rolled out pastry, humming all the while. She wore a large flowered apron over her navy slacks and fresh white blouse. Her hands were white and doughy, and a smudge of white flour covered the freckles on her nose. She turned from her rolling pin and addressed Sheila who was washing some dishes in the sink. "Will you put the light on for me, please, Sheila? My hands are all messy, and it's getting so dark in here I can hardly see what I'm doing."

Sheila dried her hands, went over to the switch and put on the light. "Is that any better?"

"Marginally. We need a stronger bulb in that crummy ceiling fixture. Anyway, it has some psychological value to know it's on. It looks as though it's going to rain. What time do you expect Simon?"

"Around six." Sheila's tone was surly. Her golden hair was damp and was pinned haphazardly on top of her head and tied with a plaid ribbon. She had finished her chore and was gazing absently out of the window.

"Say," Carol said. "you'd better hop to your room and dress. Your beloved will be here soon."

Sheila continued to stare out of the window. watching the wind play with branches of the lilac tree growing against the side of the house.

Carol expertly flipped the thinly rolled pastry on to the pie plate and sprinkled it generously with chopped apple. "Does Simon like apple pie?"

"I really don't know, and frankly I could care less," Sheila snapped.

"Well, pardon me," Carol said. "What's the matter with you? You're grouchy as an old man with gout. And you should be in high spirits with Simon about to arrive."

Sheila turned away from the window. "Nothing's the matter... except...except. Oh, what difference does it make anyway?"

She left the kitchen quickly and went to her room.

Carol shook her head in wonderment. She would never understand those two. 'I expect she'll have forgotten her rotten mood by the time Simon arrives', she told herself.

But she was wrong.

It was just after six when Simon walked into the lounge where Sheila was curled up on a chair before the fire, reading. She didn't look up when he entered and she made no effort to greet him. He threw his small knapsack on the sofa and walked over to her. "Well, aren't you going to say hello?"

Sheila ignored him. He sat on the arm of her chair. "Aren't you glad to see me?"

"Not particularly. Should I be?"

"Well, I've just flown home to spend a forty-eight with you."

"With me? With Miggles and her spooks you mean."

"Pfew! If I'd known what kind of reception I'd get, I'd have stayed at camp."

"No, you wouldn't. You'd have gone directly to Miggles."

Simon lit a cigarette and puffed on it for a moment. Suddenly his eyes softened and he leaned toward her. "What's the matter, moppet? What have I done to deserve this chilly reception?"

Sheila refused to look at him, knowing that the moment her eyes rested on that persuasive smile she would lose her resolve to have it out with him.

Ever since her talk with Jocelyn she had been promising herself this moment. She wasn't going to be cajoled out of it by his magnetic charm. He had been home twice since then, and each time he had not spent more than five minutes alone with her. He would take off for Dovedale at the first opportunity and not reappear until after midnight. She was through pretending she didn't really mind sitting home alone like a stuffed dummy. It was humiliating enough, but when Miggles started patronizing her with,

'Poor Sheila. It's a pity she isn't well enough to come out too'. Well, that was the end.

She was about to launch her protest when from the hall came the shrill ring of the telephone. In a moment, Carol called, "Simon, it's for you."

Sheila shrugged, and when he closed the door behind him, she buried her face in her hands. The moment of reckoning had come and now it was gone. 'What's the use', she asked herself bitterly.

When it was ready, Carol served the dried egg and onion omelet, mashed potatoes, and apple pie to Sheila and Simon in the dining room.

When they had finished, she asked, "What are you two doing tonight?" Whatever it is, hop to it. I'll clean up the dishes."

Simon coughed nervously. "Well, er-ah-I that is, Miggles wants us to go to a party tonight. Archie is throwing it in honour of his birthday. But, I'm not sure that we're going. It's up to Sheila."

"I've just washed my hair. It's wet. I can't go out." Sheila said, pushing back her chair and clearing the table. "I'll do the dishes, Carol. It's my turn. You made supper."

"Yes, you're off duty," Simon added. "I'll help Sheila."

"Okay, if you insist. I'll get back to my book and leave you two lovebirds alone."

Lovebirds they were not, and when Carol left the room, Simon said grimly, "For the last time, are you going to be sensible and come with me tonight? Miggles really wants you to come."

"And you? Do you **really** want me to come?"

"Of course I do."

"Well, I really don't want to go." With that, she got up, marched defiantly past him, out of kitchen and to her room.

A short time later, some of Miggles' friends arrived in a car and whisked Simon off to the party.

Sheila was no fool. She knew that her behaviour was no way to win her battle for Simon's attention. She was angry with herself for losing her temper and being spiteful. She would have to wage a more subtle and effective war on 'female dragons', as Jocelyn had so aptly described them.

At breakfast the next morning, she was immaculately groomed and her violet eyes sparkled as she slipped into her chair opposite Simon. Carol noted her change of mood with relief. She hated to witness their bickering.

Simon was at first puzzled by Sheila's apparent change of mood, then relieved.

"Did you have fun at the party?" Sheila asked lightly.

"It wasn't a bad bash. Everyone asked for you."

"I'm sure," Sheila said sweetly.

"Archie's a good sort really," Simon went on, encouraged by Sheila's congeniality. "He offered me the loan of his car today. I thought we might go on a picnic."

"I'd love that," Sheila said agreeably. "I'll pack us a lunch."

"Splendid!" Simon said, getting up from the table. "It's supposed to be a fine day. I'll dash down and pick up the car while you make the lunch."

He donned his tweed sports jacket, gave Sheila a quick peck on top of her head and left.

While he was gone, Sheila made some sandwiches out of a tin of corned beef sent from Canada, brewed a thermos of coffee, and went to her room to change into some suitable clothes for the occasion. She popped her head into Jocelyn's room and told her, "I'm going out slaying dragons!"

Jocelyn wished her good luck.

Carol came in after Sheila had left. She was carrying a fresh supply of formula for Boo, and a stack of newly laundered diapers. "Hi, is my favourite niece awake?"

"I'm not sure. You'd better have a peek. She's been awfully quiet, except for the odd gurgle and hiccough. Do you know, I'm sure that she smiled today."

Carol laughed as she bent over the basket. "Just gas," she said authoritatively.

Boo's enormous dark blue eyes stared up at her trustingly. Carol picked her up, settled her comfortably on her lap and began giving her the contents of the bottle. It had taken a few sessions with Miss Hatherley, but she finally got the hang of giving Boo her bottle without her getting any unwanted air which could cause discomfort, and also of giving her a bath, or 'top and tailing' her, as Miss Hatherley called it.

"What's with Sheila?" Jocelyn asked, as she swung her slim legs over the side of the bed and stood up. "She sounded almost happy."

"I'm not sure. They had a bit of a tiff yesterday, but all seems forgiven and forgotten."

"I hope so. While you feed Boo, I'm going to have a bath. Then I'm going to get dressed and go downstairs. I've been playing the invalid long enough."

"Are you sure you're strong enough? There's no rush for you to get up, you know."

"I know, but I've imposed long enough on your good will. As Mom used to say, it's time I shook my feathers."

She trotted off to the bathroom, her legs feeling a bit weak and wobbly. Other than that, she felt just fine. And how good it was to see her feet again!

She stayed up most of the day, but was back in bed by the time Sheila and Simon returned from their picnic. All day she had been wondering how they made out. It was the first time Sheila had been able to wean Simon away from the Dovedale menage long enough to make any progress. Miggles was terribly possessive, but Jocelyn felt sure there was no deliberate malice in her monopoly of Simon's time. She just didn't think beyond the end of her long thin nose.

CHAPTER 21

The blackout curtains were drawn and the lights turned on inside the Lodge before Jocelyn heard a car come to a halt at the front entrance. She heard the car door slam, then Sheila's short steps clicking up the walk to the door. The car drove off, the front door opened and closed, and Sheila started upstairs.

"Hi, Sheila," Jocelyn called. "Come in. I'm awake."

Sheila hesitated a second, then turned into Jocelyn's warm bright room. Her hair was tangled, she had no lipstick on, and she was on the verge of tears. She sank down on Jocelyn's bed and kicked off her sandals.

"How was the picnic?" Jocelyn asked, guessing what the answer would be.

"Fine, just fine. We had a smashing time, all five of us."

"Five of you? I thought it was just you and Simon."

"So did I, but it seemed that when Miggles heard our plans she thought it was a **divine** idea and begged to come along. That was bad enough, but she dragged along some creature called Dodie—Dodo would have been more apt. I suspect she's the one they produce when 'poor Sheila' isn't well enough to be there. And, of course, Deirdre came as well. It was a veritable Sunday School picnic."

"What a shame. I had such high hopes," Jocelyn said.

"So did I, foolishly. But you can't win a war with hope. You need long scrawny arms to twine about the neck of your victim, and bony fingers to ruffle his hair, and you need a name like Dodie!"

Sheila sat quietly for a moment, sapped of energy by her anger and frustration. Then a hard glint came into her eyes and she stood up. "I'm not going to let them get away with it. This is the last time that I take a back seat to that hussy. In future, I'll trail along behind Simon like a squaw, whether he likes it or not."

"By the way, where is Simon?"

Standing by the door, Sheila said, "They wouldn't let him come home with me. He wanted to, I'm sure. But they wouldn't hear of it. Poor Simple Simon. Just like a puppet on a string. Well, I'm going to operate the strings from now on."

"That's the stuff," Jocelyn said.

"Well, I'm off to bed. Good night, Joc. See you in the morning."

"Good night," Jocelyn said, and turned off her lamp.

In the dark she lay back on her pillow and wondered. Her first impulse was to feel sorry for Sheila. And yet, at the back of her mind, there was a seed of doubt. There were so many times when Sheila overdramatized her role as the neglected wife, almost as though she relished it. It was obvious, too, that she was purposefully contrary at times, like washing her hair just as Simon was due to arrive home. She made Jocelyn feel at times as though she were annoyed and hurt more because he humiliated her than because he didn't seem capable of giving her his wholehearted and constant love. Perhaps Sheila wouldn't know what to do with his heart if she possessed it entirely. Perhaps, if the pattern of that marriage did change course and began to run smoothly, Sheila would become bored with it all, and would stir up some mischief herself, to liven things up a bit. Meanwhile, however, she had her share of competition. Apart from Miggles and Dodie, there was the girl he had jilted in Canada who still wanted him back. What formidable odds against a successful marriage. Poor Sheila. And even more to the point, the poor baby that was to brought into the world in a few months.

Simon was scheduled to return to his squadron later the next day, and Miggles had telephoned to say that she and Deirdre would be dropping in that afternoon to say good bye to him. Carol, who had answered the 'phone, asked them to come in time for tea. When Sheila heard that, she arranged for Simon to go shopping with her and made certain that they were not back when Miggles, in her breathless fashion, blitzed in, followed by Deirdre.

If either of them had any clothes other than the black velvet or red corduroy slacks, they never wore them. Jocelyn ushered them into the lounge.

"Where are Simon and Sheila?" Miggles asked, stretching herself out on one of the chairs and lighting a cigarette.

"Down town. I'm surprised you didn't run into them."

"We got a drive with Archie," Deirdre replied, sitting down on the chair opposite Miggles and taking a letter out of her shabby red leather handbag. "I forgot to read dear Owen's letter. Will you excuse me if I open it. I'm anxious to see what my husband has to say."

"Go ahead," Jocelyn said. "I'll be back in a tick. I'll help Carol bring in the tea."

She was back in a moment and sat down on the stool by the fire. Deirdre was still reading her letter. Miggles was now standing and she was restlessly examining everything in the room without really looking. She puffed sporadically on her cigarette.

"What does my dear elder brother have to say?" she asked Deirdre who finally put the letter back in her bag.

"He's been in London for a few days."

"Oh, and how is dear Pamela?"

"Her flat has been hit by a buzz bomb."

"So?" Miggles questioned. "What does that portend?"

"It portends that we are going to be graced with her presence. Owen has invited her to Dovedale for a rest from those awful flying bombs. She's arriving tomorrow to stay until another friend can put her up."

Pamela Heathby was an exotic female in whose handy flat in London Owen Barton-Holmes was able to sample home comfort away from home, so to speak.

"Of course, Owen always was impetuous," Miggles squeaked. "but I suppose the poor lamb couldn't think of any other place to send her. Did you say she's coming tomorrow?"

Carol arrived bearing the tea tray which she set down beside Deirdre.

"Who's coming?" she asked, sitting down and starting to pour the tea.

"Pam Heathby, a very dear friend of Owen's. The poor girl has been bombed out of her London flat and he wants us to put her up for a short while."

Carol knew just how dear a friend Pamela Heathby was, and she arched her eyebrows slightly. "Oh," was all she said.

Miggles ceased pacing around the room and sat down on the chair. She immediately rose to her brother's defence. "It's really quite a good arrangement, don't you agree, Dee?"

"Of course. I owe a great deal to Pamela in a way. She keeps Owen from becoming one of those wretched husbands who are bottled up with frustrations and have fiendish tempers, simply because their wives, like me, are tied down with three monsters. Owen is always gentle as a lamb when he's with us, and he couldn't be nicer to the children."

"Well," Carol said matter of factly, "I'm a bit selfish where Dennis is concerned. I have no desire to share him with anyone, no matter how noble their motives; nor how sweet-tempered it might make him."

Deirdre's small thin mouth twisted into a sardonic smile. "But my dear child," she said patronizingly, "you don't honestly think that Dennis is faithful to you and you alone?"

"Not only do I think it, I believe it," Carol countered.

Miggled tittered and winked knowingly at Deirdre. "How quaint," she squeaked.

"Well, in any case," Deirdre said, placing her tea cup on the table and getting ready to leave, "you must come to Dovedale to meet Pam. She's really quite charming. We'll have a tea party in her honour."

"A splendid idea," Miggles chimed in. "We'll have Dodie, and, of course, Sheila."

"You **will** come?" Deirdre said, looking directly at Carol.

"Wouldn't miss it for the world," Carol replied, with a mischievous grin.

"Count me out," Jocelyn said. "Boo's a bit young for high-powered tea parties."

"Very well, that's settled then," Miggles said, glancing up at the clock on the mantel. "Oh, m'god!. It's after four o'clock. Mrs. Vale will go off and leave the brood if we don't get back before five." She stood up, brushed the cake crumbs off her lap and followed Deirdre to the door. "It's a shame we've missed Simon. Do say 'ta ta' for us."

"Yes, do," Deirdre added. "And don't forget, tea on Thursday, around three."

"I won't," Carol assured them. "We'll pass the messages along to Sheila and Simon."

Dovedale was like a circus when Carol and Sheila arrived on Thursday afternoon. Children swarmed everywhere and their piercing screams and shrill laughter could be heard half way to town.

As she ushered the visitors into the lounge, Miggles tripped over three-year old Randy and she snapped impatiently at the child, "Do get out from under foot, Randy!" She set the chubby youngster on his fat legs and apologized to the guests. "Excuse the bedlam, but Mrs. Vale didn't have any better sense than to get a chill on top of a bad throat, and couldn't come in today."

She led the way to the back terrace where chairs had been placed about a round wobbly picnic table. She introduced them to the guest of honour who looked as though she wished herself back in London with the buzz bombs.

Carol had been more than normally curious to meet the reputedly glamorous mistress of Owen Barton-Holmes, but, in truth, here was a very ordinary looking girl, with a longer than average nose, sunken cheeks and a sallow complexion. Her hair was stringy and the colour of mud. But from what could be seen of her slender long legs, small waistline, and firm breasts as she languished on a decrepit chaise lounge, Carol decided that must be what captivated Owen.

Deirdre was charming to a degree, and most conciliatory toward her rival. However, towards the end of the tea party, the subject of Owen's former mistresses mysteriously popped up in the conversation.

"Do you remember Daphne?" Miggles squeaked, her small monkey face wrinkled in humour, and smoke pouring from her thin nostrils.

Deirdre's high forehead wrinkled in a frown as though she were trying to recall the name. Then her face relaxed in a benign smile. "But of course. She was a lovely thing. A bit lanky perhaps, and flat chested, and she talked too much. At least, so Owen told me. She didn't last long, as I recall." She laughed a tinkling laugh and faced Pamela. "As a matter fact, a bit of a bitch she was. At least so Owen told me. Will you have some tea, Pam?"

"No thank you," Pam said coldly, and smoothed her thin muddy hair with beautifully manicured nails.

Miggles suddenly chuckled merrily. "Oh, yes, Dee, than there was...what was her name?... Cynthia...that was it. How could I forget?"

Deirdre smiled sweetly and again looked directly at Pam. "Cynthia," she mused, "now there was a bitch. Of course, as dear Owen always says...there **are** bitches, and there **are** bitches. But, **do** have some tea, my dear."

CHAPTER 22

Beyond the high grey stone wall that enclosed Queensbury Lodge, the ominous rumbling of war vehicles continued to intrude on their lives. In the skies the steady thrumming of heavy bombers was a constant reminder that the invasion of Europe was imminent. With grave faces and in sombre tones people discussed it, and watched, and wondered, and waited. A palpable air of tension and expectancy hung like a pall over England, and the south coast became host to the incredible variety of vehicles and troops that streamed endlessly through towns and villages en route to become part of the allied invasion force.

Simon and Dennis had very little respite from their task of low level bombing missions over France and Germany, striking at trains carrying men and supplies for the German army, and at other strategic targets. Kit's Beaufighter squadron was constantly seeking out and attacking enemy merchant vessels and minesweepers off the coast of Norway and over the North Sea. The worry for the men's safety permeated the atmosphere of the Lodge, stifling the usual lightheartedness the wives affected.

Kit was granted the promised leave and had been home for three of the nine days—three wonderful days in which he and Jocelyn were content to sit in the garden, usually with Boo nearby sleeping nearby in her pram. They tried to ignore the disturbing traffic noise beyond the stone wall of the Lodge, knowing that it was a certain portent of the greater rumblings to come.

As they reclined lazily in their deck chairs on sunny days, Kit's trained ear would identify the aircraft that droned overhead, and he attempted to school Jocelyn in the art of aircraft recognition, just as in Charlottetown he taught her to recognize the silhouettes of the enemy ships with which he, as a pilot in Coastal Command, must be familiar. She became quite good at that, and was now becoming an expert on aircraft recognition.

She had come quickly to the realization that the peace she enjoyed for that brief interlude barely a week ago, and that she prayed so hard would last, was merely an illusion, a tantalizing mirage to be glimpsed at in rare moments, but always beyond her grasp.

On Kit's first day of leave she asked him casually, "What sort of work are you doing on the squadron, darling?"

He was slow to answer. His eyes avoided hers and followed the strange antics of a lone exuberant butterfly. At length he looked at her, frowning and yet half smiling. "It's an odd sort of job, really. Quite exciting."

"And dangerous?"

Kit shrugged. "Well, it's not exactly a teddy bear's picnic. On the credit side though, I have a very fine chap for a navigator. He's intelligent and he's steady. You've heard me speak of Arthur Steel?"

Jocelyn nodded and Kit continued. "He came top of his navigation course in Canada. And I have great faith in our Beaufighter aircraft. Our job mainly consists of clearing the North Sea and the Norwegian Fjords of enemy shipping. Half of us are there to attract the attention and subsequent flak from any of our targets. The other half sneak craftily in from behind and let loose their torpedoes."

"And which are you—the dispenser of the torpedoes, or the target of the flak?"

"We take turns," Kit replied, still averting his eyes from hers.

And that ended the discussion and whatever peace of mind she momentarily had enjoyed.

It was now the sixth of June, 1944, the fourth day of Kit's nine day leave. They were strolling back to the Lodge from a shopping expedition, Kit proudly pushing the pram up the High Street, and Jocelyn gazing into shop windows as they passed by.

Suddenly, a man came running out of a shop, stopped to say something to the first person he bumped into, then ran on. The atmosphere on the High

Street, in the space of a few seconds, became charged with excitement. People gathered in small knots, making it almost impossible to make any progress with the pram. Because he was in uniform, several people tugged at Kit's sleeve and asked, "Is it true? Has it really started?"

Kit couldn't tell them, but it was true. D-Day had dawned at last. The long and tensely awaited invasion of Europe had begun. Prime Minister Churchill was at that very moment reporting the news to the British House of Commons. With more than a thousand warships taking part, four thousand landing craft, and more then eighty-three thousand British and Canadian troops, and another seventy thousand Americans, the bridgehead in Europe was being firmly established.

Kit and Jocelyn hurried as quickly as they could back to the Lodge, and were greeted at the door by Carol and Sheila.

"Have you heard?" Sheila asked.

Kit said, "Yes, we got the news as we were coming home.

"It just came over the radio," Carol said. "Will this affect your leave, Kit?"

"I'm afraid so," he replied, looking miserably at Jocelyn. "I'll be recalled immediately. That was the understanding on which I came."

The official order from his Commanding Officer arrived by telegram within the hour. He went upstairs immediately to pack. Jocelyn followed him and sat glumly on the bed while he threw things into his case. She just could not believe that this long overdue leave was to end so abruptly, and she fought vainly not to look as despondent as she felt.

Kit consoled her as best he could. "I'll be back before you know it, darling. After all, I'm not in Scotland now. I'm just thirty miles away, a mere flea hop. I'll fly home on my first day off, and you'll be able to pop over to see me often."

"I suppose you're right," she replied. "In any case, we have a great deal to be thankful for. You could easily have been sent to the Middle East, or even India." She shuddered at that thought, and made a stalwart promise not to let this parting tear her apart. After all, it would only be for a short while. He'll be back, she told herself fiercely. He just **has** to come back safely. Oh, why, why was she haunted with such a desperately lost feeling whenever he left?

She walked to the train depot with him, and he leaned out of the compartment window to hold her hand. As the train drew slowly away, in spite of her stoic determination not to cry, the tears streamed down her face. Still waving, she raised her other hand to wipe them away, and discovered, to her dismay, that she was still holding the package of lunch she had so carefully made for him.

"Silly goose," she chastised herself aloud. "That's what I get for breaking my resolution not to cry."

Then, realizing that people were staring at her, she turned and walked quickly back to the Lodge.

***

By some measures, those first few days of the invasion were the most momentous of the war, because the ears and eyes of the entire world were focused on the culmination of years of careful planning, unavoidable bloodshed, and inevitable heartache. Other epics of World War II were perhaps more grim, or more glorious, but this was the reason for it all—the beginning of the end. Most people were weary of the war, and some had almost lost sight of its real purpose. They wanted only to get it over with so that they could have their loved ones home again and return to a normal life unfettered by constant anxiety and deprivation.

The endless flow of weird and wonderful war vehicles ceased to clog the High Street of Newmarket, and the town and its inhabitants were acutely aware of the new quiet. At the Lodge there was no coming and going of husbands; nor was there likely to be until the first intense stages of the invasion were over. Jocelyn, Carol, and Sheila, like their counterparts in homes everywhere, had to sit back and wait, with as much hope and patience as they could muster.

Gradually, the pace lessened, and when Boo was about a month old, Kit called to say that, if Jocelyn could come up to Grimsby the following weekend, there was a reasonable chance that he could spend at least one day and a night with her. Carol immediately offered to look after Boo, so when Kit called the next evening she was able to tell him to expect her on Friday.

It was a gloriously free feeling to be going to see him. Had she been at Haycroft, there would have been no chance to just take off like this. Kit's mother would have had some very logical reason why she shouldn't go. Violet had written a short note when Boo was born, saying that she was pleased that all had gone well. Kit had received a lengthy letter from her in which she tried vainly to vindicate herself. Because their time together was always so short and every moment so precious, Kit made no attempt to enter into a lengthy discussion of the breakup and Jocelyn was glad not to dredge up the past. What happened, happened, and it could not be undone.

Kit regretted not having prepared Jocelyn more carefully for her stay at Haycroft, but he hadn't known that she was coming to England so soon. And after she arrived he didn't want to sour their sweet but too short reunion. As far as Jocelyn was concerned, the awful fracas with Violet was a blessing in disguise. In some unknown way, she could have been at least partly to blame, and if so she was sorry for that. But she was contented living with Sheila and Carol, and being able to share with them the heavy burden of worry and waiting. She rationalized that Violet was most likely happier having her out of her hair, even if it meant losing some face in the village.

On the Friday morning that she was to go to Grimsby she was out of bed at an absurdly early hour and was busy preparing for the trip. She was delighted to find that she could slip easily into her blue linen shirt waist dress that Kit liked. She had saved a pair of nylons for special occasions, and those, plus a pair of navy and white spectator pumps, and her blue cashmere cardigan thrown over her shoulders made up her ensemble.

She locked the small overnight case on the bed, glanced quickly into the mirror to ensure that her lipstick was not smudged, then skipped lightly down the stairs, feeling much like a bride setting off on her honeymoon.

Loud screams and cries of petulant children came from the lounge, announcing that Deirdre and Miggles had arrived. Jocelyn left her case by the front door and walked in amidst the noise and chaos that was quite normal for the Dovedale brood. Deirdre was in the act of walloping six-year old James for breaking one of the elements in the gas radiant.

When Jocelyn entered the room, Deirdre eyed her from tip to toe. "My God, Jocelyn," she exclaimed, "you look like a damnably high-paid whore." There was no malice in her voice. In fact, in her own peculiar way, she was giving Jocelyn a compliment.

Jocelyn knew this, but she was annoyed just the same, and decided she wouldn't let Deirdre get away with it. She studied Deirdre's limp colourless hair straggling to her shoulders like seaweed, her crumpled soiled blouse, her mud-spattered creased red corduroy trousers, and dusty bare toes poking out of sandals in dire need of repair.

"And you," she said softly, a deceptively sweet smile on her lips, "look like one who has been damnably underpaid."

Miggles squealed with delight. "You see, Dee, jealousy gets you nowhere. I think Jocelyn looks ravishing. I wish to God I could look like that in my clothes."

"If you had any clothes like that," Deirdre retorted sourly.

Fortunately, at that moment the door bell announced the arrival of her cab. Jocelyn said a hasty good bye and was on her way to the train station and to Kit.

CHAPTER 23

It was true, as Kit had said, that Grimsby was but a thirty-mile hop from Newmarket. But, alas, there was no means of transport across country. Jocelyn had to travel first to Cambridge, then south to London, a trip of some three hours, during the whole of which she had to stand in the corridor. Friday was a bad day to go to London because all the service men with weekend passes usually converged there. At each stop more people squeezed into the long corridored train, until Jocelyn felt like a sardine in a tin. She was practically gasping for air by the time she reached London where she had to catch another train to go north to Grimsby.

All of London's enormous stations looked alike to her, but that day there was a strange lack of the usual hustle and bustle about Liverpool Street station. The people who got off the train dispersed quickly and the odd person she encountered on her way out seemed to be walking on tiptoe, as though in fear of making any noise that might mute the sound of an approaching assassin.

The city itself was comparatively deserted, and she sensed the same ominous hush as she made her way by the Underground to King's Cross station and found her train for Grimsby. She procured a seat and, soon after she sat down, the piercing wail of an air raid siren struck cold fear into her heart. But no one in the train moved, and when she looked about she noticed that previously tense expressions were now relaxed, and the station suddenly came to life. The explanation was simple. She had arrived at Liverpool Street station in the midst of an air raid alert, and everyone who could be was in a shelter. The siren she just heard was the welcome All Clear.

A plump woman entered the compartment and sat down beside Jocelyn. She pushed her last parcel into place and settled herself into the seat with nervous jerky pats and tugs to her dress.

As the hideously scarred London suburbs slipped past the moving train, she grumbled to Jocelyn, "Thank 'eavens, I'm seein' the back end of this place. I've nivver spent sooch a week in me 'ole life."

Encouraged by what she took for interest in Jocelyn's raised eyebrows, she caught her breath and continued her complaining. "This was me first visit to Loondon since the war. I thought it was syfe to coom now that the blitz and all is over. But, what a mistake that was. Them devlish nazzies 'as invented somethin' worse than iver. Doodle bugs they calls 'em—devil's bugs would be more loike it." She smoothed her cotton print dress over her heavy thighs once more, blew her bulbous nose into a mansize handkerchief, then went on with her tale. "I'll tell you, the noise them things make is enough to deafen a soul."

"What sort of noise is it?" Jocelyn asked out of genuine curiosity.

"Joost loike a great tractor, or summit. And it 'as lights on the wing and tail, and when they go out, and the noise stops, that's when you moost watch out. You niver know where they're going to land. And sooch destruction when they do. One fell about a 'alf mile from me sister's place. You've niver seen sooch a mess as it made of the 'ouses in the area. All strewn about, they were, and the people in 'em all dead."

The newspapers had been full of lurid descriptions of the havoc these terrible weapons were wreaking all over the southern counties of England. Jocelyn remembered the destruction the one had caused in Newmarket, the night before Boo was born. And Dennis's squadron had had to move from its location outside of Gravesend because of the threat to its flying operations there. In fact, the air crews were congratulated by Air Chief Marshal, Lord Trenchard, because they managed to make the move to Thorney Island on the south west coast while still carrying out their daily and nightly strikes on the continent. And their Group Captain was awarded an Order of the British Empire. Since it was mainly the aircrews who had performed the feat, Dennis laughingly told Carol that the O.B.E. stood for 'other buggers' effort'.

Jocelyn's seat companion blew her nose again and then went on. "I tell you, luv, I've niver seen owt loike it in all me life, and I niver want to again. You can 'ave Loondon. I'm going 'ome where it's syfe."

Jocelyn marvelled once more how someone who lived such a short distance from London could have gone through four years of the war without having experienced any kind of a raid. She couldn't imagine Medicine Hat, for instance, being bombed, and towns within sixty miles not being directly affected. In fact, it had surprised her how little the war had really bothered the people in Repton. She didn't have much opportunity to mull over the phenomenon because her companion babbled continuously until they got to Peterborough, which was her final destination.

Before Jocelyn knew it, she had reached Grimsby and Kit was standing on the platform, anxiously seeking her compartment. His face wreathed in smiles when he saw her and he hastened to help her off the train.

With him was his navigator, Arthur Steel, whom he introduced to Jocelyn. She knew that Kit's life depended to a large extent on this man's caution and skill, and she was relieved to discern that here was no young reckless daredevil craving excitement. Arthur was a quiet gentle fellow who spoke of his wonderful wife and boasted good-humouredly about the baby he and his wife were expecting soon. He walked as far as the hotel with them then left for camp promising to see Jocelyn again before she returned to Newmarket.

Grimsby was a dismally drab sea coast town, and the hotel was musty and dreary. They had supper in the dining room which, although clean, was depressingly utilitarian—like a railway hotel in a small Canadian town. It was crowded with naval and airforce uniforms, and Jocelyn noticed that other wives were there who, like herself, were snatching a few brief precious hours with their husbands.

While it was still light, Kit showed her what little he could of interest in the town, and as they wandered hand in hand back along the promenade on the sea front, a formation of thirty Beaufighters swarmed over their heads flying out over the grey sea towards the horizon. In a matter of seconds they were lost to view.

"Are they from 254 Squadron, Kit?"

"Yes, my friend Don Rowe is with them. He had hoped to meet you tonight, but was on deck. You'll like him, and his wife, Ellen. They both were out in Canada for a time."

"Does Ellen live here?"

"Yes, just on the outskirts of town."

"Why couldn't I come here to live, Kit? It's safe enough, I should imagine. The lady I travelled with from London lives only a few miles away and she hadn't heard an air raid siren until she went to London."

"Oh, it's safe enough," Kit agreed. "But I've put a great deal of thought into the idea and you know there's nothing I'd like more than to have you near. But it wouldn't be fair to you, darling."

"How do you figure that?" she asked, not hiding her irritation.

"I know it sounds odd, but it's true. Living this close to an active squadron is no picnic for a wife. Don has found that out and Ellen is moving away soon."

"But why? I don't see...."

Kit interrupted her. "I know you don't, darling, because you haven't experienced it. You see, the wives always know when their husbands are flying. They watch the aircraft go out—just as you did a moment ago. They know that their husbands are up there, and they count the planes.

Then they wait to hear them return—one by one. You can imagine the rest. It's a form of self torture, but they can't resist it. There's a lot to be said for the old adage, 'what you don't know can't hurt you'."

"You're right, of course," Jocelyn admitted ruefully, remembering that Dennis had said the same thing to Carol.

Kit stopped outside their hotel and placed his hands on her shoulders. "I couldn't bear to think of you being hurt needlessly, darling. Nothing's going to happen to me, believe me, but I must have my wits about me when I'm flying and I can't do that if I envision you in some dreary digs eating your heart out."

She looked away quickly to conceal her disappointment and the sudden fear that clutched at her heart. She knew her eyes would mirror her feelings. Forcing a smile of resignation, she said again, "You're right, of course."

Kit left for camp before breakfast the following morning, and Jocelyn went to the dining room by herself. It was an ugly room, ill-lighted and panelled in cheap dark stained wood and furnished with utilitarian chairs and tables—early Salvation Army, she judged. She smiled to herself at that old joke.

She sat alone in the drab, austere surroundings feeling cold, inside and out. Her thoughts would not stop returning to their discussion of the previous evening, and the awful implication it contained. It was like the proverbial hand writing on the wall at Balshazzar's Feast. It was a slightly muddled parallel, but she needed no Daniel to interpret it. It was she who had been weighed and found wanting—wanting in the courage and faith sufficient to prevent these morbid thoughts from torturing her. Her hands trembled and she felt utterly miserable. Leaving her breakfast untouched, she walked mechanically upstairs to the dingy room where she threw herself on the bed and wept bitterly. It was only now that she truly knew that Kit was right. She simply could not live here because she was not brave enough to take it.

What Kit could never have described to her was how awful some of their sorties were. After his last trip, he recorded in his log book, " There were no balloons or enemy aircraft. Attacks were made on the vessels and the leading centre E/V (enemy vessel) was seen to blow up, hit by a torpedo and was seen to be ablaze. At least 4 ships were on fire when the convoy was last seen. Intense light and heavy flak was encountered, accurate at first but decreased considerably. It was like flying into the mouth of hell as we dived to attack. But we emerged without a single hole. Others were not so lucky."

Some fifty years after the war ended, the Lord Mayor of London, Sir Brian Jenkins GBE MA DSc. would write to all surviving members or the R.A.F. North Coates Strike Wing on the occasion of their reunion in Den Helder, Holland: "It was above this place along the Dutch coast, in the stirring days between 1943 and 1945, that the intrepid 148, 236 and 254 Squadrons of your Strike Wing signed the skies with their honour in a determined and effective offensive against enemy shipping...Each one of you made a great contribution to our ultimate victory in World War II, and at this special reunion I ask all veterans of the North Coates Strike Wing to remember that old airmen never die. Neither does the memory of the part they played in the service of their country."

***

Kit returned to the hotel in time to have dinner with Jocelyn that evening, and immediately afterwards they telephoned Carol to see how their precious baby daughter was faring.

"She's just fine," Carol assured them, "But I'm afraid I have some unpleasant news. We've received notice from Mrs. Lee to vacate the Lodge. It seems that her husband is returning to his old posting in Newmarket and they want their house back."

"When do we have to leave?"

"The end of June."

"That doesn't give us much time," Jocelyn said worriedly.

"No, it doesn't, but we have no choice. We did sign an agreement that she could reclaim the house whenever she wanted it," Carol reminded Jocelyn.

After the call, she and Kit found two secluded seats in a corner of the lounge and sat until bedtime thrashing out this new development.

"You must find a place in or around Newmarket, if possible," Kit said. "Somewhere safe and central, so that I can get home often."

It was an excellent idea, but might not be so simple to put into effect, Jocelyn suggested.

"We can but try," Kit replied.

Sunday was a quiet uneventful day. After dinner, they took a long leisurely stroll along the rocky beach. They talked and laughed, as they reminisced about the good times they had enjoyed in Canada—riding madly over the brown prairies, tobogganing and skiing on the hills outside of the town, the perfect picnics they enjoyed in the Cypress Hills, the Mess parties, and especially the dances, the bonfires and corn roasts held in the autumn on the sandy banks of the South Saskatchewan River—all the wonderful memories they shared.

For two nights at least, and for the first time since Jocelyn arrived in England, they could make love and try to obliterate the miserable months they had been separated. But it was not easy to blot out the fact that Kit had to leave her again early Monday morning.

Before he left for camp, he leaned over the bed to give her a good bye kiss. She clung to him tightly for a few seconds and then he was gone.

After breakfast, she made her own way to the station, feeling indescribably lonely and dejected. The train left on time and the return journey to London went very quickly. There was no garrulous seat companion to listen to, so Jocelyn sat watching the fleeting countryside pass, and thought how flat and uninteresting was this so-called Fen country compared to other parts of England she had seen. But her mind dwelt mainly on the dilemma now facing them, the problem of Sheila's confinement in August being far from the least serious. Perhaps now that the invasion had begun, she would be able to persuade the hospital to accept her. If Simon approached Dr. Bailey, he might be more amenable to a man's appeal.

She would miss the Lodge, she thought. It had become more than just a place to hang their hats. It was home. Where would they find a place as convenient and accommodating?

When the train drew into King's Cross station, she got off and found her way to Liverpool Street, again via the Underground. There was no repeat of the air raid that she had described to Kit, but he made her promise she would call him the minute she got home. The rest of the journey, first to Cambridge and thence to Newmarket was uneventful. She managed to secure a seat on the Cambridge run this time and was soon in Newmarket, hastening home to ensure that Boo had not suffered in her absence, and to call to reassure Kit.

CHAPTER 24

When Jocelyn arrived back at the Lodge, she found Carol and Sheila already feverishly searching for a new home. They had put advertisements in both The Woman, and The Lady, and had bought copies of other magazines containing rentals.

After she had been up to see Boo, Jocelyn joined the others who were sitting around the fire in the lounge. A strong wind had come up and was hurling rain against the windows. The room seemed even cosier and more inviting than usual, and Jocelyn thought again how much she would miss the Lodge.

"Have you heard of any places likely to be available around here?" she asked.

"We've looked at a couple," Carol answered, "But they were hopeless. They either had no plumbing, no heating, or they came equipped with cockroaches."

"What about Miggles? Has she any leads?"

"She says that all of a sudden Newmarket is besieged by people from the south who are desperately trying to get away from these awful German doodle bugs. People are taking any kind of accommodation, at any price."

"I don't blame them" Jocelyn said. "Kit says they are far worse than piloted aircraft because they're being directed willy nilly over the countryside. What does Dennis think of the situation, Carol?"

"He's frantic of course. He's such a worry wart. You know that his squadron had to leave Gravesend because of this new menace. He's not keen on us moving any further south, that's for sure."

"Neither is Kit. He thinks we should try to stay around here. It's central to both squadron locations and it is safer than anywhere in the south."

"Simon was home for a few hours," Sheila said. "He wasn't much help. I think he couldn't care less if I end up having this baby in a telephone kiosk."

Carol and Jocelyn ignored the barb at Simon who actually had been quite helpful when he was around. He had looked at least two places and discounted them.

"Well, Mrs. Lee can't cart us out bodily," Jocelyn said. "In any case, I'm dead beat. I think I'll turn in."

Sheila was not long in following her and, when Carol had finished another chapter in her book, she, too, started up the stairs on her way to bed. Half-way up, she was summoned to the telephone. Her heart sank and a worried frown creased her forehead as she hurried to pick up the receiver. The frown smoothed instantly when she heard Dennis's voice. "Darling, what a lovely surprise," she bubbled.

Dennis's tone was solemn and secretive. "Listen carefully, darling. I can't say much. Is Sheila around?"

"She just went to bed. Why?"

"Did she hear from Simon yesterday?"

"Yes, He arranged for her to meet him in London tomorrow. Dennis, what's wrong?" she demanded.

"You must stop her from going," he said, his tone becoming even more urgent.

"Why, for goodness sake? She's looking forward to it."

"She mustn't go. Simon won't be there."

"Dennis, what is wrong? Has something happened to Simon?"

"We don't know for sure, darling. But if no word has come from me or the Wingco tomorrow, see that she doesn't leave the Lodge."

"I'll try, but...."

The operator cut in. "You're time is up, Sir." And the line went dead.

Carol stood for a few moments, her mind confused. How... what could she tell Sheila? She must have time to think. Perhaps Sheila and Jocelyn hadn't heard the 'phone ring. That would eliminate any immediate explanation. She went upstairs stealthily. Jocelyn's light was out she noted, and there had been no sound coming from Sheila's room. She lay awake for hours, worrying, wondering, hoping, and praying alternately.

As dawn broke, she fell into a troubled sleep, disturbed by nightmares in which she saw Simon's handsome face laughing at some joke, and then the laugh turning to a scream. Simultaneously, the ringing telephone wakened her and she sat bolt upright in bed, wondering momentarily why she felt so wretched. Then she remembered.

She jumped out of bed, grabbed her dressing gown and struggled into it as she flew downstairs to answer the telephone, in case Sheila might have heard it and reached it first. She picked up the 'phone and panted into it, "Dennis, is that you?"

"Yes, it is. Did I get you up?"

"Yes, but that's okay. What time is it?"

"Seven o'clock. Is Sheila up yet?"

"Not at this hour. What is the news?"

"The Wingco gave me permission to call, in view of Simon's plans to meet Sheila in London. He didn't return from his last sortie, and he's listed as missing. Sheila will hear officially today. But if you bring her to the 'phone, I'll break it to her gently. And don't worry, for heaven's sake. There's a very good chance he'll be found."

Carol tried to speak, but she had no power to do so. She placed the receiver gently on the table and went to summon Sheila.

Sheila listened to what Dennis had to say, thanked him politely, put the receiver down gently, went back to her room and shut the door. She lay on her bed, wondering why she couldn't cry and what she was going to do if Simon was not found.

The atmosphere in the Lodge quickly became subdued and permeated with gloom. The housing problem was entirely set aside while they waited anxiously for news. Miggles offered to come up when Jocelyn told her about Simon, but she took the liberty of asking her not to come. She felt certain that Sheila would not want to see her at this time.

The only news that day was the telegram from Air Ministry stating that Simon was listed as missing. Sheila read the message, then crumpled it up and threw it away. She had taken the news calmly, and had shed no tears. "It had to be one of them, sooner or later," was all she said, her voice dry and emotionless. "Perhaps it's...." She didn't finish the sentence, but turned and went to her room.

The following morning, Jocelyn received a mysterious call from Miggles, asking her to meet her at the Dutch Tea Shop around four o'clock. Hurrying along the High Street in a drizzling rain, she tried to imagine what Miggles wanted. She sounded very secretive. A rust-coloured coat sleeve waved frantically at Jocelyn as she entered the tea room, and she zig-zagged over to the table where Miggles was seated.

"No news, I suppose," Miggles said, the usual cigarette dangling from her thin mouth.

Jocelyn shook her head and sat down at the table.

"Poor dear Simon," Miggles said, a tear stain on her dry brown cheek.

"Dennis feels quite sure that Air Sea Rescue will pick him up, Miggles. They know approximately where he went down, and it's just a matter of waiting. So try not to worry."

"That's easier said than done. Especially in the face of this other horrid business that has cropped up. Oh, God! why does everything have to happen at once?"

"What has happened?" Jocelyn demanded. She hadn't taken Miggles' summons very seriously until now.

Miggles fished in her bag and pulled out a letter. "It's this," she said, handing the envelope to Jocelyn.

"It came for Simon yesterday, and I recognized the writing. Under the circumstances, I opened it. Thank God I did. Dede was all set to hand it over to Sheila. It would have been fine consolation for a widow."

"She's not a widow yet," Jocelyn retorted, "and likely won't be, if Dennis is right. But what's with this letter. Who is it from?"

"You can read it later, but I'll explain briefly. You know, of course, about that girl that Simon had been sort of involved with in America, before he met Sheila."

"Vaguely, yes," Jocelyn said, resisting the impulse to remind Miggles that it was Canada, not America. It irked her the way the British made no distinction between the United States and Canada.

"Well, she has never given up on Simon, poor demented girl. She's quite mad, and so are her parents. They keep writing to Simon and pestering him to leave Sheila and return to their Carolyn."

"Has Simon considered the idea?"

"No, of course not. He adores Sheila. But this letter is from the father, and he says that he's going to stir up mud, whatever that means, if Simon won't agree to their crazy scheme. He claims that Simon broke their daughter's heart, and endangered her health, etc. etc."

"What do they propose to do about Sheila? Exterminate her?"

"Oh, poor Sheila. They'd like to. They claim that she vamped Simon away from their Carry."

"That's nonsense," Jocelyn said. "Sheila didn't even know of the girl's existence until after she and Simon were married."

Miggles stubbed out her cigarette and lit another. "Yes, I believe that's so. Unfortunately, these people are desperate and determined to make trouble regardless of the facts of the case. Dede and I are wondering if they might really have something to go on. Maybe the girl is pregnant." She clasped and unclasped her fingers nervously and looked at Jocelyn as though hoping she had a solution to this 'nasty business' as she called it.

But Jocelyn had no more idea than Miggles what to do. After a moment, she said, "I hope you won't think I'm unsympathetic, Miggles, but I'm wondering why you asked me to come here."

Miggles' wrinkled brown face bore an apologetic expression. She dabbed her thin nose with a grubby handkerchief and sniffed. "I don't know,

Jocelyn, really I don't. Except, except you're a bit more conventional in your views, and we thought that talking it over with you might help us sort things out."

"I'd be happy to do anything to help. But I can't think what I could do at this moment."

"Well, it's probably a crazy idea," Miggles said, "but we wondered if we wrote to this man and told him that Simon was missing believed killed, it may shut him up." She sniffed into her grubby handkerchief again and looked imploringly at Jocelyn. "What do you think?"

"It might work, and it's probably worth a try. I can't think of any other way to discourage them."

"Neither can we." Miggles sank back into her chair, her hand on her forehead. "My God! When I think what a blow it would have been for Sheila to have opened that letter at a time like this, it makes me shudder."

Jocelyn handed Miggles back the letter and got up to leave. "I must get back to Boo," she said. "It's mealtime."

"Thanks for coming, Jocelyn. I feel better just for having talked it over with you. I hope to God we hear some news of Simon soon."

"So do I. I'm sure we will. Try not to worry."

"You'll let us know the minute you hear, won't you."

Jocelyn promised, and at the same time she decided that for now she would say nothing to anyone, not even to Carol, about this strange encounter.

CHAPTER 25

Two and a half timeless days elapsed without any news of Simon. A grey twilight crept into the lounge where they sat before a glowing fire. Carol was reading aloud in her low pleasant voice. At last, unable to see the small print in the dim light, she closed the book and placed it on the end table. Jocelyn and Sheila scarcely noticed that she had ceased reading. Sheila's intensely blue eyes stared unseeing into the fire, and Jocelyn closed hers and her knitting dropped on to her lap. Only the incessant ticking of the clock on the mantel intruded on the silence that permeated the room.

The harsh ringing of the telephone jarred them to consciousness. No one spoke, but Sheila rose calmly and walked into the hall to answer it. A strange look of assurance came into face as she left the room, almost as though she were hearing those wonderful words before they were uttered: 'He's been found! Alive!'

A passing warship had chanced to spot the tiny dinghy with Simon, delirious from exhaustion and exposure, clinging desperately to its side. It had been sixty hours since he had parachuted into darkness and plunged into the icy waters of the English Channel. His navigator, a gentle boy affectionately nicknamed Bambi by his fellow officers, was never found, and it was a miracle that Simon had survived. He had been taken to a hospital on the south coast.

It took time for the effects of this near tragedy to wear off, and for a short while house hunting was set aside. Mrs. Lee was sympathetic, and allowed them three weeks' grace on their eviction notice. Meanwhile, Carol took the opportunity to spend a week with Dennis down in Hampshire, not too far from where 21 Squadron was operating.

While she was gone, Jocelyn and Sheila began once more to follow up on possible leads. Even though they had no success and places they investigated were disappointing, still Jocelyn's heart was infinitely lighter. Somehow Simon's ordeal had cleared the air of tension, and she convinced herself that they had had their share of bad luck. Surely lightning would not strike twice in the same place.

Sheila received two shakily written letters from Simon, but he had no idea when he might be allowed out of hospital. She could not go to him, even if she had wanted to, because he was in a restricted coastal area.

Carol had been gone five days, and Sheila, following a pattern she began after Simon was reported missing, had gone to bed immediately after supper. Jocelyn sat on the bed in her room describing yet another unsuccessful housing sortie. Suddenly, Sheila cocked her head and frowned. "Did you hear the doorbell, Joc?"

Jocelyn listened. "Yes, there it is again" She hopped off the bed and hurried down the long hall to answer the door, wondering anxiously who it could be at this late hour. She peeked through the side window to get a preview of the caller.

It was Simon! He was holding his large frame erect with the aid of two canes. His baggy uniform revealed the tremendous amount of weight he had lost, and his handsome face was barely recognizable. His cheeks were hollow and his skin was scorched by sun and wind. Salt sores covered his swollen lips, but they were parted in his usual engaging grin as he noticed Jocelyn's face peeping out at him.

She unlocked the door to let him in. Her eyes filled with tears. How he must have suffered, she thought. She quickly forced a smile and pulled his bag into the hall.

"Simon, how marvellous to see you. However did you manage to get home so soon?"

He grinned. "I have influence, Jocelyn. They brought me here in an ambulance. Where's Sheila?"

"In bed. Here, let me help with those things."

She took his haversack, kicked his larger bag into the corner, then followed him down the hall to Sheila's room.

Sheila looked up when he hobbled in. Her blue eyes seemed to be mocking him as she greeted him casually with, "Well, will you look what the wind blew in."

Simon was home for a whole month on convalescent leave. His normally strong constitution and tremendous will had been instrumental in saving his life, and it also allowed him to recover remarkably quickly. He was soon spending much of his time helping in the critical search for a house. Hardly a day passed that he didn't go off somewhere to view a house or to worry the estate agents both in Newmarket and Cambridge.

But, by the middle of July, still nothing suitable had turned up. The only thing that was achieved, and it was a great weight off their minds, was a promise extracted by Simon from Dr. Bailey at White Lodge Hospital to reserve a bed for Sheila's confinement in August. Jocelyn figured that he must have been under special constraints when she asked him to help in early May, probably because of the imminence of D-Day.

Sitting around the supper table that evening, they discussed the situation. Simon had met with Mrs. Lee earlier in the day and she had made it clear that she was not pleased with their lack of progress. They were mulling over possible strategies when the 'phone rang.

Jocelyn took the call and she heard a woman's shrill voice say, "Is this the party that advertised for a cottage to let in The Lady?"

"Yes, it is," Jocelyn said, putting her hand over the transmitter and shouting excitedly into the lounge, "It's an answer to one of our ads."

She spoke, rather listened, to the caller for a few minutes, after which they were cut off. She returned to the lounge and told the others what had transpired.

"The woman's name is Marshall, and the place sounds great. It has plumbing, electricity, a fire place, bed linen, dishes, etc. etc. I can't believe it."

"What's the catch?" Simon said dryly.

"Well, there is one all right. It's in Sussex, right in the middle of buzz bomb alley."

"Did she say whether any bombs had fallen nearby?"

"Yes, she admitted that a few had fallen in the area, but not for a week or so."

It was true that a special R.A.F. bomber group had been given the task of trying to combat this menace. The pilots would manoeuvre close to the missile and tip its wing thus intercepting its course and causing it to fall into the channel where it could do no damage. They had been quite successful in their dangerous endeavours, but the threat was by no means eradicated and Simon was very skeptical about renting a house in that area.

"How did you leave it with her, Joc?" Simon asked.

"I said, we'd think about it and get back to her if we are interested."

"Good," Simon replied. He got up and put on his coat. "I'm going back to Mrs. Lee and ask her to give us a bit more time. Surely we can find somewhere less vulnerable."

He returned to the Lodge within the hour with the news that they could have one more week. But that was it.

"Well, if all else fails, I guess we can take Mrs. Marshall's place," Jocelyn said without enthusiasm. Upon reflection, she realized it was not such a great prospect after all.

The following morning she pushed Boo in her pram along the dusty High Street en route to buy the week's rations. The hot July sun enthroned in a deep blue sky dotted with puffs of white wooly cloud, the aimless breezy whirls of dust, the friendly 'hellos and good mornings' were so reminiscent of a summer day in her childhood that she felt a sudden sharp twinge of homesickness. It passed quickly as she wove Boo's pram in and out of the slowly moving crowds of shoppers that clogged the narrow High Street.

It was market day and the pavement on both sides was edged with the rickety stalls of the street vendors. They offered everything imaginable, on ration or off, for a price—buttons, zippers, pins, elastic, slippers, dresses, toys, pots and pans, girdles and corsets immodestly hung from pegs on the makeshift counters. There was nothing in this scene to remind Jocelyn of home where on market days farmers drove to town on Fridays with their truckloads of produce: vegetables, eggs, butter, cream, turkeys, chickens, which they either sold at the covered market, or peddled from door to door. The idea of street stalls was a purely European custom which would not find its way to Canada for several decades after the war.

Arriving at the door of Mrs. Vanner's shop, Jocelyn parked the pram under the shade of the awning and applied the brake. Boo was sound asleep. On the other side was another pram whose cherubic occupant was helping himself to a fistful of his mother's precious butter ration. The mother emerged, retrieved the mutilated package and smacked him soundly. His outraged howls soon ceased as he busied himself licking the rest of his plunder from oily dimpled fingers.

Jocelyn smiled as she passed by the mother and entered Mrs. Vanner's shop. She was greeted warmly by the rosy-cheeked proprietor, who asked her how their house hunting was coming along.

"Not too well I'm sorry to say. I don't suppose you know of anyone who wants to let their house, or part of it?"

"I'm afraid not. Newmarket seems to be right full up at the moment. And more folks keep coming, to get away from them awful doodle bugs."

Jocelyn picked up her parcels, said good bye to Mrs. Vanner and left the shop. She put the rations at the foot of the pram and turned it towards the Lodge.

The crowds on the High Street had thinned somewhat and she made better time going home. Boo was still sleeping so she placed the pram in a sunny spot in the garden and carried the rations into the kitchen.

She was about to put them away when a familiar sounding chuckle sent her flying into the lounge and into the arms of Kit.

"Darling, why didn't you let me know you were coming?" she asked, still hugging him.

"I didn't know myself until about an hour ago," he said. "I struck it lucky. Someone was heading this way and I hitched a ride. But, before you get too optimistic, I can't stay long. He'll be returning to North Coates after lunch and I must fly back with him."

"I don't care. You're here, and that's all that matters." Jocelyn led him back into the garden and he went over to the pram to look at Boo.

"She's getting so big," he marvelled. "Look at her chubby legs."

"She's over ten pounds," Jocelyn said proudly. "Miss Hatherley weighed her yesterday."

They sat in the garden beside the pram and Jocelyn updated him on the housing search. He was not pleased with the idea of Mrs. Marshall's offer. "It's too risky," he said firmly. "Anyway, I've got an idea. I've also got some very good news. I have seven days leave coming up."

Jocelyn's eyes gleamed. "Oh, Kit, how wonderful! When? Soon, I hope."

"At the end of this week. My idea is that we should go down to Sussex and see for ourselves whether the place is feasible. What do you think?"

"It's fabulous. I'm sure Carol will look after Boo while we're gone. I'll call Mrs. Marshall and ask her if she'll hold the place until we can get down to look at it. That is, if we haven't found something else in the meantime."

Before Kit left that afternoon, Jocelyn had telephoned Mrs. Marshall and arranged for them to go to see the cottage. She said she was delighted to wait for them.

That night Jocelyn was too happy to knit or read as she sat before the fire with Carol and Sheila. "Just think, seven whole days! I can't believe it."

She was so elated by Kit's flying visit and they had spent such a perfect few hours together and had planned so many things to do on their leave. One of them was to go to Repton and see his parents. She wasn't thrilled with that prospect, but it had to be done because Kit had business to attend to. Something to do with his estate.

A wisp of a smile played at the corner of her mouth as she pictured him waving good bye and getting into the cab. It was the first time in recent memory that she had been able to let him go without that sickening fear taking a strangle hold on her heart. Surely, that was a good sign.

CHAPTER 26

Despite the proposed plan for Jocelyn and Kit to investigate the cottage in Mayfield, Sussex, the search in the vicinity of Newmarket went on with renewed vigour. Simon met with Mrs. Lee once more but he gained no further concessions from her. They must vacate the Lodge within the week.

For the first time in his life, Simon was conscious of the heavy hand of responsibility on his shoulders. He was in the thick of the situation, rather than being on the squadron and thereby able to avoid direct involvement. Considering how unaccustomed he was to facing up to his responsibilities, Jocelyn thought he was doing a creditable job. Sheila gave him no credit, however, and seemed to enjoy taunting him every time he returned from his less frequent visits to Dovedale with childish barbs: 'And how are the spooks at Dovedale? How's dear Dodo? As dumb as ever?'

Simon took it with surprising grace and resignation, usually laughing it off. However, Jocelyn found their incessant bickering very irritating, and she resolved to ask Sheila to give Simon more of a chance. He was obviously trying to be more considerate of her. Carol and Simon had gone off to view two different housing prospects, and Jocelyn took the opportunity to speak to Sheila. They were lounging in the garden enjoying the warm rays of the sun. She chose her words carefully. "Simon is surely working hard over this house business," she remarked casually.

"I suppose so. It won't put undue strain on him."

"Couldn't you encourage him a little?" Jocelyn asked.

"I could," Sheila said flatly.

"But you won't?"

"I might," Sheila said, a wicked glint in her eyes. "But he might not like me as well if I were always nice."

Jocelyn knew when she was beaten, and she abruptly changed the subject.

Meanwhile, in Cambridge, Carol and Simon were outside an estate agent's office tossing a coin to see which of two houses each of them would view. Carol won the toss to visit a place with the intriguing name, Susan Plum. It was located in Balsham, a village nine miles out of Cambridge.

She got instructions on how to get there and took off for the bus station where she joined the short queue that formed under the sign for Balsham. Soon she was sitting in an ancient vehicle which wound its way noisily through the narrow busy streets of Cambridge and finally out into the peaceful countryside.

After a half hour of bumping along on an ill-kept road, with little sign of habitation, she began to wonder where this place could be. It was surely desolate country.

Just as she was beginning to think she would never arrive, the bus dipped into a valley and lumbered up to a quaint village inn. The sign bearing the figure of a sly looking red fox proclaimed that it was called The Fox.

The bus driver called out, "Balsham", and Carol hurried to the door and got out.

She was standing outside of the entrance to the inn, wondering which way to go when an elderly man in heavy tweeds, plus-fours, belted matching jacket, and a deer stalker hat emerged. She decided to check with him before going any further. He confirmed that she should indeed go off to the right and follow Fox Lane to its end.

The village of Balsham was as quaint as it was ancient. The shady lane along which Carol walked was banked by trim hedges enclosing loosely spaced whitewashed cottages whose thatched roofs glinted golden in the sunlight. The sky was almost as intensely blue as a prairie sky and she felt a twinge of homesickness.

'Susan Plum', she mused. 'What a strange name for a house. That must be it on the right. The man said it was the last house on this lane'.

The house was low and rambling, and its many sloped roofs cut into the cloudless sky at odd angles. Passers-by could almost touch the sturdy oak door and peer easily through the leaded casement windows. Carol was enchanted.

Her summons with the large brass gargoyle knocker brought someone to the door instantly.

"You must be Mrs. Carter," the attractive young woman in a W.A.A.F. uniform said, motioning Carol into the hall. "This is my mother's home. I'm interviewing prospective tenants. Do come into the lounge."

Carol followed her into the spacious room and was charmed at once with the brightly coloured chintz-covered furniture and matching drapes and the glossy dark oak end tables.

"I've already fallen in love with Susan Plum," she said, sitting down in an easy chair beside the huge fireplace which was commodious enough for a person to stand up in.

Hilary Case immediately got down to business, explaining the terms of the lease and then offering to show Carol the rest of the house.

So overcome was she with the charm of this lovely old world cottage that she scarcely heard her companion's studiously practical sales chatter, pointing out the spaciousness of the house, the modern bathroom, the rustic open fireplaces in which one could actually sit, the spectacular view of the garden from the French doors in the lounge.

Carol completely overlooked the ugly black space heater which sat glumly in the centre of the open fireplace in the large square front hall. Had she noticed it, she might have been forewarned that quaintness and charm in old houses always had to be paid for in dampness and cold draughts. Neither did she notice that there was no electricity or telephone. Instead, her eyes were drawn to the dark brooding oak beams, worm eaten and irregular but satiny with preservative, the antique linen press, and a century-old oak cradle sitting in the corner of the dining room which she was sure would be just large enough to hold Boo now that she was growing out of her bassinet.

Miss Case hurried through a wide dark hallway, urging Carol to be careful of the step down into a small square vestibule leading into the kitchen. Here she pointed to some stone steps which she said led to a cellar and a very deep well. She explained that this was where the provisions were kept in the days when Susan Plum served as an inn.

Carol thought it would be very useful to keep Boo's formula and their own perishable food.

The kitchen had an irregular brick floor in the centre of which was a long beautifully preserved antique refectory table. Behind it was an enormous coal stove and, in the corner beside that, stood three small oil-burning heaters. Carol failed to notice them. She went over to the tiny casement windows and gazed out over the loveliest garden she had ever seen.

Emerald velvet lawns wandered haphazardly over a half acre or more of grounds, encircling brightly laden flower beds, nudging trim hedges, sloping to the verge of a lily pond, and spreading gently to the foot of an ancient walnut tree. She stood still, absorbing the peace that emanated from the pastoral scene until her hostess, impatient to be on her way, snapped her out of her reverie.

"Come along. I'll show you the grounds."

The rear portion of the house was in a hollow, and from the back door they mounted a low bank to reach the path leading to the garden. Had Carol not been so utterly bewitched by the place, she might have noticed that this dip would act as a trough to collect rain water which would eventually seep into the kitchen.

Miss Case didn't mention it. She pointed to the left. "Those are the stables. We haven't used them since father died, but you may find them useful for storage purposes."

"That one with only three sides and a roof will be ideal for putting the babies out for their airing, if it's wet."

"**Babies**!" Miss Case exclaimed, her dark eyebrows suddenly arching well above the slanted green eyes. "Is there more than one?"

Now it was Carol's turn to be vague, as Miss Case was when, on their rounds, Carol asked about shopping and mail delivery.

"Did I say babies? How silly of me. No, there's only one." Under her breath she said, 'at present'.

Miss Case clearly was relieved. She probably had envisioned Susan Plum being turned into some kind of shelter for homeless waifs.

She led the way to the end of the path where, well hidden behind tall raspberry canes, was a chicken coop, housing five small pullets and an old hen.

"If you take the house, you must buy the fowls," Miss Case said matter-of-factly.

Carol would likely have agreed to buy a boa constrictor if it meant being able to live in this enchanting place. She virtually committed them to renting it, although she did say that she could not sign a lease until she had conferred with Simon. She asked, and was given, another day for this.

It was not until she was back on the bus, gazing out of the window at the flat countryside stretching as far as the eye could see with very little evidence of habitation, that some of the impracticalities of Susan Plum surfaced in her mind. The faint recollection of seeing oil lamps hanging in odd places and sitting on end tables in the lounge spelled out clearly that there was no electricity and no telephone. And she remembered Miss Case saying something about it being two miles to the shops and post office. She had forgotten to ask about milk or bread delivery.

Nevertheless, the vision of the tastefully decorated lounge and the exquisite garden was still fresh in her mind. Besides, they were not in a position to be fussy. They had to leave the Lodge by the end of the week, whether they had anywhere else to go or not.

Simon met her at the bus depot where he had been waiting for some time. "I hope your trip was more worthwhile than mine," he said despondently. He took her arm and led her across the street. "Here's a tea room where we can exchange notes and wait for our train," he said, ushering her through the doorway.

The frilly white eyelet lace curtains over leaded windows and the blue checked tablecloths helped to dispel Simon's gloom and whetted Carol's enthusiasm. Over a pot of tea and delicious scones, she extolled the beauty and charm of Susan Plum while he listened intently.

"It sounds perfectly charming," he said. "But is it a practical place for you to live?"

He was weary of this fruitless round of looking at barns and pig sties that passed for homes and wanted only to get the business of house hunting over so he could return to his more enjoyable activities.

"I think it will be fine," Carol said. "It's certainly large enough. It has five bedrooms."

"How did you leave it with the owner?"

"I said that I had to speak to you and that we would get back to her tomorrow."

"Good. That's settled then," he said decisively. "Now, we just have time to catch the next train. Finish up your bun and let's go."

They sat facing each other on the train, and Carol continued her glowing account of the wonders of Susan Plum. Simon was impressed. It was the kind of place he would like to own: lots of atmosphere, space, antiques, open fireplaces. But he was also fond of modern conveniences and he interrupted her with, "It does have electricity, doesn't it?"

Carol looked sheepish. "Well, as a matter of fact, it doesn't. But there are scads of wonderful oil lamps around."

For the life of her she couldn't have told him what was so wonderful about oil lamps, but she was relieved to hear him chuckle.

"Carol, you're the limit. Tell me, what other wonderful conveniences, or lack of same, are there that I should know about. Does it have indoor plumbing?"

"Of course. As a matter of fact, it has a very modern bathroom and a powder room on the main floor."

"Well, I'm prepared to go for it, if you think the three of you can cope with it."

"There is one more thing," Carol admitted guiltily. "We have to buy an old hen and five pullets if we take it."

Simon roared. "Good Lord, Carol! And who'll look after the beasts? I'm sure that Sheila's knowledge of fowls is confined to southern fried chicken and avoiding the parson's nose. Have you or Jocelyn any related experience?"

"Well, not exactly. But Miss Case said that there is really not much to caring for them. And there is a gypsy who lives across the road who Miss Case says will give us a hand if we get into difficulty."

"Gypsy!" Simon roared again. "Where did you say he lives?"

"In a caravan, just across the road. But Simon, he's harmless. In fact, he has five growing children."

"What's so harmless about that," Simon grunted.

The train reached Newmarket and Carol led the way out of the carriage on to the platform.

"What a heavenly day this has been," she commented. And a familiar voice behind her agreed, "Yes, hasn't it?"

Carol swung around and cried out, "Dennis! What are you doing here?"

"That's a fine way to greet your husband. I might ask the same of you."

"Simon and I have been house hunting in the Cambridge area. Where is he? He was right behind me a moment ago."

"He stopped to chat with some fellow who got off the train. Here he comes now."

Simon's limp, the legacy of his ordeal in the Channel, was barely noticeable now, and his clothes no longer hung baggily about his large frame. He had also lost the gray pallor and the salt sores that had marred his good looks. Nonetheless, Carol thought smugly, Simon may be more handsome in a college football hero sort of way, but Dennis, with his almost gaunt features, well-trimmed mustache, and impeccable dress was much more distinguished looking. She linked her arm in his and they walked towards the Lodge, she babbling all the way about the charms of Susan Plum. She was quite out of breath from her chattering, and with trying to keep pace with the two men. Before long, she had to beg them to slow down.

CHAPTER 27

In the absence of Simon and Carol, Jocelyn had left Sheila in charge of Boo while she went to the ration office, a short walk from the Lodge. There was always a long queue for the vitamins and orange juice provided free by the National Health Service and, today, although it took her only ten minutes to reach the office and ten minutes to walk back, she was away from the Lodge for an hour.

She arrived home, all set to have a good grumble to Sheila about the lack of efficiency in such places, and the shocking exhibition of bad manners and ill temper on the part of both customers and clerks. Entering the house from the garden, she walked out of the bright sunlight into the dark cavernous kitchen and set the basket of rations on the table.

"Sheila, hi, Sheila," she called. "I'm back."

There was no answer. The house was strangely silent as she walked through the hall and into the lounge. Sheila was sitting by the fireplace, holding Boo on her knee.

"Didn't you hear me calling?" Jocelyn asked.

"No, I mean, yes," Sheila mumbled.

Jocelyn didn't notice Sheila's confusion. "And what is my precious babe doing up at this hour?" she asked.

"She was unhappy, so I brought her in for a while. She's okay now. I think it was just a bit of gas."

Sheila was white and her eyes tense, as though she were trying not to cry.

"That's good. I'll put her back in the garden. What's new? Anything from the house hunters? Are they back?"

Sheila shook her head miserably, and finally Jocelyn noticed her stricken countenance.

"What's the matter, Sheila? Are you ill?"

Then it suddenly crossed her mind that perhaps she had had a letter from that girl or her parents in Canada. Jocelyn had never mentioned the conversation she had with Miggles at the time of Simon's ordeal.

Sheila got up from her chair and put Boo safely in an arm chair. She said falteringly, "I...when...oh, how can I...?"

Her voice stumbled and then stopped altogether and she looked at Jocelyn, her blue eyes brimming with tears, tears she had not shed when she had learned that Simon was missing. She removed a small yellow envelope from the mantel and handed it to Jocelyn.

Jocelyn took it, all the life ebbing from her face. In a hollow, far-away voice that was not like hers at all, she said, "It's Kit...it's Kit...isn't it?"

Sheila nodded mutely. Jocelyn's legs suddenly refused to support her, and she sank into the nearest chair. She sat for a moment staring at the envelope, her fingers numbly disobeying the impulse to open it.

"It came just after you left," Sheila said softly. "The delivery boy gave me fair warning. I hope you don't mind my opening it."

Jocelyn forced her fingers to move and take out the message from Air Ministry. She read: We regret to inform you that your husband, Flight Lieutenant Christopher Wallace Ford, 88654, is reported missing believed killed, following air operations against the enemy. A letter is forthcoming.

Jocelyn re-read the telegram a dozen times, trying to find some ray of hope in the stark message. Simon came back, she reasoned. Why couldn't Kit? But deep inside she knew that here was the answer to that gnawing fear that had haunted her, those dreaded moments of farewell. There had, after all, been no time to waste. Kit was gone, really gone, gone forever. His wonderfully generous nature, his gay twinkling eyes, his broad happy smile, his gentleness, his tenderness, his love—all gone.

She sat for a long time, feeling as though she had been hurled to the bottom of a deep black pit. Finally, she got up, and in a daze carried the yellow message, tightly clenched in her hand, up to her room where she threw herself on the bed and succumbed to the heartbreaking sobs that shook her body.

Queensbury Lodge, for the second time in a month, was in the grip of the cruel hand of fate. But now its grip was firm and unrelenting.

Later that evening, Dennis called Don Rowe, Kit's friend on the squadron, who merely confirmed their worst fears. There had been a miracle, but this time the fates decreed that it was the navigator who was saved and the pilot lost.

Kit was killed on Thursday, July 20,1944. On July 23, the adjutant of 254 Squadron wrote the following letter to Jocelyn:

Dear Mrs. Ford:

It is with deep regret, I have to confirm our telegram of 21st July, notifying you that your husband F/Lt. Kit Ford is missing from an operation on the 20th July, 1944.

The Squadron Commander, W/Cdr. R.E. Burns, D.F.C. has only recently returned from leave, and operational commitments have prevented him from writing to you; however, he hopes to advise you more fully in the course of a day or so. Meanwhile, I am afraid there is no further news I can give you.

Your husband's personal and private effects are being collected, and in accordance with R.A.F. practice will be forwarded to the Standing Committee of Adjustment, R.A.F. Central Depository, Colnbrook, Slough, from whom you will receive a communication in due course.

May I offer the sincere sympathy to you in your great loss, of all personnel of the Squadron.

Yours,

R. Termayne,
Flight Lieutenant,
Adjutant, 254 Squadron.

On the same day Jocelyn received another longer letter from Kit's

navigator, Arthur Steel. He wrote:

Dear Jocelyn:

I have only just surfaced after two days on my back, and am trying to balance the pad on my lap to write. To be quite honest, I don't know how to begin. It seems so futile to say how sorry I am. That doesn't begin to cover it. I know that it sounds childish and weak, but every time I start to think about it, I can't stop crying—just stupidly weeping. That doesn't help at all, I know, so I'll start right at the beginning and go through, hoping you'll forgive the faults.

On Thursday dinner time we heard that there was a job on, but we weren't on it. Then, they changed their minds and we had a mad scramble to get ready in time. Kit helped me to carry all my junk, and I gave him his bar of chocolate as he knew that if I kept it, I should only break it, or step on it, or something equally silly. We always did that since the time I stepped on two oranges as well as the chocolate.

There was nothing wrong at take-off. All his engine readings were O.K., and we were both nicely settled in. We had flown in that plane often, and regarded it as our own particular one. After getting into formation, we set off roughly north and then altered course out to sea, both about our own work.

Then Kit called me up over the intercom and told me that the port engine was going wrong, and he was afraid he would have to turn back. Neither of us wanted to do it, but it would have been foolish to go on, so we broke out of formation at eleven minutes to three, told the Squadron Leader that we were going back, then set course.

I worked out a rough course to get us back to base and Kit acknowledged it. Just after that, the port engine started vibrating, and it got steadily worse. Kit tried to get rid of it, and I could see him working his throttles to keep steady. The vibration got so bad that I was being thrown about and couldn't do anything about it. Kit couldn't hold it any longer so he headed roughly for some trawlers a few miles away. We were only at about five hundred feet to start with so had no height to play with.

We went sweeping around in wide circles with the wings dipping to each side alarmingly. Kit was trying to fight the plane, but couldn't. It went mad, and we got into a spin. We went straight in at over three hundred m.p.h. and went over on our back, breaking up as we hit.

Kit shouted to me about two seconds before we hit, "**Arthur! Look out!**"

That two seconds seems endless now, from the things I remember. I saw the time was eight minutes to four from my watch as I braced myself. I saw the speed—280 knots, and I looked down the fuselage, seeing Kit's helmeted head and shoulders and the sea coming up at us.

I prayed, don't ask me what I prayed because I just don't know. The peculiar thought crossed my mind that right then I should find out whether one dies instantly. I don't know any more of what happened until I came to, in a light green world deep under water, drinking gallons of it.

Then I knew I was drowning and it seemed rather interesting. Suddenly, I broke surface, but I didn't grasp what was going on for several seconds.

I was floating, supported by my Mae West, and the tail of the plane was about eight feet out of the water. As I watched, it just went straight down.

My mind wasn't working very much then, and I felt no sensation of pain. Some of the petrol tanks from the wings were floating, and I floundered between two of them to get support. I know that I was shouting for Kit and sobbing too, but I knew that I shouldn't get a reply. There was no sign of him floating around.

Our dinghy was floating about twenty five yards away, but I had no strength to reach it. After a bit, I began to take stock. Every few seconds I went under and drank petrol and sea water, but that seemed to make no difference. My right leg was floating out straight—bent out at right angles from the knee and bleeding. I know that I looked stupidly at it for awhile, then realized that I couldn't do anything about it.

The nearest trawler was about a mile away from where we hit, with all its nets out. I knew it would come, but not whether I could last until it did.

I tried to climb on the tanks, but couldn't; tried to get into the dinghy, but started sinking so came back. I ended up with my whistle between my teeth blowing constantly, and hanging on grimly to a tank with each hand.

They say they reached me in twenty minutes, but I haven't the haziest notion how long it was. They had to come into a minefield to reach me too. On the first run, they fouled some of our wreckage and went past.

I'm afraid I just broke down completely then, and nearly let go. Eventually, they got round again, and one of the chaps dived overboard with a rope. Somehow, it wrapped round my neck and I was dragged under the stern by the propellers.

They pulled me round, and when they started to push me aboard, I passed out again.

I know very little of the trip back except that those tough trawler chaps were infinitely tender with me, and treated me like a baby, dressing my cuts and stopping the blood. They even pulled my leg out of dislocation. They told me afterwards that I was shouting for Kit, and for them to get him, but I remember nothing of it.

There isn't much else to tell you. They got me into hospital and I was transferred here yesterday. I haven't been bothering much about what has been going on. All I have is a lot of cuts and bruises, and all the ligaments of my right knee are ripped, and my right leg is broken.

I shall never know how I got out of the plane, or why I wasn't killed. It doesn't make sense. As soon as the lads got back from Norway, and found that we were missing, some of them went straight out again for a couple of hours, but could find nothing. Don Rowe came to see me, and promised to write to you as I couldn't hold a pen properly.

That is the whole tale as I know it. If there is anything at all that you want to know, please don't hesitate to ask. If I can do anything at all to help you, believe me that I will do anything in my power.

Losing Kit is like losing a brother. In fact, it seems even worse than that. We depended on each other utterly. My navigation had to get him around, and on his skill as a pilot my life always depended. I never hesitated to trust it with him. At the last, it was his warning that saved my life. I am sure of it. Why he was killed, and I got away, is something I cannot explain.

There is so very much that I want to say, but can't put into words. One point that may seem quite irrelevant is that Kit and I drew our will forms from the Adj. together. He left his in his locker, saying that it didn't matter because you were to get everything of his in any case. That will offer an explanation if no will can be found. To the best of my knowledge, it is still there, uncompleted.

I know that this is pretty useless as a letter of consolation, Jocelyn, but I had to write to tell you all I could, and I'm not thinking clearly yet. Nothing has registered properly, and I may wake up suddenly, and find I am just having nightmares. I'll write again as soon as I can get things sorted out in my mind.

I can't think of any inspiring phrases that might help. All I can say, from the bottom of my heart, is that I'm sorry, and that I'm thinking of you and praying for you constantly.

Sincerely,

Arthur.

As promised, on July 24, Kit's Wing Commander, Richard Burns, wrote a personal letter to Jocelyn.

Dear Mrs. Ford:

It is with deep regret that I have to confirm the telegram of 21st:July, informing you that your husband Flight Lieutenant Ford is missing and believed to have lost his life as the result of an aircraft accident on operations on 20th:July, 1944.

He took off with the Squadron on an anti-shipping strike but soon after leaving our own coast on the outward journey, he reported on the radio that his port engine was failing and was seen to turn for home.

Nothing further was heard until later that day, when a British trawler reported seeing an aircraft dive into the sea, and picking up one survivor. The survivor was Flying Officer Steel, your husband's navigator.

In spite of the most thorough searches, nothing further has been heard or seen of your husband,and it is regretfully believed that he lost his life in the crash.

Flight Lieutenant Rowe, who was a close friend of your husband, will be visiting you shortly and no doubt will be able to clear up any details which I am not permitted to cover in this letter.

Kit Ford had been with us only a short time, but he had rapidly proved his worth as an operational pilot. He was extremely popular, and we all miss him sadly.

On behalf of all members of the squadron and myself, may I offer our sincerest sympathy to you in your sad loss,

Yours sincerely

Richard E. Burns,
Wing Commander.

In the light of these three letters, Jocelyn could find no reason for hoping that at any moment a message might arrive to say that Kit had been rescued. Nonetheless, every time the telephone or doorbell rang, her heart would leap involuntarily, and for a split second she almost believed it was happening.

However, on the 29th of July, she received a final, official message from the Casualty Branch of Air Ministry which read:

Madam:

I am commanded by the Air Council to express to you their great regret on learning that your husband, Flight Lieutenant Christopher Wallace Ford, Royal Air Force, is missing as a result of air operations on 20th July, 1944, when the Beaufighter aircraft of which he was pilot crashed into the North Sea during a patrol off the Norwegian Coast. The navigator was later rescued but no trace of your husband could be found.

Any news which may later become known will immediately be communicated to you.

The Air Council desire me to convey to you their sympathy in your great anxiety.

I am, Madam,
Your obedient Servant,

Charles Evans

After reading this letter, in her numbing grief, Jocelyn could only think of something so mundane as, how odd that this man's surname was the same as her maiden name.

CHAPTER 28

Jocelyn was sensible enough to realize that she could not escape unhappiness by pursuing it, and she kept busy enough during the day so that she had no time to sit and grieve. There were all the preparations to be made for the move to Susan Plum, and she had the comfort and distraction of company. She had Boo, and she had Carol who was always there when needed.

But the long nights were another matter. It was then that the agonizing finality of death would crush her heart as a hammer will crush an ice cube. She wanted to cry out loud in the darkness, Oh, why, why did it have to be Kit? He was good, and kind, and loving, and honourable. Most of the things in fact that Simon was not. Was this justice? If so it was a kind she did not comprehend.

It was not that she felt it so unfair to herself. She knew that she was but one among thousands of bereaved wives, including two of her own friends who, since D-Day, had become widows. And she was aware, too, that time's discriminating fingers would pluck the thorns from her heart that now caused this unceasing pain, and would leave only faint scars that poignant memories of the happiest moments of their short life together would anoint. It was for Kit that she felt her grief so keenly. That he who so loved the life they shared, and had hoped to share for a long long time, should be denied it—that he would not see his child grow up—that all their wonderful plans for the future would be unfulfilled. And what made it even more cruel was to see before her very eyes each day two people who, for some inexplicable reason, had been spared to go on living together in the most wanton incompatibility.

There were moments when she felt a pressing impulse to shout at them, "Stop! Stop this futile childish bickering!" But the words always failed before the aching constriction in her throat.

***

Before Simon went to see the owner of Susan Plum about signing a lease, another prospect came to light. It was in the guise of an answer to another one of their own ads. A Mrs. Butler from the small village of Swaffham in Norfolk called to say that she would be happy to rent them her home if they would like to come up and look it over. Since it was a long journey, whoever came could stay overnight.

She explained that she was leaving England on a kind of mission of mercy to Italy to try to locate her only nephew who had been shot down over some remote area. She evidently had some connections in high places to get permission for such a risky junket in the middle of the war.

With the thought that Jocelyn would benefit from a change of scene, Carol suggested that she should be the one to go and investigate the place. It might be a better bet than Susan Plum. Still too numb to care much what she did, Jocelyn agreed to go. She did after all know the route, having gone that way to visit Kit.

In bleak contrast to the lighthearted mood in which she had left for that journey, with a heavy heart she boarded the train for London, via Cambridge, thence to Peterborough and on to the village of Swaffham by bus

She found a taxi and asked the driver to take her to Mrs. Butler's house. He was a local and knew the place. Soon he dropped her at the front entrance to the property, agreeing to come back for her the following morning.

The paint was peeling from the wooden sign loosely hanging at an odd angle on the gatepost. It proclaimed that the house was called Four Winds. It was a huge rambling old brick structure dating back to the 16th century which now boasted several added turrets and a great deal of incongruous lacy once-white wooden trim gracing the peaks. The expansive grounds were uncared for and the whole place was in need of some loving care. Jocelyn learned from the owner, Mrs. Butler, that this was where Lord

Nelson was said to have run away to sea as a young lad. His grandfather was then the rector of the village church.

Mrs. Butler, a tall angular woman about fifty, lived alone. She was an artist of some note and the walls of the cavernous rooms and halls were lined with samples of her work—mainly chillingly wild land- and seascapes. But she was a warm charming hostess and made Jocelyn feel very much at home. She led her up the staircase to the guest room which was adorned with gaily flowered chintz curtains and matching bed spread and easy chair. There was an en suite bathroom also nicely appointed and with thick soft towels and abundant hot water. Mrs. Butler left her to freshen up after her trip and went down to make tea.

Jocelyn soon followed, finding her hostess in the kitchen. This room was a classic Victorian horror—cavernous and dank. A monstrous yellow enamel Aga Cooker sat against one wall and Jocelyn thought it would take some getting used to. In addition to the relatively modern kitchen sink, there was the old original pump, still operative, standing in one corner. It looked as though the adjuncts to the house had been built around it.

Certainly the place could easily accommodate everyone, and it did have both electricity and a telephone. However, Jocelyn could see several drawbacks. It would be draughty and difficult to heat; it was not close to any shopping; it was not an easy spot for Dennis or Simon to reach; and, last but hardly least, instead of at Susan Plum where they would have only five chickens to look after, here, as well as chickens, there were several dogs, cats, and two bad-tempered goats. To Jocelyn's practical mind it just didn't seem to fit the bill. However, she would have to talk it over with Carol and Sheila, and especially Simon.

After a very pleasant evening listening to the details of Mrs. Butler's proposed venturesome trip to Italy, Jocelyn enjoyed a good night's rest. The following morning, after breakfast, she thanked Mrs. Butler for her hospitality and promised to call her as soon as they made a decision, one way or the other. Then she left Four Winds in the taxi in order to catch the train back to London and on home.

She got a seat in a compartment and dozed most of the way to London, partly in order to avoid staring out of the window at the desolate countryside and partly to avoid dwelling on the happier time she had taken this train. She couldn't bear to think how wonderfully convenient this place would have been for Kit to come home to.

When she reached London she was early enough to find a seat on the Newmarket train which soon filled up with G.I.s returning from their weekend passes. Loud, cocksure, and carefree, they joked with one another in their nasal drawls, and laughed as though the world were theirs to do with as they wished.

Jocelyn tried to concentrate on her book, but found herself listening to the banter. One was saying "I'll bet you dollars to doughnuts she's an American. Look at her clothes. They sure aren't English."

His pal drawled back, "You look at her clothes. I'm looking at her legs. Jee-zus! they aren't English either."

A serious, good looking lad with a crew cut, dark brown eyes and a round cherubic face mumbled apologetically to Jocelyn, "Pay no attention to them, Ma'am. They don't mean anything by it."

Jocelyn smiled warmly and said, "I don't mind, really, but if you are taking any bets with them, I'm not an American, I'm a Canadian."

"So that's it! I just knew you were different. What are you doing over here, anyway?" He spoke in a true Bostonian drawl.

Not wanting to invite sympathy, Jocelyn chose not to say anything about her present status and she answered casually, "I'm married to a Raf pilot."

She expected he would lose interest as soon as she admitted to being married, but his eyes lit up. "Say, I wish my wife could be over here. I'm having, at least we're having a baby soon."

"Really? We have a baby daughter, just over two months old."

"No kidding! Say, you don't happen to have any pictures of her do you? I've never seen a real small one."

"Now isn't that a coincidence," Jocelyn grinned, opening her purse and taking out a folder of snaps of Boo. "I just happen to have a dozen or so." She handed him the pictures.

He studied them carefully. "Say she's real cute. But isn't she awfully small? Are they really that tiny?"

"Actually Boo is quite a large specimen. She was over eight pounds when she was born. Most babies weigh in at around seven or so. She was nine weeks old when those snaps were taken."

He was looking at a snapshot of Kit, sitting in the garden of the Lodge, concentrating intently on giving Boo her bottle.

Finally, he asked, "Is that your husband holding the baby?"

"Yes. it is," Jocelyn replied. "She was nine weeks old when that picture was taken." She didn't add that this was the last time Kit had seen his baby daughter.

"Is that right?" the G.I. incredulously. "I don't suppose I could see her? I mean,...golly, you must think I'm awfully nervy. But I'd really like to see what I'm going to be missing."

"I'm sure Boo would be delighted to meet you. Where are you stationed?"

"Just outside Newmarket. Gee, I expect you live miles from there," he said, sounding disappointed at the thought.

"As a matter of fact, I live right in Newmarket."

"No kidding? Could I have your address?"

"Of course," Jocelyn said, getting a piece of paper and a pencil out of her bag and writing it down for him.

His fresh boyish face beamed with pleasure as he took the paper and put it in his wallet. "Gee, thanks. That's mighty fine of you. By the way, my name's Eddy, Eddy Johnston."

"And mine's Jocelyn, Jocelyn Ford."

While his pals played card games, she and Eddy exchanged trivia about their backgrounds, and Jocelyn kept to her resolve not to mention Kit's tragic death. When they reached Newmarket station, she said good bye and reiterated her invitation for him to come and see Boo whenever he had any time off.

The sky was threatening, but it hadn't yet begun to rain, so she walked quickly past the taxi queue. As she strode off in the direction of the Lodge, it suddenly occurred to her that she had given the American boy an address that would not be valid for very long.

When she arrived at the Lodge, Carol made some tea and brought it into the living room where Jocelyn reported on her visit to Swaffham. She told them the good things first; that it was very roomy, well furnished, and for the most part pleasantly bright. Then she told them about the kitchen, its accoutrements, and, finally, about the menagerie they would inherit. That, plus the rather inconvenient location, convinced them that they should stick with Susan Plum, despite its lack of electricity. And five hens seemed considerably less of a challenge than a dozen or more hens plus domestic pets and two contrary goats.

When Simon arrived home later in the evening, Jocelyn repeated her story and he agreed with their decision. He immediately called Mrs. Case, the owner of Susan Plum, and made an appointment to see her the next day to sign a lease.

CHAPTER 29

On Saturday, the day chosen to move, Carol wakened suddenly, jumped out of bed and ran to the window. "Oh, no!" she whispered as she looked out upon a day dreary beyond belief with a heavy sky pressing in low and ugly. "Why couldn't it have been sunny so that Jocelyn could see Susan Plum as I first saw her?" she asked herself miserably.

She slipped into her slacks and sweater which felt uncomfortably clammy, brushed her hair, and began stripping the bed, carefully folding the bed linen. Surely by the time we're ready to leave, the clouds will lift. It can't stay gloomy all day, she told herself.

But, by 10 o'clock, a cold persistent rain was falling from the dirty grey skies, and occasional gusts of wind defiantly hurled the drops against the windows as though to prove that nature always holds the trump card.

Simon had been summoned to a rehabilitation centre for therapy and so was not present to help with the move. Sheila cynically insisted that he had arranged it on purpose. She was ready to accuse him of anything at this moment she was so annoyed with him. Before he left the Lodge, he asked her to mail a letter for him. When she noticed that it was addressed to an officer in the W.A.A.F., without hesitation she opened it and read it. She knew that he was keen on one of the nursing sisters who had looked after him when he was in hospital.

She was standing white faced and fiery eyed when Jocelyn happened to come into the lounge, and she threw the letter down on a chair angrily. In a low dry voice she asked, "What would you do, Joc, if your husband asked you to mail a letter to some woman he intended to spend the weekend with?"

Jocelyn felt her heart's wound open. "I'd tear it up and let the wind deliver it," she replied bitterly.

The hurt in her eyes and the apparent lack of sympathetic interest in her tone went unnoticed by Sheila who wasn't really hurt by Simon's indiscretions and needed no sympathy. This sort of thing merely added the piquant flavour to her life which kept it from becoming humdrum, much like putting bay leaves in a stew.

There was a wickedly satisfying gleam in her violet eyes now as she tore the letter into tiny pieces and let them fall into the waste basket. "That's that," she said, and continued with her job of preparing to move, as though from the incident she had drawn new life and vigour.

***

Because of the petrol shortage and the fact that it was nine miles to Balsham, they had some difficulty persuading anyone to move them. However, in the end they managed to hire a small lorry. It arrived at eleven o'clock, with a short rotund rosy-cheeked woman at the wheel. Their instant dismay quickly turned to admiration when the stout Mrs. Murphy began tossing heavy trunks around as though they were made of cardboard and filled with feathers. She rapidly loaded everything neatly into the back of the lorry and, after giving a final push to a jutting pram, she said, "Coom along now luvs. 'op in and we'll be off."

Sheila, now heavy and awkward in the final weeks of her pregnancy, and Jocelyn with Boo on her lap, squeezed into the front seat beside Mrs. Murphy. Carol manoeuvred herself into the back on top of a trunk and under a tarpaulin.

The rain was now coming down in sheets which turned the gravel road to Balsham into a quagmire. When they turned on to it from the paved highway, Carol began to feel much as she often had aboard the Bonaire. It was not quite as rough in the front seat, but it was more terrifying. The antiquated lorry gasped and choked up inclines, then slid and slithered down the other side, and when not fighting deep ruts or plunging into pot holes whose water emptied in a muddy spray on the windscreen, it skidded and shied from one roadside verge to the other.

Sheila clung grimly to the door handle with one hand and to Jocelyn with the other. The only ones unconcerned were Boo, who had fallen asleep as soon as the wheels started turning, and Mrs. Murphy, who hummed nonchalantly, and swore only once when a larger lorry almost forced her ancient vehicle into the ditch.

At last, they came to a jolting halt in front of Carol's dream house. She crawled out stiffly from under the tarpaulin and, with bewildered eyes, beheld a new Susan Plum hunching dark and mournful under the sorrowful sky. The leaded windows now seemed small and baleful, and the heavy oak door with its grotesque knocker was forbidding.

She gasped. "It couldn't be! It must be a mistake, an illusion, or a horrible malevolent prank." She stood in the rain, shocked and stupefied, until Mrs. Murphy's commanding voice urged her back to reality.

"Ere we are, luv," she said. "Let's 'ustle now and get these things in out of the wet."

Carol trudged slowly up the path, and fumbled for the keys with wet trembling hands. She unlatched the door. It stuck fast; then, as she pushed hard on it, it gave unexpectedly flinging her into the dank, dim interior. Recovering her balance, she shivered as she gazed about her. From the eerie gloom within, the ugly oil heater thrust itself forward defiantly. Surely this was not the same gracious hall over which she had exclaimed so rapturously just a week ago.

Jocelyn stepped in behind her and she, too, paused as though loath to venture further into the hostile atmosphere.

Carol dared not look at her. "The kitchen is this way," she said with feigned nonchalance. "We'll get a fire going and...and warm the place up a bit."

She led the way and Jocelyn followed, silently, carrying the sleeping baby. They groped their way along the dark corridor and Carol warned her to watch for the steps leading into the kitchen. With windows on both sides, this back room was slightly brighter than the front of the house, but it was just as intensely damp and cold.

Sheila came in, pushing Boo's pram. "Here's the chariot," she announced cheerfully. "Mrs. Murphy was sure you would need it right away so she uncollapsed it."

"Thanks," Jocelyn said, and placed Boo in her pram. "Now you be good and have a long snooze," she whispered, tucking the bankets around the baby. "We've got a lot of work to do around here." She placed the pram near the window and returned to the front of the house to bring in more of their possessions.

Carol meanwhile was trying without success to light a fire in the big coal range. Giving up in disgust, she tried coaxing one of the small oil burners to light.

Mrs. Murphy came in, edged her aside, and said, "Ere, what's up with it? Let me 'ave a go. I've 'ad some experience with them devilish things." She picked up the small stove and shook it vigorously. No sound came from the fuel chamber. "It'd work better with some oil in it," she said wryly.

Before long this resourceful woman had found the oil supply, filled the burners, started a fire in the stubborn coal stove, got the kettle boiling, as well as removing everything from the van into the front hall. Carol wished that she could stay longer. Her homespun cheeriness dispelled some of the choking gloom of the weather and the surly mood of Susan Plum.

When the door finally closed behind her comforting presence, Carol faced Jocelyn and Sheila. "I'm so sorry," she apologized miserably. "Really, it didn't look like this when I saw it before. I just can't understand it."

Jocelyn took her arm as they walked back to the kitchen. "Don't feel badly, hon'," she said. "It's just the day."

Carol brightened. "I'm sure it is. Honestly, you'll love it when the sun shines."

But the skies prolonged their doleful weeping, and Jocelyn began to doubt whether the sun would ever shine in her life again. Her day began before dawn with Boo's first gurgling hint that she was hungry. For one split second, Jocelyn would lie in bed wondering why she had been so loath to waken from the blessedness of sleep. Then the awful truth would engulf her like a tidal wave, leaving a loneliness and yearning within her that made her despair as to how she could face another long pointless day.

In the clammy darkness, she would creep out of bed and tackle the oil lamp and then the stove on which she warmed Boo's milk. Then, while the clouds shed their noisy tears on the slate roof, hers fell silent and unheeded on the pink blanket wrapped around the baby cradled in her arms.

With the onset of daylight, and its accompanying activities, the insidious shadow of grief trailed her at a distance, reluctant to leave her even for a moment.

To make matters worse, pools of water collected and seeped into the kitchen from the trough outside the door, keeping the room in a constant state of flood. The rain gushed down the wide chimneys into the fireplaces, defying all attempts to light fires in them. Without the magic touch of Mrs. Murphy, the oil lamps and stoves persisted in their spiteful stubbornness, and at least once in every attempt to light one, an angry oily cloud was spat in someone's face.

The house itself was dark, cold, and sinister. And, as there were no daily papers, no radio, and no telephone, they felt the remoteness of the place more acutely. Even Pete the gypsy, in his caravan across the road, made no attempt to become acquainted.

However, they were finally forced to appeal to him for help. Jocelyn had been down to the chicken run to feed the hens, and when she returned, she kicked off her Wellingtons and gingerly removed her dripping raincoat, giving it a vigorous shake before hanging it up behind the kitchen door. Carol looked up from her kneeling position on the floor where she was mopping up water.

"Hey, don't shake that wet thing on this lovely polished floor," she warned.

"Sorry, hon." Jocelyn responded with a grin. She put her boots in the corner by the stove and remarked with disgust, "I think chickens must be the dumbest creatures on earth."

Carol protested. "I feel I must stick up for dear old Gastronomika," she said, on behalf of the hen to whom she had affixed that name. "Any bird that will lay one egg per day in these eggless times has my unqualified support.''

"Well, she's a bit dense in some respects," Jocelyn said. "I've just been down there and the whole kit and caboodle—including your precious Gassy—are sitting in puddles shivering and shaking with cold, and not one of them has the sense to go in out of the rain.''

"That's odd," Carol frowned, wrung out her cloth in the pail and stood up. "I hope Gassy doesn't catch cold and stop doing her daily good deed. If it weren't for her I'd have forgotten what a real egg looks like.'' She put the pail in the corner, and took her coat from the door.

"Do you have some formula for making stubborn hens change their minds?" Jocelyn queried.

"No, but I'll go and investigate.''

Jocelyn put her coat and boots on. "I'll come with you, although they just stared at me dumbly before when I suggested that they go inside their hut.''

They picked their way carefully around puddles covering the sodden path to the chicken coop. Carol walked around the henhouse, peering through the wire at the bedraggled looking birds.

"They do look as though they've been on a lost weekend, don't they?'' She continued her inspection, then examined the hut. She turned to Jocelyn, a curious expression on her face. "It's a smart chick that can lift a latch," she said wryly. "They're locked out of their house.''

"Oh, no, Carol. What a chump I am. Poor things. What shall we do?''

"I haven't the foggiest. But Miss Case said that Pete would help us if we got into trouble. I'll go and ask his advice.''

Pete was almost as bedraggled looking as the hens, with his long wispy hair falling over a narrow forehead, his cabbage leaf ears and sallow complexion. Carol couldn't help thinking that with his sad bleary eyes sunk in a long thin face, his unkempt clothes, and his inarticulate mumbling he looked and sounded as though he had accompanied the hens on their lost weekend. At first he played an exasperating game of pretending to be mentally dense, but after Carol explained the problem for the third time at varying speeds, he finally grunted that he understood and led the way across the road to "look at 'um".

When he saw the pitiful creatures, he became a different man, stirring suddenly into action and taking complete charge. In three days he had successfully doctored the birds and grunted a promise that they would survive. Gassy missed those three days, but then forgave and forgot and thereafter continued her daily offering.

***

Every second person in Balsham was called Strump, and their next encounter with the outside world was in the person of Sam Strump who introduced himself when Carol answered his heavy knock on the kitchen door. Without waiting to be invited, he walked past Carol into the kitchen. Where he stood, a large puddle formed as water dripped from his boots, rain slicker, sou'wester, and his scraggly black mustache.

"Oi'm Sam Strump," he announced gruffly. "Oi've coom to deliver the tumston ordered last Easter. It's taken a tidy toime to git what you wanted. Things is 'ard to git nowaday."

Jocelyn backed away from him and leaned against the table. "What is it that you've brought?" she asked.

"The tumston the loidy ordered, last Easter. It's out in yon van."

Jocelyn appealed mutley to Carol but received a blank look and a shrug.

"What is it exactly that you've brought?" Carol asked.

"Ben't this Mrs. Case's 'ouse?" he inquired testily.

"Yes, it is. But we're just her tenants."

He started buttoning up his coat readying to leave.

Jocelyn interposed quickly. "Wait a moment. If you've got something for Mrs. Case, it's all right to leave it."

"You're sure this is 'er 'ouse?" he asked suspiciously.

"Quite sure," Jocelyn said. "In fact, she's coming here sometime in the next few days. We can give it to her then."

"Well, oi guess it's all roight then. Whar'll I put it?"

"How big is it?" Carol asked.

He scratched his head and said impatiently, "It's a reglar sized tumston—just loike the lady ordered. Now, whar'll I set it?"

"Just roll it in," Carol said flippantly, still without the vaguest idea what it was.

He cast a suspicious glare at them and shuffled off to his van, reappearing shortly staggering under the weight of a large marble tombstone. He put it down in the corner of the kitchen while Carol and Jocelyn watched in horrified silence. Jocelyn at last forced herself to examine the inscription on the monument. It read, 'In loving memory of dear George. Died April 2, 1944. We loved him to the end.'

She made a mental calculation. That's four months ago. Could this George person possibly be buried on the premises?

Sam finally found a piece of paper he had been searching for in his pockets, and nudged Jocelyn's arm.

"Soign this, roight 'ere," he said, handing her a small chewed pencil.

She took the paper over to the window and examined it. After reading it, she suddenly began to laugh. "Carol, it's okay," she said. "George is a dog."

"Thank heavens!" Carol exclaimed with relief. "All we need in this spooky place is a dead body buried somewhere on the premises."

Sam carefully folded the receipt and put it in his coat pocket. He put on his hat and turned to leave shaking his head sadly as he went off down the path mumbling, "There be some queer folk about."

CHAPTER 30

Just when Jocelyn felt certain that she could not bear another day of incessant dreary rain, or another hour being trapped within the damp eerie confines of Susan Plum, the sun thrust itself through the thick grey blanket of cloud and poured its bright golden rays through the leaded windows, lending warmth and colour to all it touched. The magic that Carol had experienced on her first visit had returned.

Jocelyn could scarcely believe her eyes that morning when she awoke and saw a touch of blue in the sky. She got out of bed, threw open her bedroom window and breathed deeply of the sun-warmed air. Oh, this is better she thought. The garden below was transformed, almost pulsating with life and colour. It made her want to live again, when only the night before, in her abject misery, she had not cared whether she ever saw the light of another day. The throbbing ache was still there in her breast, but now the grim hopeless shadow of grief was dimmed in the warmth and brightness of the sun.

At breakfast, she said to Carol, "We need some groceries badly. Shall we cycle to the village later on?"

"All right—unless Sheila would rather go with you."

"Go ahead," Sheila said amiably. "I'd look pretty silly on a bicycle right now. You two go. I'll watch Boo."

"I'll put her in the garden," Jocelyn said. "It's time she got reacquainted with fresh air and sun."

"We could walk," Carol said. "And then you could come."

Sheila shook her head. "No, thanks just the same. I've got some washing to do and I may as well do it while the sun is out and I can hang it outside."

Before they left, Jocelyn wheeled the pram out to a secluded spot in the garden, then placed Boo in it and wrapped her up warmly. True, the sun was out, but it was still damp and a bit chilly. There, protected from any wind, or direct sunlight, with garrulous birds chattering overhead, Jocelyn left her and she and Carol pedalled off to the village.

As they cycled along the muddy road, they revelled in the warmth of the sun and the quaintness of the thatched cottages leaning over the road as though trying to touch each other, and in the fragrance of the cleansed countryside. Carol partially recaptured the magic that she had felt on her first visit to Balsham. It was so peaceful, so removed from the hurly burly of the war-wracked world.

"It's just like a picture on a calendar, isn't it," Carol commented.

Jocelyn had turned her wheel quickly to avoid hitting a stray white hen on the road. "Yes, it is. I can well understand how you fell in love with it when you first saw it."

"I'd almost begun to think I imagined everything," Carol admitted. "I'm just glad that Dennis hasn't been here yet. He would have had a fit to see us wallowing in all that miserable rain."

"That looks like the post office over there," Jocelyn said. "The tiny cottage with the kiosk outside."

The shop where they had registered for rations was just next door so they decided to buy the groceries before picking up the mail.

There was a musty odour about the small general store, but there were pleasant overtones of spices, leather, dry goods, and the earthy smell of freshly picked vegetables. Behind the cluttered counter was a tall, lean, bespectacled man, and a short, roly poly woman with ruddy cheeks. A bit like Jack Spratt and his wife, Jocelyn told Sheila later. They were another branch of the prolific Strump family. They made up the order for Susan Plum in a brusque business-like manner, with more suspicion than curiosity in the question, "The noime, please?"

Carol answered, spelling out all three last names very deliberately. She received a scowl in return for her friendly smile. Evidently, the villagers did not take kindly to strangers in their midst, especially ones who were from some strange country overseas. As they left the shop, they called out a cheery thank you and good-bye, but there was no response from the Strumps.

Their next stop was the tiny white-washed cottage which housed the post office. The room used for this purpose was really the entrance hall. It contained makeshift counters and several drawers and cubbyholes, all filled beyond their capacity. Much of the material consisted of the mounting collection of information pamphlets issued by the civil service, but there were, as well, odd bits of crockery which could not be accommodated in the small kitchen just behind. It was all very homespun and most unbusinesslike, reflecting the characters of the two middle-aged spinsters who shared the role of postmistress. They were, of course, named Strump—Minnie and Myrtle.

At the tinkling sound of the old fashioned bell over the front door, Miss Minnie bustled in from the kitchen. She wiped her pudgy hands on her white apron. Her huge round face folded in a benevolent smile as she said, "Good morning, loidies. I be thinking you must be the new folk at Susan Plum, be I roight?"

"Yes, you be," Carol responded, smiling. "I'm Mrs. Carter, and this is my sister, Mrs. Ford. There's also a Mrs. Barton-Holmes living with us."

Jocelyn acknowledged Miss Minnie's friendly greeting and was totally amazed to see her manoeuver her well larded torso into the narrow space behind the counter. From the grey knot of hair on top of her large head, to where her volumninous skirt touched the floor, she was like a huge bell. It was like watching an ocean liner edge skilfully into its narrow berth.

Having safely installed herself behind the counter, she said proudly, "Oi'm Minnie Strump, the postmistress. What can oi do for you? Oi 'ave some mail for you, I know that. And there's a letter for the other lydy—Mrs., Mrs. ah..."

"Barton-Holmes," Carol interposed.

"That's it. Queer name that."

Miss Minnie rummaged among the papers on the counter, then peered into one or two cubbyholes, but found no mail. Finally, she turned and called into the back room, "Myr—tul, 'ave you seen them letters for the new folk at Susan Plum?"

A shorter, thinner counterpart of Miss Minnie bustled in from the kitchen, and squeezed in behind her sister. She gave Jocelyn and Carol a quick shy smile, and then removed her gold-rimmed glasses and began to search for the missing mail. Presently, she held up a bundle of letters and said smugly, "Ere they are, luv. You never 'alf look for things."

"Thank you, luv," Miss Minnie replied politely. She glanced at Miss Myrtle, then at the two girls. "My sister, Myrtle. She 'elps me sort the mail."

Miss Myrtle darted another shy smile over the counter, replaced her glasses, then pattered back to the kitchen.

They bought a supply of stamps and air letter forms, then said good bye and went out to their bicycles. They put the mail and provisions into the bicycle baskets and took off in the direction of Susan Plum.

Jocelyn was the first to drive up the gravel path. She caught sight of a blue uniform in the far corner of the garden, bending over the pram. Her heart made a sudden foolish leap, then dropped back into place. "When will I ever learn?" she asked herself sadly. She had hoped to avoid these crushing moments of unwarranted bittersweet pleasure once they left the Lodge with its ringing doorbell and telephone and its proximity to things she preferred to forget. But her heart was very hard to convince that never again would there be any thrill-giving calls or joyous unexpected arrivals for her.

It was Simon this time who had raised the false quickening in her breast. She waited while Carol put her bicycle in the shed and then walked across the grass to speak to him. He had left the pram and was sitting in a deck chair, engrossed in a book on spiritualism. The book shelves in Susan Plum were replete with such literature, much to his delight. Sheila was sitting beside him, feigning sleep. He put his book down and stood up to greet Jocelyn and Carol.

"How nice to see you, Simon," Carol said. "How's the therapy coming along?"

Simon sank back in his chair. "Fine thanks. You and Jocelyn are looking as beautiful as ever."

"Flattery will get you nowhere," Jocelyn said. "But if you are angling to stay for dinner, then perhaps a bit of flattery isn't wasted. We've just picked up the rations."

Sheila opened her eyes. "Flattery will get you nowhere with me," she said sourly. "I know you too well."

"Quiet, bitch," he said with a charming suavity which diluted the insult. He turned his charming smile back to Carol and Jocelyn. "Can I get you some chairs?"

"No thanks," Jocelyn replied. "I'm chief cook today and must go in and begin lunch."

"I'll put away the groceries," Carol offered, pausing for a moment to ask, "How long are you staying, Simon?"

"Until they call me back, and I hope it won't be too soon. This place is very tempting."

"You'll soon change your mind on that score, when we hand you the axe and lead you to the wood pile. This is no holiday resort. It's all hands to the plough," Carol teased.

"Ah, well," he sighed, "for the moment allow me to lounge in my ignorant bliss. We should always have weather like this." He stretched his long legs out from the chair, and lit a cigarette.

The kitchen window overlooked the part of the garden where they were sitting, and Jocelyn leaned out and called, "Simon, would you do us a favour? We need some kindling."

Sheila burst into a trill of laughter. "Your hands, my dear spouse, are needed at the plough," she mocked.

He grinned as he slowly eased himself out of his chair, ground out his cigarette, took off his coat, rolled up his sleeves, and went over to the wood pile. When he had finished his task, he returned to his chair beside Sheila and said casually, "By the way, darling, I ran into Mrs. Case in Cambridge and we had a nice chat."

Sheila arched her finely shaped brows. "Mrs. Case? Oh, you mean our landlady?"

"Yes, she asked me if I would put some tombstone at the head of her dog's grave. Have you any idea where he's buried?"

The tombstone was sitting in the kitchen where Sam Strump left it.

Sheila said, "No, we haven't a clue. We just hope it isn't down that creepy cellar next to the kitchen."

"Not to worry," Simon said reassuringly. "She says it's somewhere in the garden. Down by the raspberries, I think?"

"Oh, that's much better," Sheila said sarcastically.

"Well, if you really have no idea, I guess I'll have to check with Mrs. Case when I see her tonight."

"You're seeing her tonight?" Sheila asked in astonishment. "What for?"

"She's having a seance at her home and she asked if I'd like to attend."

"And you said, yes, of course." Sheila said dryly.

"Naturally, I wouldn't miss such an opportunity. She's an excellent medium, I'm told."

Sheila's blue eyes smouldered with anger. "First it's Miggles dragging you off to those idiotic seances, and now it's that daft landlady." She pulled her blue cardigan over her shoulders, got up, and strode across the lawn and into the house.

It was approaching dusk that evening when they sat down to supper around the refectory table in the kitchen. A mauve twilight was seeping over the sky, and Venus, proud and solitary, displayed her matchless beauty and brilliance like a priceless diamond on soft deep blue velvet. The kitchen door stood ajar and the casement windows were wide open, admitting the sweet heavy scent of the nicotine plants growing beneath them.

Sheila had finished her dinner, and sat waiting for the others, before pouring coffee. She was still petulantly silent, feeling very annoyed with Simon for leaving her to go to Mrs. Case's seance. She sat, rolling her napkin into a tiny ball, trying to think of some way she might even the score. At length, she said provocatively, "Has Mrs. Case seen any good ghosts lately, darling?"

Simon lit a cigarette and inhaled deeply, then exhaled slowly. "No, but she did tell me that she got through to her husband last week."

"Really?" Sheila said, her lips curving into a sardonic smile. "That's nice. And what did dear Mr. Case have to say?"

Simon was well aware that he was being mocked but he answered her seriously anyway. "He said he's happy and that some of his favourite horses are with him."

"Galloping across the Elysian fields, I suppose?" Sheila teased.

Simon was about to retort when, through the open windows, came a sudden draught of air laden with the most pungent smell of sweaty horse. Sheila glanced at Carol and Jocelyn, then she jumped up and ran to the door. She climbed the slope and scanned the open meadows. There wasn't a horse in sight. And even more strange, not a leaf was moving in the still twilight air. She came back, faced Simon's triumphant smile with anger replacing the mischievous look on her face.

"Simon, we are nervous enough as it is with no man around except Pete," she raged. "Let's hear no more about spirits."

Simon laughed. "You started it, my dear. Maybe now you won't be so quick to ridicule my beliefs."

Many things occurred within the thick stone walls of Susan Plum which could not be readily explained. Unidentifiable noises, sudden draughts, occasional sounds of light footsteps—and after the incident of Mr. Case and the horses, they were convinced that the house was haunted.

They were abetted in their conviction by the noises made by a harmless wind as it rattled along the eaves, banging windows, slamming doors; and also by the presence of numerous cats that stole in and out of open windows at all hours. Fertile imaginations supplied the rest.

All of the 'supernatural' happenings were blamed on the spirit of Mr. Case. He was the pet ghost, and upon occasion he was mischievous. One of his favourite pranks was to slam the lavatory lid down on the back of an unwary sitter. Another was to meddle with the lamps. In the evening, when they were sitting reading, knitting or sewing in the dim light of their amber glow, one by one the lamps would suddenly begin to smoke, blacken their globes and become utterly useless.

After several unsuccessful attempts to fix them by trimming the wick, someone would 'damn the man' and go in search of the candles. But Mr. Case was not to be outwitted. At the point where the staircase took a sharp turn, an inexplicable draught would snuff out the candle, leaving the bearer to stumble up the remaining steps in impenetrable darkness. The stairway was a menace in itself being composed of three short flights, two small landings, and two right-angled turns with lethally low ceilings. Thus, it was very hazardous to the uninitiated, or the absentminded.

Sheila didn't bother to forewarn Simon of its pitfalls and when, on his first night at Susan Plum, as he ascended the stair and his taper had been mischievously blown out by Mr. Case, he punctuated each landing with a loud, "OUCH! What the hell! Ooh, damn!"

His visit lasted just one week. Since Sheila's confinement was near, he had made arrangements with the Potts that she should return to Surrey House to await the event. He was scheduled to report back to the convalescent hospital on Friday, and he planned to escort Sheila to Newmarket that day. However, on Thursday afternoon, an ancient flivver chugged up the driveway of Susan Plum. After it had finished a series of hiccoughing jerks, it stopped and the Potts family emerged.

When old Mrs. Potts alighted, complete with straw boater resting on the verge of her grey bangs, she shouted, "MY WHAT A NICE PLACE YOU HAVE HERE!"

The birds went scurrying off in all directions, Pete the Gypsy's dog came barking out of the caravan, and even Pete, himself, overcame his usual inertia and got up from his rocker to see what all the commotion was about.

Sheila and Simon greeted the guests and showed them around the house and grounds. They went into the kitchen where Jocelyn was preparing vegetables for an early supper. She immediately invited them to join them.

In their high-pitched voices, inflecting the proper intonation of surprise and protest, Rose and Jean chorused, "Oh, no we couldn't think of doing that."

Mrs. Potts looked up quickly and shouted, "WHAT'S THAT? WHAT DO I THINK OF WHAT?"

"Nothing, Mother," Rose said gently. "Jocelyn has asked us to stay for a meal, and we said we couldn't think of it." She turned to Jocelyn and held up a small paper bag. "You see, we've brought some food for a picnic."

Jocelyn eyed the small bag and wondered if they had some biblical miracle in mind. She rather doubted it and felt that a little persuasion was called for. "We just got our rations," she said convincingly. "There really is plenty for everyone."

"No, we simply couldn't," Rose said firmly.

"Well perhaps Simon can persuade you. I'll do enough veggies for everyone, in any case."

Later in the afternoon, Jocelyn caught Sheila's eye and beckoned her over. "Are they going to eat with us?" she asked.

"They say not, but I notice that their picnic fare consists of a small raisin cake. I don't know why they are being so stubborn."

"Ask them again. Supper is almost ready."

Sheila returned to the chattering group on the lawn and pressed them again to stay for the meal.

They protested vigorously, but after Sheila made one more plea, Rose said, "Well, perhaps we could have just a teeny bite with you. But we won't touch your meat ration. We simply cannot do that."

"But Jocelyn says there's plenty for everybody."

"No, that's final. No meat. And just a few vegetables."

Sheila gave up and reported to Jocelyn. So the Potts sat down to potatoes and green beans, while everyone else enjoyed potatoes, green beans, and roast lamb, which was just a euphemism for English mutton. Rose and Jean looked very noble throughout the meal and afterwards Jocelyn said that she felt mean about it.

Sheila replied, "Nonsense! Methinks, the ladies did protest too much."

CHAPTER 31

The Potts insisted that Sheila go back to Newmarket with them, thus saving Simon the trouble of delivering her. They left immediately after supper. Simon returned to the therapy centre the next morning.

As Carol had discovered to her chagrin, Susan Plum did have a whimsical moody side to her, and now, in the absence of the Barton-Holmes who tended to have a slightly ruffling effect upon her, a soothing calm permeated her ancient rooms. Jocelyn sensed it immediately and acquired from it a measure of peace within herself.

Since Kit's death she had been living in a kind of vacuum, where everything around her moved in its normal course while she remained inert. Physically she was the same person she had always been. Except for a deep sadness in her eyes, she looked the same, behaved the same; and yet, she was not the same person at all. In one fatal moment, she had been relegated to the ranks of widowhood. Widow, she thought, what a horrid word. It brought to mind spiders.

It was not that her new state had come as a surprise. It seemed that she had always known that she and Kit were working against time to cheat death. In one way, it had been a terrible release, for no longer did she have anything to fear. She had fought a losing battle with fate all along, and, subconsciously, she had known it. It had just been a matter of time. And now Kit was gone. He would never come back; and she was left behind. She was twenty-one, with a whole lifetime stretching ahead of her like a blank never-ending road. What should she do? Where should she go? How could she bring up a child on the miserable pension of five pounds a week allowed by the British government?

She was thankful for one thing. Her mother, wisely, had made her take a business course after she and Kit were married. This was in lieu of going to university. Her mother had a firm belief in education. It doesn't cost anything to carry around, she always maintained. At least I can type and take shorthand, Jocelyn reminded herself. But then she would think, even if I can get a job, who will look after Boo?

Another of her worries stemmed from the fact that Kit had not completed his will form, and it was going to take months before his estate was settled. Meanwhile, how was she to carry on? She was no longer in the same category as Carol and Sheila. They had husbands. They still had hope and happiness for the taking, while she was a soul without a country, a hopeless wanderer on an unchartered sea. She wondered when she would become acquainted with this person, and when, if ever, she would come to accept her as her new self. All she knew for certain was that it would take time.

***

Three days after Sheila left for Newmarket with the Potts, a telegram was despatched to Susan Plum. Jocelyn and Carol were enjoying tea on the lawn when a lad cycled up the drive and handed them the message. Until Carol quickly tore open the envelope and read the contents, there was fear in her eyes and in her nervous fingers. But she relaxed and smiled as she relayed the good news to Jocelyn.

"Sheila has a son. Simon won't have to disown them."

Jocelyn sighed. "Some people always manage to get what they want, whether they deserve it or not. But I'm glad for Sheila. Perhaps they'll get along a bit better now."

"I don't blame you for feeling bitter," Carol said.

"Oh, I'm not really. I was at first, especially at the Lodge when they kept up that incessant bickering. But I can see things differently now. I've come to the conclusion that it was a miracle my coming over when I did. I believe Kit was meant to have that brief interlude of happiness and to see our baby before he was killed. There was something too incredible about the way things happened for it to have been mere chance—his posting being changed from the Bahamas to England, my almost disastrous departure for the West just before getting a passage, having you come on the same boat.

No, it was just too many things pointing in the right direction for there not to have been some instrument of divine providence at work."

Carol poured them another cup of tea. "It sounds as though you've become a confirmed fatalist," she said.

"No, I'm not a confirmed anything. I must admit my belief in divine compassion and wisdom was shaken. It just didn't make sense that someone as worthy as Kit should be snatched away and someone as profligate as Simon be saved."

"Well, you know what Mom always said, the devil always takes care of his own."

"Yes, I remember. But perhaps that is too unkind. It's just that Kit and I were so well suited to each other. And I like to think that we had a great deal to offer the world in our own small way. I always imagined that it was people like us whom God wanted on this earth to try to make it a better place."

"Possibly that was His original intention.."

"It was the mark of innocence or naivety I suppose. Anyway, I've stopped trying to ferret out the whys and wherefores. I just feel that I'm richer for having known someone as fine and good as Kit, and I'm prepared to be grateful for the few precious years we shared. I wouldn't trade them for a lifetime of the future I can see for Sheila and Simon."

"Do you think you could ever marry again?"

"Kit and I had something that perhaps is quite rare—a love based not so much on physical attraction, but rather a meeting of minds. We liked the same things, laughed at the same things, even sometimes cried about the same things. But I don't think that we were

so naive as to believe that we might not have been lucky enough to find another kind of love with someone else. Right now, however, I can't think farther than the end of my nose. The future is a blank sheet. I suppose I should be grateful that I'm young enough to warrant a second chance. But, at the moment, I can't imagine availing myself of it, if it did come along."

"I'm sure Kit would never begrudge you any happiness you might find," Carol said.

"No, I don't think so either. But I'm sure that a lot of other people would. I suspect that public opinion tolerates a wanton wife more graciously than it does an unwailing widow." She turned her head suddenly. "Did you hear someone opening the gate?"

Footsteps crunched on the gravel path and in a moment Eddy Johnston, the young American sergeant whom Jocelyn had met on the train on her return from Swaffham, appeared. A broad grin spread over his boyish face as he recognized Jocelyn.

"Hiyah," he drawled, walking across the grass. "Gosh, I thought I'd never find you."

"Eddy, how nice to see you," Jocelyn said. "I'd like you to meet my sister, Carol Carter." She turned to Carol. "You remember my telling you about Eddy, Carol?"

"Of course. You were to come to the Lodge for a visit."

"That's right, M'am. I tried real hard but I never seemed to make it. Then, when I did get there, the lady said you'd moved. Golly, I was disappointed."

"I only remembered after I left you at the train station that day that I had given you an address that would not be valid for long. How did you find us?"

"The lady at the Lodge gave me this address, but did I ever have a hard time finding it. I thought I'd lost you for sure."

Jocelyn offered him a chair, but he declined and sat cross legged on the grass.

"Did it take long to get here?" Jocelyn asked.

Eddy grinned. "Well, I left camp at ten this morning, and it's now nearly three o'clock. I guess you'd say that was fairly long."

"You must be starved. Would you like some tea?"

"No thanks, but I will have one of those cookies."

Jocelyn passed him the plate. "I've been wondering if you got your wish for a baby girl."

"You bet I did. That is one of the reasons I wanted to find you. To show you what a beautiful little girl she is. We call her Fredel—my name's really Frederick, and my wife's is Ellen."

"I hope you brought some snaps of her," Jocelyn said.

"You bet I did," Eddy replied, taking an envelope out of his jacket pocket and handing it to her.

She took the pictures out of the envelope and studied them. The tiny baby had her father's round pleasant features and dark hair.

"She's a beauty all right," she said, handing the snaps to Carol, who examined them and heartily agreed with Jocelyn's assessment.

"How long can you stay, Eddy?" Carol asked. "If you have a forty-eight, and want to spend it here, you're welcome. Our other inmate, Sheila, is away at the moment, having just had her first baby in Newmarket. So, we have lots of room."

Eddy flashed an embarrassed grin at her. "Gosh, I do have tomorrow off. And if you're sure I wouldn't be too much trouble."

"Not a bit. We've just had a parcel from home, so I may be able to whip up something special for supper."

Eddy rummaged in his kit bag and handed a brown parcel to Carol. "Here, I brought this. It's just some gum and chocolate, but I figured it might be welcome."

Carol accepted the parcel. "Thanks heaps. It is indeed welcome. I'll get another plate of cookies. Be back in a minute."

Eddy sat down on the grass beside Jocelyn's chair and said in his soft Bostonian drawl, "You know, I came here for another reason today." He hesitated, searching for suitable words. Jocelyn's eyes continued to study one of the baby pictures she held in her hand. Eddy's coming had brought back with painful clarity the memory of her last visit with Kit in Grimsby.

He finally went on. "I came to tell you—-well, just to say that I'm awfully sorry. Your former landlady told me what happened. I never did get to meet your husband, but I know he must have been a swell guy."

In spite of the aching constriction in her throat, Jocelyn managed to say a brief, "Thanks Eddy. That's just what he was, a swell guy."

She was relieved to see Carol coming out with another plate of cookies.

Although Eddy was warned about Susan Plum's ghost and other strange phenomena, especially the hazards of the staircase, that night on his way to bed he suffered the same fate as Simon had on his first visit.

Tenderly nursing the bumps on his head, he scoffed, "You and your Mr. Case. I'll find the origin of that draught, or my name isn't Frederick Patrick Johnston."

He spent a long time the next morning searching for its source, but he left for Newmarket that afternoon, still a very puzzled young man, and almost convinced that Mr. Case was really lurking about and haunting Susan Plum.

Jocelyn walked with him to the bus. While waiting for its arrival, he said shyly, "Golly, you know, this has been almost as good as going home for a visit. Do you think I could come back sometime? I'd like to get better acquainted with that little girl of yours. She sure is a cutie."

"After all that wood you chopped this morning, I think you've earned the status of a relation. The house might be a bit more crowded the next time, and less peaceful with two babies, but feel free to come anytime you like."

"I'll look forward to meeting the rest of the clan," he said happily.

The bus arrived then and he stepped inside, found a seat by a window and waved to Jocelyn as the bus drove off.

When she returned to the house, Carol ran out to meet her, her cheeks flushed and her eyes sparkling with excitement.

"Did you see it?" she called out.

"See what?"

"That Mosquito that flew over a moment ago."

"We have wasps, ants, and flies, but I really haven't seen any mosquitoes," Jocelyn said, smothering a laugh.

"Oh, Joc, you know what I mean. I'm sure that Dennis flew over a few minutes ago. He dipped his wings and then headed for the R.A.F. station at Fiddler's Common."

"Do you really think it was his plane?"

"I'm sure of it. I'll bet you a shilling that he'll be walking through the gate in about—let me see, how long should it take to get here? About fifteen minutes."

"I'm a poor widow on a very small fixed income, " Jocelyn protested. "Make it sixpence and I'll take you on. Just in case I lose, I'll take Boo for a ride down to the farm and see if I can wheedle some fresh eggs out of Mrs. Hurlburt."

While she was away, Carol rushed about straightening the house, hiding unfinished ironing in a cupboard, leaving herself barely enough time to change from her slacks into a pale yellow cotton dirndl dress, and to dab some perfume behind her ears.

It was closer to a half hour before Dennis arrived. In answer to his loud, 'Hello, is anybody here?' Carol called, "Up here, darling. Come on up."

He bounded up the stairs two at a time, barely missing hitting his head on the low beams. Within seconds he was holding Carol tightly in his arms.

He had three days to spend with her. Carol was ecstatic, and Jocelyn immediately began wracking her brains how she could give them the maximum time to themselves. She decided that the next morning, as soon as Boo was tucked away in her pram in the garden where she spent all fine mornings, she would take the bus into Cambridge and explore the town.

By ten-thirty, she was wandering around the ancient university, marvelling at the lovely old buildings and the quad which was alive with young men in their grubby academic gowns that billowed behind them as they hurried to or from their tutorials. Some were lounging under the trees by the river; others were out punting on the river's glassy green surface. It was a perfect summer's day and Jocelyn envied them their relatively carefree existence.

The beautiful town was so steeped in history, so peaceful, and such a contrast to the war-wracked world beyond the ancient walls of this venerable institution of higher learning.

She had great difficulty tearing herself away, but her watch told her she must hurry back to the bus which left for Balsham at noon. The decrepit vehicle was waiting at the depot and she climbed aboard and took a seat at the front behind the driver.

She settled down with a book she had brought to read and soon the bus was rattling through the streets of Cambridge and on into the country,. After a while she had the acute sensation that someone was staring at her. She raised her eyes from her book and glanced across the aisle where a young and very handsome R.A.F. officer was sitting, his oval grey eyes studying her intently. She noticed that he was wearing pilot's wings and had the three rings of braid on his sleeve indicating his rank as a squadron leader.

Having gained her attention, he questioned in a deep resonant voice, "What are you reading?"

She was startled by his audacity but she answered, "Oh, it's just an Agatha Christie 'who dunnit'."

"She's one of my favourite authors," he said, his lips parting in a most engaging smile.

Before Jocelyn knew it, he had moved over to her side of the bus and they were exchanging information about their backgrounds, past and present.

His name was Derek Stewart and he was stationed at Fiddler's Common as an instructor, having already completed two tours of ops. in Bomber Command.

On his lapel Jocelyn noticed he was wearing the tiny gold caterpillar pin indicating that he must have parachuted from his aircraft at some time.

Jocelyn found herself telling him about how she had come to England, how Kit had met his death, how she and Carol came to be living in Balsham, and, of course, about Boo.

By the time the bus reached Balsham, he had invited himself to Susan Plum to meet Boo and Carol and, to her amazement, she heard herself asking him to dinner the following week.

When she reported her actions to Carol, she said, "I can't think what got into me—inviting a perfect stranger to dinner. I must be daft."

Carol repressed a smile and said, "What's he like?"

"He's over six feet tall, extremely good looking, has a narrow face with rather hollow cheeks and an aristocratic nose. He has a twin brother who is called Rex. Their mother called them Derek and Rex because both names mean 'king'."

Carol was finishing up the supper dishes and she dried her hands on the towel and tossed it on the maiden by the fire. "I can hardly wait to meet him," she said, and gave Jocelyn a sly grin.

***

Carol and Dennis thoroughly enjoyed their peaceful interlude and before he left he delighted her with a promise that in a couple of weeks she could come down to stay for a few days near the station.

Derek Stewart turned up at Susan Plum the following Monday and stayed for dinner. Carol showed her approval of him by giving him an invitation to come anytime he wished. Hence, from then on, whenever he had time off, he would hop on his bicycle and drop in at Susan Plum. He kept their woodpile stacked high and their kindling box filled, mended the oil stoves, cleaned the lamp chimneys, and generally made himself useful.

He obviously adored children and liked nothing better than to accompany Jocelyn on her daily walks with Boo bouncing happily in the pram. Jocelyn felt nothing for him but warm friendship and gratitude for his companionship and help with the chores. But Carol was quick to notice that there was a great deal more to Derek's feelings for Jocelyn. Secretly she wondered how this relationship would work out. Characteristically, she took the most sanguine view of the situation and was just glad that Jocelyn was enjoying some male company.

Sheila was still in Newmarket and was intending to stay close to the doctor, until baby Christopher was settled into a satisfactory routine. Meanwhile, another friend of Jocelyn's from home, who also had married an R.A.F. pilot instructor, came to stay at Susan Plum.

Joan Flemming was a stunning looking girl with jet black hair, large round eyes as black and shiny as coal, long dark lashes, high cheekbones, and a perfect olive complexion. She was as petite as her husband, Ralph, was tall. His colouring almost exactly matched hers and they had an 18 month old son who was a replica of his mother.

They appeared to be a perfect family. But underneath Ralph's suave and gentlemanly exterior was a strange man with a violent temper and an insanely jealous nature. When he was instructing in Medicine Hat, he used to lock Joan in their apartment when he went night flying, to ensure that she made no contacts with anyone after dark. Not even her girl friends were allowed to visit.

When Ralph returned to Britain from Canada he was assigned to a Pathfinder Squadron. These pilots, flying a stripped down version of the Mosquito bomber, went out ahead of the big bombers and dropped flares over enemy territory to make it easier for the bomber pilots to find their targets. It was a very high risk job and, after only one mission, Ralph found it so terrifying that he suffered what was known in the services as L.M.F.—lack of moral fibre.

He was taken off flying and was waiting to go to an establishment where this problem was treated. Joan had come to Susan Plum to stay with friends until his future was decided. There was no question of him going back on ops. But he would remain in the service until he was demobilized.

Thus, when Sheila returned with Christopher, there were four wives and three babies sheltering within the stout walls of Susan Plum. With all this company, plus Derek's visits, Jocelyn found life easier to bear.

Joan and her small son left at the end August to stay with Ralph's sister until he was discharged from hospital and likely thence from the R.A.F. For them, to all intents and purposes the war was over, as it was for Simon. Neither of the men would ever again do any hazardous operational flying.

CHAPTER 32

August slipped unobtrusively into September, offering those all too short crisp autumn days with hazy mauve skies, frosty mornings, and the delightfully pungent odour of smoke from burning leaves which filled the air with a nostalgic tang. The war seemed a long way from Susan Plum. Only the newspapers they received spasmodically, recounting what was happening on the war front, served to shatter the illusion of peace that prevailed in this sleepy old world village.

The latest reports revealed that the Allies were now firmly entrenched in Belgium. Elsewhere in Europe, the cities of Lyons, Pesaro, and Pisa were taken, and it was announced that British Empire casualties for the past five years of the war amounted to 1,091,628. Hitler and his formidable war machine had been significantly thwarted, but still the slaughter went on.

Jocelyn recently received a sad letter from another friend from home whose R.A.F. pilot husband, Dick Saunders, had been reported missing. His wife, Frances, was living in Bath and was in hospital having their first baby when she received confirmation from Air Ministry that his wrecked plane had been found and he had not survived the crash. She asked if Jocelyn would come and visit her some time in the near future to lend her some moral support. She had suffered much the same treatment from her mother-in-law that Jocelyn had experienced, but had no one like Carol to turn to. Jocelyn answered with a promise to go as soon as she could get away.

Dennis's squadron was still busily engaged in the incessant low-level bombing of industrial targets and railway supply lines in Germany and he had made no more visits to Susan Plum. However, as promised, he made arrangements for Carol to go down and stay near the station so that they could have some time together. She left the day after she received his letter.

The following Friday, a pleasantly warm bright day, found Sheila and Jocelyn kneeling in a far corner of the garden stripping the aromatic narrow leaves and small lilac flowers from lavender shrubs on to paper spread out on the grass. So engrossed were they in their task, that neither of them heard footsteps approaching.

It wasn't until a shadow fell across the grass in front of her that Sheila looked up quickly and exclaimed, "Simon! You startled me. What's the idea of creeping up on us like an Iroquois?"

"I wanted to surprise you," he said, a broad grin on his handsome face. "How is my son? Is he any better looking than he was the last time I saw him?"

"What did he look like then?" Sheila asked, sounding a bit piqued.

"A crimson prune," Simon said.

"Well, he's more a tan shade now, thanks to the sun, but you should watch your language when you speak about Christopher's looks. It is unanimously agreed that he's the mirror image of his father."

"God forbid!" Simon exclaimed, walking over to the pram where the baby was sleeping. He looked intently at the fair silken hair and rosy cheeks of his baby son. "I do believe he's improving," he said, dumping his bulging parachute bag down on the grass.

Sheila looked at it. "Is that all laundry, I hope not," she said. "Or have you come for a month?"

"No, just two weeks."

"Two weeks! Simon, you're joking."

"No, I'm not. I've been given two weeks respite from those damned therapeutic exercises."

"Why, that's wonderful. In that time, I can easily teach you to bathe and feed Christopher, and wash nappies."

"Who, me! I planned to take you up to Scotland to meet some more friends and relatives of mine."

"And where did you think of parking your son and heir while we go gallivanting up to the wilds of Scotland? Or did you plan to strap him on my back like a papoose?"

Jocelyn was listening to their banter, and she caught the fleeting look of disappointment on Simon's handsome face. For once she sympathised with him. She understood that it wouldn't be much of a holiday for him here at Susan Plum, sharing Sheila with a new and not very interesting infant, to say nothing of the ever increasing number of guests who now kept dropping in—mainly Canadians who were serving overseas and, who, like Eddy Johnston, found that a visit to Susan Plum was as close to a taste of home as they would get until the war ended.

Jocelyn enjoyed the diversion the company created, especially since Derek Stewart's drop-in visits were curtailed while he was on a refresher course somewhere in the north. Carol and Sheila also enjoyed the constant coming and going of friends from home, but Jocelyn was sure that Simon would soon tire of it.

On impulse, she said, "Cheer up, Simon. I'll take over Christopher while you and Sheila go to Scotland." Her aching heart silently added, and laugh and play together, and love, and dream and plan—'Kit, oh, Kit, how I miss you'.

They were thanking her but with a forced smile she turned abruptly and walked to the far end of the garden. She thought that she had herself well in hand now, and was angry because she had given way to self pity. Realizing that they would want to make plans right away, she returned quickly to the house and found them in the drawing room. They were as usual arguing about something, but stopped when she entered the room.

Jocelyn sat down on the bench by the fireplace. "Well, when do you leave on this wonderful vacation?"

"Did you really mean it, Joc?" Sheila asked.

"Of course I did. You can leave tomorrow if you want."

"That's awfully decent of you," Simon said. "I'm really keen to take Sheila to Scotland. A friend is loaning us his hunting lodge and it's a super place." He turned to Sheila. "When can you be ready to go, darling?"

"Hold your horses," Sheila cautioned. "We can't just pack up and leave Jocelyn here alone with two babies to care for, to say nothing of Mr. Case and his cohorts."

"I won't be alone, Sheila. Remember, Don and Ellen Rowe are arriving tomorrow, and I've asked Ellen to stay a while because her new flat in Swindon isn't quite ready. They hope it will be finished in a week. Don will be going right back to the squadron, of course, so Ellen will keep me company until Carol comes back."

"That's splendid!" Simon exclaimed happily. "Then we can leave here early tomorrow. We'll spend the night in London, then leave for Scotland the following day."

They were away by nine the next morning and, for a few hours, Jocelyn was alone. The house was eerily quiet. Despite the fact that she had no real belief in Sheila's theory that Susan Plum was haunted, either by Mr. Case or any other departed spirits, she felt uneasy indoors. Perhaps it was because the empty silence of the rooms, broken only by the sound of her solitary footsteps, emphasized her own emptiness. In the presence of others, she was able to set it aside in a corner of her heart. Whereas now, like some evil genie, it pounced out of hiding and followed her from room to room as she completed the job of tidying up after the whirlwind, chaotic departure of Sheila and Simon.

When at last, to her exacting satisfaction, she had readied the house for the new guests, she was only too pleased to go outside and sit in the garden, close by the prams in which tiny Christopher and Boo, who had grown plump and rosy in the country air, slept soundly.

A hazy sun provided enough warmth to offset the coolness of a gentle breeze that shook and dislodged the reluctant yellow, bronze, and scarlet leaves from their branches. Jocelyn watched them flutter to the ground and surveyed the decaying garden, feeling quite sad with the realization that winter would soon be upon them. Her first winter without Kit. There would be so many firsts from now on, and she wondered if they would become any easier as time passed.

In a way, it would be better to face each season, redolent as they were with their own special memories, here in England, far from the place where she and Kit had been so happy. The coming winter, for example, would not in any way resemble the invigorating, fun-filled winters with which she was familiar and which would inflict deeper wounds with every fresh fall of tiny star-like snow flakes.

She smiled to herself as she recalled the first time Kit had tried skating. How they had laughed as he struggled to maintain his balance on the treacherously slippery ice; and later at his comic attempts to don skiis and stay upright as they descended the snow-clad hills. He had been such a good sport, and tried very hard to become more proficient so that he could keep up with her.

Yes, it was as well that she couldn't leave England just yet. A recent letter from Air Ministry assured her that they would send her home but that she might have a long wait for a passage. So, she would likely be here for some time.

It's curious, she reflected, as she sat there in the solitude and fading beauty of the garden, how chance so often prevented one from meeting people. Several times in the past few months, she had been on the point of making the acquaintance of Kit's good friend on the squadron, Don Rowe and his wife, Ellen. But something had always turned up to thwart the proposed meeting. When she visited Kit in Grimsby, Don was to have to come to the hotel to meet her, but instead had to go out on a strike. And Ellen was confined to bed with the flu.

Then, after Kit was killed, Don wanted to come to Newmarket and bring Ellen, but the move to Balsham had prevented that meeting. However, they were really coming today, and she felt a keen interest in seeing them both.

At noon she went into the house to start lunch, and to warm some formula for the two babies who would be waking soon. Boo, in fact, was already kicking her chubby sun-browned legs up in the air having tossed off the blanket that had covered them.

By the time Jocelyn had fed, changed and made both babies comfortable back in their prams in the garden, there was a knock on the door announcing the arrival of the Rowes.

Don Rowe, tall and slightly inclined to corpulence, with very dark brown eyes, curly black hair, and a ruddy complexion, commanded with his easy charm the rather awkward business of introductions. He said he would have known Jocelyn anywhere from the photograph of her that Kit kept on his dresser. Within moments Jocelyn felt as though they were old friends who had dropped in after a long absence.

She escorted them into the lounge, and directed Don to their room, making sure to warn him about the hazards of the stairs. Ellen followed her into the kitchen and insisted on helping with the lunch preparations.

She was an uncommonly pretty girl with large olive-green eyes, a small nose and mouth, a cap of light brown curls, and a specially happy countenance. They were a handsome couple, Jocelyn thought.

She told them that after Don left, she and Ellen would be alone and she hoped that Ellen didn't mind ghosts. "The landlady's deceased husband shares the house with us," she joked. "And sometimes he's very rude."

"I believe implicitly in ghosts," Ellen said, her sweet mouth parting in a smile revealing white, even teeth. "I expect between us we can cope with this one."

After lunch they sat in the garden until Don said he must leave. His infectious laugh and Ellen's sense of fun had made a perfect afternoon. The only off note was when, just before leaving, Don gave Jocelyn a package containing the gold cufflinks she had given Kit as a wedding gift, his fountain pen, and his wallet, as well as a formidable stack of letters. There was one for every day she and Kit had been parted. She took them in her hand and stood looking helplessly at them.

"I was able to rescue these from Kit's room before they packed up his things to be sent to the central depot in Colne, Buckinghamshire," Don said. "You'll likely be hearing from someone in that establishment at some point."

Jocelyn forced back the tears that welled up in her eyes and managed to find voice to thank Don for his thoughtfulness.

He placed his forage cap at a jaunty angle on his black curly head, and said, "Well, I must be going, or I'll miss the train in Cambridge. Thanks for the splendid lunch, Jocelyn. And thanks for putting up with my wife while she is out of house and home.''

He gave Ellen a warm embrace and a lingering kiss and took off down the lane to catch his bus.

Jocelyn immediately took to Don's sweet-natured unaffected wife and she was sure they would have a pleasant week together. Ellen was delighted with the two babies and took charge of Christopher without hesitation. She and Don were expecting their first child early in the new year, so she welcomed the chance to get in some practice handling a small infant. She was also anxious to make the acquaintance of the village characters, Minnie and Myrtle. Hence, two days after Don left, they wheeled the babies to the post office.

At the sound of the tinkling bell above the door, Miss Minnie bustled in from the kitchen, squeezing and wheezing until she was behind the counter.

"Good morning, Miss Minnie," Jocelyn greeted her. "This is my friend, Mrs. Rowe, who is staying with us for awhile.''

Miss Minnie beamed at Ellen, and her several chins quivered. "Is your husband a flyer, too?" she asked.

"Yes, he is.''

Miss Minnie's broad forehead suddenly crinkled into a frown. "It seems to me that I've seen that name of late, or heard it somewhere," she said.

"Perhaps some mail came for me,'' Ellen suggested.

"No, it wasn't that. Now let me see, where did Myrtle put it. It was a telegram that came last night, too late to have it sent down to you.''

A telegram! Harbinger of doom! Levity dropped at once and Ellen's face drained of colour. Jocelyn, too, went ashen.

Miss Minnie, innocently unconcerned, thumbed through the untidy pile of papers on the counter, opening and shutting drawers in the disorderly filing cabinet. She edged her great bulk sideways from one end of the counter to the other, searching in a leisurely calm through the messy piles. No telegram.

Finally, she called loudly into the back room. "Myrt-ul, 'ave you seen that there telegram for a Mrs. Rowe?"

Miss Myrtle emerged from the back room drying her pudgy hands on a large print apron, and pushed her way in beside her sister.

Jocelyn and Ellen stood tense and silent while Miss Myrtle repeated the same fruitless search with the scattered papers and bulging file, chatting amiably with Miss Minnie the while.

They argued over who had it when and where and accused each other of always losing things. Minnie said that Myrtle had a memory like Sally Strump's water bucket—full of holes. Finally, Minnie looked up and saw the stricken faces of the two girls. "Oh, cheer up, lassies. It wasn't bad news, was it Myrtle?"

Miss Myrtle shook her head. "Not as I recall," she agreed. "In fact, I believe I remember what it said." She tapped her forehead thoughtfully, then repeated the message from memory. 'Have been given a forty-eight. Will meet you in Swindon, Friday. Love, Don'

Miss Myrtle looked singularly proud of herself and Miss Minnie gazed at her sister admiringly. "Really, Myrtle," she said. "you do have a wonderful memory. Why, I declare this place would be in a downright muddle without you."

CHAPTER 33

Most of the leaves had deserted the trees and scattered themselves about the garden in untidy profusion. Derek had returned from his course and resumed his drop-in visits. On the afternoon after Carol's return from the south, with Derek's help, she and Jocelyn raked the leaves into a neat pile intending to burn them the next day. But a spiteful wind came up during the night and sent them scurrying back to the lawns and flower beds. There they remained.

The days were becoming depressingly short, and there were fewer of them which lent themselves to sitting outside. The warmth of the sun and the freshness and beauty of the garden were forsaken, and traded for a heartwarming, if back-chilling fire and the cosiness it lent to the cheerful drawing room.

A stiff wind of near-gale proportion was now lashing the bare shrubs against the leaded windows. However, with its assistance, Jocelyn was keeping a fire burning in the otherwise stubborn fireplace. She pulled two easy chairs up close to the hearth and then returned to the kitchen to help Carol carry in their supper.

Carol asked her if she had lighted the lamps in the lounge but Jocelyn said she hadn't. She thought they could get through supper without them. Since their oil quota for the quarter was almost gone, she thought they should try to conserve.

Carol lifted a plate of toast from the stove, and firmly grasped the brown betty teapot, then followed Jocelyn through the dark hallway into the drawing room where they intended to eat their supper of scrambled dried eggs and toast by the fire. Jocelyn placed the tray on the low table between the two easy chairs, sat down, and poured the tea. The grey veil of dusk filled the room, but the glow of the firelight transmitted a softness and warmth to the panelled walls.

"It's not too gloomy in here," Carol commented. "Those French doors allow more light, which I suppose compensates for the draughts they also let in. When do we get our next quota of oil?"

"November," Jocelyn replied. "But we'll run out long before then, I'm sure."

"That's a dreary prospect," Carol said, spreading some of their Canadian jam on a piece of toast.

"We might as well be realistic about it."

Carol screwed up her nose. "Yes, I suppose so. But let's not spoil our evening thinking about it. This jam Mom sent is scrumptious, isn't it?"

"We've made it stretch out quite well. Incidentally, Ellen Rowe said that when she comes back, she'll help us do something with all the tomatoes on the vines."

"There are still oodles of beans, too, but with all the company coming this weekend, we'll be able to get rid of a lot of them. Have you thought how we're going to put everyone up?"

"We'll manage. Sheila and Simon will have their own room, and I can give Ellen and Don mine. Don will be here only one night."

"What about Ellen?"

"She's staying until the damage to their flat is repaired. Just when it was all set for them to move into, a stray doodlebug landed down the street and blasted out all of the windows."

"I'm looking forward to meeting them," Carol said. "Let's see, they'll be arriving on Friday, and Simon and Sheila tomorrow, probably. Dennis said he'll be here by Friday evening. It's going to be like playing chess trying to fit everyone in."

"It'll liven things up a bit. This place is becoming dismal now that summer is on the wane. I shudder to think what the winter will be like."

"Don't think about it," Carol advised. "It will only make you miserable."

Jocelyn sat for awhile in silent meditation. Then she got up to put more wood on the dwindling fire. Settling down once more in her chair, she said, "I was just thinking. Do you know what would be a great idea?"

"No, what?"

"Since we're going to have quite a houseful here this weekend, why don't I have Boo christened?"

"That's a wonderful idea. Who will be godparents?"

"You and Dennis, of course, and I'll ask Don and Ellen."

"Can you arrange it on such short notice?"

"I'll pop over to the rectory tomorrow and ask."

The week unfolded with Simon and Sheila's return from Scotland and the arrival of the Rowes and Dennis. Eddy Johnston showed up unexpectedly as well as Ricky Damico, a friend of Jocelyn and Carol's brother. He was stationed in Ireland but had come over to England for some leave. Jocelyn's plans for the christening materialized without complication and, although the day dawned cloudy, by midmorning a benevolent sun sent the threatening clouds scurrying, so that a blue sky crowned the heavens.

As the small procession made its way leisurely along the winding lane to the 12th-century Anglican church where the ceremony was to take place, Ellen asked, "Did you order this day specially, Jocelyn? It certainly couldn't be nicer."

"She said a few prayers last night, I'll bet," Carol suggested.

Jocelyn smiled wistfully. "They say that more things are wrought by prayer than this world dreams of?"

Carol's eyes rested on the slender form of Dennis striding along ahead of her. She sighed and said, "Amen, to that." She was thinking, if only prayers will keep him safe.

Ellen, who was walking beside her, looked ahead at Don and echoed softly, "Amen."

They turned a corner shaded by three large evergreens and were now able to see the weathered twelfth-century stone church with its ancient oak doors opened wide, and the Vicar in his snow-white surplice waiting for them.

It was a short solemn ceremony and Jocelyn was filled with an unbearable sadness that Kit could not be there—a sadness reflected in her eyes, which stung with unshed tears. Then, quite suddenly, stray ribbons of golden sunshine stole through the beautiful stained glass windows and touched off a magic chain of smiles on the solemn faces encircling the font. They rested on the baby's rosy cheeks last, and lingered there as the Vicar made the sign of the cross on her forehead and repeated the familiar words: "I baptize thee, Constance Kendall, in the Name of the Father and of the Son, and of the Holy Ghost, Amen."

He then read the duties of the godparents and they solemnly promised, "I will, the Lord being my helper."

Finally, through her tears, Jocelyn heard him say the last prayer, "Grant, O Lord that this Child may by Thy mercy grow in health of body and mind, and serve thee faithfully according to Thy will all the days of her life; through Jesus Christ our Lord."

After he said the final blessing and dismissed them, Jocelyn walked out into the churchyard feeling strangely refreshed, as though she had been individually blessed. Subconsciously, she had been dreading the event, but, having faced it, she felt a new strength with which to face the future. She was certain that Kit's spirit had been present throughout the service, and that he would always somehow be with her as she raised their daughter without his physical presence.

The christening feast was assured of success by the timely arrival of a food parcel from Canada, by Eddy's generous contribution of G.I. candy and biscuit ration, and by a parcel of goodies brought by Ricky from Ireland.

After the dishes were done that evening, they all gathered around the fire in the drawing room. With the sun's early departure for the west, a damp east wind blew up and was now moaning soulfully down the chimney, making the crackling fire dance to its sombre notes. The flickering flames threw weird shadows on the panelled walls, lending an eerie note to the subject under discussion, namely Mr. Case.

Simon, ever hopeful of interesting people in his favourite subject, pulled out a large volume on spiritualism from the book shelf near his chair. The gap revealed one end of a black lacquered board that was tucked away behind the books. He drew it out and examined it.

"Now here's something that will interest you," he said, handing the board to Don who studied the strange figures and letters embossed on the black surface and the triangular marker in the corner.

"I give up," Don said. "What is it?"

Carol took it from him and exclaimed, "It's a ouija board. I might have known there would be one here."

"Oh, heavens," Sheila said in disgust. "One of those dumb things."

Curiosity shone in Don's brown eyes. "Come on, let us in on the secret. What is it anyway?"

"It's a kind of fortune teller," Simon explained. He inclined his head toward Don and they made a strange contrast side by side in the glow of the fire—Simon with his ash blond hair, and Don's a deep ebony.

Simon was delighted to demonstrate the use of the Ouija Board. He placed it on the low table in the centre of the group and said, "Each person must think of a question to ask. Then we'll take turns placing our fingers lightly on this sensitive marker, and allow it to guide them over the letters, and it spells out the answers to our questions. You must frame your question so it can answer a simple, yes, or no."

No one but Simon had any faith in the mystic powers of the lacquered board, and it is doubtful that even he had much. However, everyone was willing to join in the game.

Jocelyn took the first turn asking, "Will I be returning to Canada?" The marker spelled out, NO, and Jocelyn said, laughing, "Ask a foolish question, get a foolish answer."

Eddy was next. He asked, "Is it true that it's Mr. Case who blows out our candles on the staircase?"

As the marker moved to answer, there came from above their heads a deep rumbling sound as though the whole place were falling down.

"The babies!" Jocelyn cried, and dashed out into the hall and up the stairs without any thought of the darkness. She felt her way along the upper hall to the nursery and leaned over the two cribs. Both Boo and Christopher were sleeping peacefully, evidently undisturbed by whatever had caused the clatter.

Satisfied that the babies were all right, she returned to the drawing room and found the French doors wide open and everyone gathered on the terrace.

Dennis had the situation in hand. He had found a torch and was shining it upwards. The bright beam cut into the darkness showing that one of the five chimneys was missing, and also some of the black slates. That would explain the noise. There was also a pile of rubble on the patio.

"Well, I'll be darned," Eddy drawled. "If Mr. Case hasn't knocked down the chimney and part of the roof into the bargain."

No one disputed his theory and, although they laughed at the idea, when they gathered once more around the fire, there was no more delving into the future with the help of the ouija board. It was put back behind the books from whence it came.

When viewed in the grey light of morning, the damage to the roof did not appear to be great, although there was an astonishing pile of debris on the flagstone patio. After making a thorough inspection of it, Dennis decided that Mrs. Case ought to be notified at once.

"It's my turn to pick up the mail," Jocelyn said. "I'll call her from the kiosk outside the post office."

The very next day, Mrs. Case, clad in heavy tweeds and canal barge oxfords, arrived at Susan Plum to view the damage. She was openly sceptical about the account that Jocelyn gave her, and emphasized her doubts by repeating at frequent intervals, "I simply can't understand it. It's most peculiar indeed."

"We can't understand it either, Mrs. Case," Jocelyn said.

Mrs. Case snapped back, "I've never had trouble before. The roof was in perfect order when I saw it last."

She made it seem as though they had worn out the roof in their short tenancy, and Jocelyn was tempted to be facetious and ask her if she thought they had used it as a toboggan slide. However, she restrained the impulse and, instead, offered the lady a cup of tea, a courtesy which was declined rather rudely.

After another sweep with her small squinty eyes around the garden, a very ruffled Mrs. Case got into her car and drove off, promising that they would hear more from her later.

The next morning a paunchy overbearing man in a brown felt porkpie hat and trench coat arrived on the terrace. Jocelyn greeted him and he told her that he had come to assess the bomb damage. From a large pocket in his coat, he pulled out a pencil and a pad. With these utensils poised and an officious eyebrow cocked toward Jocelyn, he asked, "Now, Miss, just exactly where did the bomb fall?"

Jocelyn blinked. "The bomb? What bomb?" she asked.

"The bomb that landed on this property the night before last," he replied testily.

Jocelyn pointed to the rubble on the patio and said, "I don't know about any bomb, but the chimney landed there, where all that mess is."

He stared at the pile of bricks and mortar lying outside the French doors. "That's where the bomb fell?" he queried, evidently very perplexed.

"Did you say that a bomb fell around here two nights ago?" Jocelyn asked, equally puzzled.

"Madam, I was informed that a bomb fell on this property two nights ago doing considerable damage to the roof."

"Oh, really? Where did it fall?"

"That, Madam, is what I am trying to find out from you."

He was so typically the bombastic officious civil servant that Jocelyn had to stifle the urge to laugh. She said mildly, "I really don't know anything about a bomb."

He looked past her and saw someone coming towards them. His beady eyes gleamed with hope as Carol approached. He addressed his question to her. "Perhaps you can me tell me where the bomb fell?"

Carol looked puzzled. "A bomb? Fell around here?"

He wiped his brow and looked at them both pityingly. "According to the owner of this property, yes, a bomb fell on this house two nights ago. All I want to know is, where exactly did it land?"

"Well, if you mean the chimney, it landed right there at your feet, and it brought down some of the slates with it."

"That's right," Jocelyn interposed. "It nearly scared us out of our wits." She gave Carol a sly wink.

The harrassed man took out his handkerchief and mopped his glistening brow. In one final attempt to get the desired information, he said, "If you didn't hear a bomb fall around here, do you happen to know anyone who did?"

"No, we don't, I'm afraid, Mr....what did you say your name is?"

"I didn't say," he snapped. After a curious appraisal of the two girls who were standing with deliberately blank faces, he put away his pencil and note pad and stomped off.

They heard no more from Mrs. Case or her attempt to con the government into paying damages to the roof by claiming that they had been caused by a bomb. Later in the week, someone came out to repair the chimney and replace the tiles.

***

After the christening, Ellen Rowe stayed on at Susan Plum and she had just spent a few hours with Don who had flown in that morning. It was late in the afternoon when he was obliged to leave, and she persuaded Jocelyn to accompany her to the outskirts of Fiddler's Common to watch him take off. They stood watching as the zooming Beaufighter circled above them, dipped its wings in salute, and faded quickly into the distance.

Suddenly, without warning, Ellen was crying. "I'll never see him again," she sobbed. "Never, I just know it."

Jocelyn took her arm and tried to comfort her. "Now, Ellen, you know that is ridiculous. You're just feeling low because he has left. And maybe you're overtired. It has been rather a strain on you, with all the company we've had. You should try to take things a bit easier until the baby comes."

Ellen regained control of herself and said, "You're right, of course, Jocelyn." But, at the same time, she shook her head as if in silent certain contradiction.

A few days later, she left for Swindon to move into her new flat, and she promised to telegraph Jocelyn when she was settled. Miss Minnie sent a village lad to the house with the message on Monday morning.

Jocelyn took the envelope and called to Carol, "Ellen's wire arrived, so I guess she...." Her voice stopped as her eyes rested on the word 'missing'. She read on. 'Don and Allan reported missing believed killed. Will write later'. Allan Wilcox was Don's navigator. Ellen's premonition had been prophetic. She would never see Don again, and he would never have the joy of seeing his child.

Filled with a numbing despair, Jocelyn handed the wire to Carol and went into the house.

CHAPTER 34

The remainder of September was windy, wet, and cold.

Susan Plum became their enemy once more, and with the tragic loss of the attractive, witty, and lovable Don, a heavy gloom permeated the house, despite good intentions and determined efforts to ward it off. The stoves and lamps devoured their quota of oil in much too short a time, as Jocelyn had predicted, and they could now be used only when absolutely necessary. All cooking was done on the coal range and the lamps were saved for the late darkness. The candles, used as a substitute, flickered and threw sinister shadows making it difficult to read or work or to ignore Mr. Case's pervasive presence.

Sheila complained so often and so bitterly to Simon about the cold, the gloom, the dampness, and the isolation that he at last agreed to move her away. While she was loath to desert Jocelyn and Carol, she could no longer tolerate the dreariness of Susan Plum.

Carol was confined to bed with a severe cold which threatened to turn into pneumonia when Sheila broke the news of her departure. A recent near disaster had hastened her decision. Christopher had been put to bed one evening, and as Sheila sat knitting in the lounge, she thought she heard him crying. An investigation revealed that the oil heater left there to keep the room dry and warm had started belching out black oily smoke. The baby's face was covered with soot and his tiny nostrils were so clogged that he was close to being suffocated. That had convinced Simon that they must move and he set about finding some alternative accommodation for Sheila and Christopher in the south of England.

Sheila relayed this news to Carol and Jocelyn. After she left the room, Jocelyn sat on the edge of Carol's sickbed and they considered their own plight seriously.

"We can't stay here on our own," Carol said in her rheumy voice. "Apart from the high cost, we'll either freeze to death or be frightened to death."

Jocelyn nodded her head in agreement. She sat, silently thinking, a cloudy worried expression in her soft brown eyes. Then suddenly she brightened. "Carol, I wonder if that cottage in Mayfield is still on the market. You know, the one Kit and I were going to go and see."

Carol sat up, pulling her heavy cardigan about her shoulders. "That's an idea. If the flying bombs have stopped peppering the countryside, it may not be, but if they're still a menace, then it will likely still be up for grabs."

"Beggars can't be choosers," Jocelyn said. "Let's pray it's still available. Miss Minnie told me they're still coming over. She said that eight thousand have been launched so far and twenty three hundred have reached London. There may still be hope."

"What hope? I can't even remember the owner's name, let alone the address," Carol said hoarsely.

"Despair not. Her name was Mrs. Marshall and I have the 'phone number somewhere. So concentrate on getting better and I'll get after this right away."

Carol sighed with relief. She was pale and weak from the high fever that had accompanied the virus she had picked up. But she was immensely cheered by Jocelyn's suggestion.

Jocelyn quickly donned her coat and wellingtons, pinned the hood of her coat firmly to the front of her head, muttering mild invectives about the weather the while. When she stepped outside, a gust of wind hurled rain in her face, and she walked backwards to the shed to get the bicycle.

The wind was at her back en route to the village, so she made good time and was soon inside the kiosk. The rain had gathered into rivulets in the creases of her hood and then trickled down her nose as she fumbled with wet fingers to make the call. Luckily, she had made a note of the 'phone number in her address book and, by a phenomenal piece of luck, she got through almost immediately. And luckier still, the woman remembered her.

"Has your cottage been let?" Jocelyn asked anxiously.

A flood of relief overwhelmed her as she heard the reply. "No, it's still free. I'm in no hurry to let it, you see. I'm waiting for the right tenant. If you are still interested, I'll be glad to let you have it. Such sad news about your husband, my dear. I can sympathize with you. I've been a widow for ten years. Poor Mr. Marshall died very suddenly leaving me with four stepchildren. You see, I was his second wife. Of course, he was a very important man...."

"Your time is up," the operator cut in, and Jocelyn barely managed to say they would take the cottage before they were cut off.

Pedalling back to the house, fighting the wind every inch of the way and constantly wiping the rain from her face to enable her to see where she was going, it occurred to her that she'd neither discussed the flying bombs nor the rent.

If that omission worried Jocelyn, it bothered Carol not one bit. She had had enough of her dream house and was anxious to move away where the climate was reputed to be more agreeable and she would be closer to Dennis. Mr. Case and his fellow spooks could have Susan Plum.

Although devastated that they were leaving the area, Derek Stewart generously offered to drive them to their new home. He had no intention of losing touch with Jocelyn, even though she had made it clear that she looked upon him only as a good friend. He, on the other hand, was prepared to bide his time, and hope he could win her over. So he would continue to play the part of the good Samaritan and do anything he could to make life easier, not just for Jocelyn, but for Boo and for Carol as well.

They packed up their possessions once more and sent the bulkier items on by train. Then they squeezed everything else into Derek's little car and bade farewell to Susan Plum. It was on the same kind of cheerless day that they had arrived, and they were glad. There were no pangs of remorse at leaving her which they might have felt had it been a sunny fragrant morning when she was at her tempting loveliest.

Carol was convinced that she was a witch, a temptress, winning you with a soft golden smile, drugging your senses with her irresistible charm; then, without warning, turning morose, ugly, and sinister. So real and compelling were her effects that they could never recall, without sinking hearts, her darker moods; nor could they remember her winsome ways without a subconscious smile.

With Derek at the wheel, they sped through the flat uninteresting landscape of Suffolk. He had a thorough knowledge of the route which eventually took them around London and finally into the lush counties of Kent and Sussex.

Although in Canada by this time the trees would have flaunted their splendid fall regalia in a few glorious weeks of wild and riotous colour, and the Indian summer sun would be warming bare branches and toasting the coarse prairie grass to an even deeper shade of brown, here in the heart of the Sussex Downs, the trees and hedges were still green, and the fields were covered in umber fern and soft moss.

The winding dirt road leading to Sharnden Brooks Farm where Mrs. Marshall's cottage was located took them far past the ancient town of Mayfield where at one time in England's distant past, St. Dunstan, as Archbishop of Canterbury, had presided over the early Christian church.

Here was a very different England than they had experienced in Suffolk. Instead of thatched cottages leaning over the streets, there were trim, orthodox whitewashed, timber-trimmed houses that looked smug and prudish in their tidiness. The road, bordered by high hedges entwined with holly, curved across broad meadows and narrowed here and there into a rustic bridge spanning a racy brook.

At every bend in the road crossing the deep valley, Jocelyn expected to turn in at one of the driveways adjoining the road. But it wasn't until they had climbed another long steep hill that Derek veered the car off the main road and passed through a partially concealed entrance.

They then bumped and rattled down a steep deeply rutted track which, according to Carol's rough calculation, took them half way back to Mayfield. Finally, in the distance, they could see a neat, vine-draped, cream and brown farmhouse standing on a treeless knoll some five hundred feet above the floor of the valley of Sharnden.

As they turned in the gate, a tall broad-shouldered woman with a disproportionately small head and large hips strode out of the house to greet them. She was clad in a tight bright red sweater that emphasized her generous bosom, tan jodhpurs stretched to their limit over her heavy buttocks, and her pert freckled face was leather tanned and wrinkled.

When she saw Derek, she jumped to the conclusion that he was Carol's husband. Carol set her straight and explained that Derek was a good friend who had been kind enough to bring them here. Mrs. Marshall extended her large rough brown hand to Derek, and then to Jocelyn.

"Hello there," she simpered. "So you are Jocelyn, and this is your darling baby. Poor lamb, with no papa."

Jocelyn said, 'How do you do', then turned to help Derek unload the car. He put all of their luggage inside the cottage and then, declining Mrs. Marshall's offer of tea, and brushing aside Jocelyn and Carol's sincere thanks, he got into the car and retraced his route back into Mayfield and thence on to Fiddler's Common.

Before he said good bye to Jocelyn, he assured her that he would be back for a visit as soon as he could get away.

Mrs. Marshall babbled on, hardly stopping for breath, as she led Carol and Jocelyn into the cottage which was situated a hundred yards from the large main house. It was a very long, flat-roofed, partially stuccoed outbuilding resembling exactly what it had been originally built for—a greyhound kennel.

Mrs. Marshall continued her monologue. "It's not much to look at," she apologized. "But you'll find it very cozy and pleasant inside. And it has an incredible view of the valley."

She was right about the view. The lush green valley of Sharnden was framed in every window of the cottage. Nestled on the verdant slopes were several magnificent mansions whose leaded panes gleamed golden in the setting sun.

But in fact the cottage did have much more to offer than the view. Inside, the drab functional exterior was more than compensated for by a tasteful decor, and furnishings which obviously had been chosen with a discriminating eye to comfort. The living room was in the centre of the building and on the floor was a faded but rich old Persian rug, its soft colours blending with the gay chintz coverings of the easy chairs and love seat.

A small brick fireplace was set in the centre of the back wall and a cheery log fire burned in the grate. An antique tea wagon, invitingly set, was placed in front of the fire. Mrs. Marshall, her wagging tongue for once at rest, stood silently relishing their expressions of pleasure. Then she showed them through the adequately furnished bedrooms, a large bright and airy kitchen, and the modern bathroom. Jocelyn noted with satisfaction that there was a large warming cupboard filled with towels and linen .

"I've made an old fashioned hot pot," Mrs. Marshall said, when the tour was over. "Indroo, my stepson, will be bringing it over shortly."

As Carol and Jocelyn smiled and mouthed the appropriate words of appreciation, the lady babbled on. "I do hope you'll be comfortable. I worked very hard making it cozy for you. You see, I had so much furniture when we left our country estate in Cornwall, and I thought I may as well share it with someone less fortunate. Well, it seemed a good idea."

Her cupid lips smeared with bright red lipstick, puckered in a smile, revealing small yellowed teeth. She fluttered her hands over her large breasts.

"Sharnden is by far the weeniest house I've ever lived in," she said. "My husband was an important man, you see."

Someone approached the door and she opened it to admit her stepson, Andrew, carrying the brown tureen containing the hot pot. He was a tall gangly youth of seventeen, with a nose too large for his face, an unruly mouse-coloured thatch of hair and small shifty eyes. He could scarcely bear the embarrassment of the introduction, and escaped as soon as he had placed the tureen on the stove.

The stove! Jocelyn could hardly bear it. Another black monster like the one at Susan Plum, and it would be just as ornery, she was sure. However, that was the only bad feature she had noted so far and she was sure they would cope.

Mrs. Marshall had noticed Jocelyn's jaundiced look at the stove and she hastened to explain. "There is one thing I forgot to mention. I've had the most dreadful luck with the stove. When Indroo lit it the other day, to try it out and to air the cottage, the hot water section burst. I suppose it was bound to go wrong. I bought it in a second hand shop. So I suppose it's quite old. Indroo and I worked all day cleaning up the mess. I was exhausted when we had finished. But Mr. Benson, the plumber in the village, has promised he will be here tomorrow to fix it. I shall remind him again in the morning. Until then I fear there will be no hot water for bathing or laundry. For cooking you can manage on the oil stoves. I'm told they are quite efficient."

Jocelyn and Carol exchanged dubious glances, and looked sourly at the black monsters, just like their cousins at Susan Plum. Mrs. Marshall twisted knobs and shook the oil burner, reminiscent of the efficient Mrs. Murphy who had performed the same task in Balsham.

While she was intent on lighting an oil burner, and was quiet for a blessed moment, Carol said, "About groceries, and mail. How do we manage for those?"

Mrs. Marshall stood up, wiped her greasy hands on her jodhpurs and replied, "Oh, you needn't worry about those things. You'll have plenty of time to see about them. Meanwhile, just make yourselves at home in my cozy little nest, and don't hesitate to call me if you need anything. I must run along now, and let you eat your supper. I've put some milk, butter, and bread in the larder to tide you over. You can boil your kettle on the oil burner until the coal stove is mended."

Carol was irked at being so neatly sidetracked, but she didn't pursue the issue because she was hungry and was afraid that if she asked any more questions, the lady would launch into another monologue. She didn't know exactly why the woman irritated her beyond reason. She hoped she would overcome her antipathy towards her.

Jocelyn escorted Mrs. Marshall to the door, thanking her profusely for her kindness. But she made no move to leave. Instead, she shrugged off Jocelyn's thanks and said, "I know you'll love it here. It's quiet, but then one needs peace and quiet these days, with the world in such turmoil. Isn't that so?" She didn't give Jocelyn a chance to reply. She rattled on. "Purchase, that was my chauffeur when I lived at Chalmers, our country estate, such a lovely old mansion, 25 rooms, but I'm digressing, and keeping you from your supper."

She finally left, and Jocelyn closed the door behind her and leaned against it. "Whew!," she said. "That's going to be hard to take if she keeps it up."

Noticing the mutinous look on Carol's face, she added. "But we mustn't prejudge. When she's got it all off her chest, she'll give us a break, I'm sure."

"But what a mammoth chest," Carol said, and they both had a good laugh.

The hot pot was really quite good, even though it had cooled considerably between delivery and Mrs. Marshall's lingering departure. When they had cleared up the dishes, emptied their suitcases of things they needed right away, Jocelyn settled Boo down for the night, and they relaxed in front of the fire. Andrew had left them a supply of dry logs which would last them a few days.

Carol expressed concern about how they were going to cope with this broken record, especially since she was right on their doorstep. However, Jocelyn reminded her that they were lucky not to be back in draughty spooky Susan Plum and that she was so much closer to Dennis and really the landlady did mean well.

Carol grumbled again about her eternal yapping and Jocelyn said soothingly, "You're just tired. and not quite recovered from that bug. You need a good night's rest. You'll feel better tomorrow."

CHAPTER 35

The following morning, while a dense fog was still hanging low over the meadows, the shrill yapping of a small dog, accompanied by a shrill, 'yoo hoo', just outside her window startled Jocelyn out of a deep sleep. She sat up with a jolt, rubbed her eyes, and squinted at her watch.

"Six o'clock! Who on earth could be calling at this ungodly hour?" Fearing that something dreadful must have happened—she dare not even think of Dennis—she hurried into her slippers and dressing gown and went to the door.

Eileen Marshall was standing outside, dressed as she had been the day before, her pepper and salt hair like a bird's nest, and a small pekinese dog dancing about her legs and yapping incessantly. Her small yellow speckled eyes travelled accusingly over Jocelyn's slippers, gown, and tousled hair.

"Why, I had no idea you wouldn't be up and about. I thought with a baby in the house. Well, you see I'm up at five every morning. I have to be to milk Bobo and Pansy, my two darling cows, and to feed the hens. My war effort you know. The morning air is so refreshing, and one can really get so much more done then. Don't you agree?"

Jocelyn decidely did not agree.

The tireless tongue wagged on and brown freckled arms were extended in an offering. "I brought you some fresh milk and some eggs for your breakfast. You can buy them from me...and butter, too, when I have some to spare."

"Won't you come in?" Jocelyn said, stifling a yawn. She was so relieved to find that there was no bad news attached to the visit that she hadn't noticed the damp frigid breeze creeping up under her dressing gown. Now, however, she was acutely chilled and she urged Eileen to come inside.

She led the way into the living room, put the provisions in the kitchen and rejoined Mrs. Marshall. She sat down in a chair before the fireplace which still cradled a few pieces of burnt out log and some forlorn grey ashes. She was prepared to sit out the visit with as much grace as she could muster in her semi-conscious state.

"Did you sleep well?" Eileen asked. "I'm sure you did. I didn't spare any expense to get good mattresses for the beds. Mr. Marshall always believed in buying quality, and I agreed with him. Penny wise and pound foolish, is my motto. I'm fortunate that having a farm opens up some doors that otherwise would...." She left that enigmatic sentence hanging and changed the subject. "Mr. Honeybone, the grocer in the village of Sharnden, will be calling on you on Saturday. He delivers all the other things you'll require for the house—you know, soap, candles, matches, cereal. And the butcher delivers once a week as well. But he's a very stupid man. I don't get on with him at all. You'll have to go into Mayfield to register with him. But, of course, you know the routine."

She stopped for breath so Jocelyn darted in, "How far is the village?" she asked.

"About two miles. Just a nice walk across the fields. Do you like walking?"

"Yes, we do. Mrs. Marshall, does one...?"

"Please, my dear, you must call me Eileen. It's so much more friendly, don't you agree?" She smoothed her large hands over her bosom, drawing Jocelyn's eyes to the ample breasts. "I'm your friend, you know. You poor lamb, left so young, and with an infant to cope with." Her monkey like face was set in a pitying expression and Jocelyn wriggled uncomfortably in her chair.

"I was going to ask if we register with you for the eggs and milk. I mean in the usual way," she ventured to ask.

Eileen's smile was conspiratorial. "Oh, the Ministry of Food doesn't bother with the likes of me, my dear. I've only a few hens and the two cows, and they are really pets."

That was something new, having cows for pets, Jocelyn thought, but she lied politely, "Oh, I see. You mentioned it was your war bit, so I just wondered...."

Eileen interrupted this line of thought in short order. "It's so rewarding working on the land," she said. "Of course, you know, I had never done work of any kind before. But then my husband died, and then the war came, and the servant problem. Well, I felt that I must do something. He was a widower, you see, with four young children, and I was their governess. At least, I wasn't really a governess. You see, their mother and I were cousins. And when she married I often used to spend my vacations with her. Mr. Marshall had business dealings in the Pacific and was absent a great deal. When Elspeth fell ill, she asked me to stay with her permanently, so what else could I do? The children knew me and loved me, so when their dear mother died, I just naturally stayed on." She fluttered her large hands over her breasts and then went on. "After I had cared for them for a year, well, he proposed, the dear thing. He knew that I was in a difficult position, and wanted to make things easier all round. His friends and neighbours resented me being mistress of Chalmers when I had no real claim to the position. So he asked me to marry him, and I knew that I could do so much for him and the children, so I agreed. He was due to be knighted the following year. But he took ill suddenly and died. Such a pity. I might have been Lady Marshall. Oh, well, he was very kind, and I truly believe he loved me although we never lived together as man and wife, if you know what I mean." More bosom stroking. "He used to say, I have a real lady as head of my household. Purchase, my chauffeur, too, always referred to me as 'Milady'." She tittered. "You can't imagine how that irritated the neighbours. It was so loyal of Purchase. I do miss him."

Jocelyn finally got up. Her legs were stiff and her feet were frozen. She said she must go into the kitchen and get Boo's milk warmed. She had heard her gurgling. Eileen followed her, continuing to relate all the trials of being left a wealthy widow. The most irritating complication, it seemed, was the irrevocable fact that children grow up and develop minds of their own. And then they turn the ugly face of ingratitude on the one who has devoted her life to their welfare.

Jocelyn half listened while she was preparing Boo's breakfast. She concluded that Eileen suffered from a deep-seated inferiority complex, and that Purchase had been a past master of taking advantage of it.

Carol wandered into the kitchen just as the door banged shut behind Eileen. "For the love of mike, when does she sleep?" she said grumpily.

"She's been up since five, feeding and milking the cows. Doing her war bit, don't you know."

"What war bit? She'd make a good frogman, the way she can hold her breath for hours on end."

"She's really pathetic," Jocelyn said. "She's just bottled up with complexes."

"Well, I wish she'd take them somewhere else to uncork them," Carol grumbled. "I heard her say she and her husband didn't consummate their marriage. That's likely her problem."

Jocelyn fed Boo and then served up some hot tea and toast in an effort to put Carol in a better mood. One thing they could not afford to do was antagonize their landlady.

Within two weeks, the garrulous Eileen had exhausted her supply of anecdotes and was on the second round. However, to their relief, Carol stumbled on a way to cut her off. She had bustled in for what had become her usual dawn dissertation, and the moment she paused to take a breath, Carol, whose turn it was to sit out the early morning shift, darted in quickly. "You know Eileen, that just reminds me of the time...."

Eileen quickly cut in. "I must hear about that some other time, my dear. I'm sure it's a fascinating story, but I must get back to my chores. I'm so very busy these days." She smoothed her hands over her breasts and made for the door. She called, "Cheerio," as she strode down the path towards her own house.

A triumphant gleeful smile crossed Carol's lips as she went into the bedroom to relay to Jocelyn the magic formula for getting rid of the pest.

***

Sharnden Brooks was, if anything, less accessible to the outside world than Susan Plum had been. And, living as they did on Eileen's doorstep, it was impossible to ignore her. She proved to be more of a menace than did the much dreaded doodle bugs which so far had sailed over Mayfield in their wanton path of destruction.

***

Carol and Jocelyn gradually settled into a routine and it became difficult to distinguish one day from another. Much of their time was taken up in the struggle to keep warm. Thanks to double summer time, it stayed light until late evening, but the pale winter sun had little warming effect on the near freezing outside temperatures. They scoured the nearby woods for old dead logs, dragging them home, chopping them up and then trying to persuade them to burn in their sodden state in the uncooperative fireplace. The wet wood was part of the problem. But they also concluded that the grate was not deep enough and the chimney did not draw properly. In order to get a fire started, they had to cover the opening with a newspaper and then make sure that the paper didn't catch fire when the logs burst into flame. It was a hazardous task, especially when Carol insisted on reading items in the paper and didn't notice it beginning to scorch prior to going up in flames.

There was no constant stream of company whose coming and going had been such a welcome diversion at Susan Plum. Hence, the routine of letter writing, sewing, knitting, reading, and simply waiting, which had filled the evenings at Queensbury Lodge, was once more their only resort.

The electricity that Eileen had boasted of so proudly, and to which they had looked forward so eagerly after being deprived of it at Susan Plum, proved only a qualified blessing. When they needed it most in the evenings, it would fade away to a feeble glow, necessitating bringing out the candles. Eileen, being of the early to bed, early to rise school, more often than not forgot to refuel the power plant. They suspected she did it on purpose to save fuel. Whatever the reason, it was impossible to work or read in candle light, so they were left with waiting—an occupation that required more skill and patience than any other, and one which practice had the reverse effect of making perfect.

Jocelyn was mainly occupied with sorting out and assembling her resources for her eventual return to Canada and trying to plan for the uncertain future. Kit, not having completed his will form, had severely complicated the task and she was having to deal with a very cold and unhelpful ministerial bureaucracy in London who in their frequent missives always addressed her as, Madam.

"You'd think they were writing to a brothel keeper," she complained to Carol.

Carol's whole outlook was focussed on the day that Dennis would finish his first tour of operations and come home to be safe for awhile. Waiting for this was slowly but surely affecting her whole personality. She had begun her stay in England a light-hearted, fun-loving optimist, but the past eight months of strain and heartache had taken their inevitable toll. For the first time in her life, she really and truly knew fear, and she had no weapons with which to combat it. When constant worry undermined her own weakened defenses, fear took over, and by degrees it refashioned the gay carefree Carol into a nervous, moody, irritable companion.

Jocelyn watched the metamorphosis in helpless sympathy and understanding. She recognized her own old fear and heartache, and knew only too well that until the root of the trouble was removed there was no way to bring back the old Carol who had been such a joy to live with. She only hoped and prayed that Dennis would be spared for the day that peace would come and drive away this fear which was almost as destructive in its way as any of the lethal weapons of war. Its power over her had vanished with dear beloved Kit, but nothing, she felt certain, would ever completely erase the awful memory of it.

Like the electricity, most of Eileen's magnaminous promises did not live up to expectation. She had offered to drive them into the village whenever she was going in her car. But, always when ready to leave, she would wave an airy good bye to them, and drive off through the gate and up the rocky road—alone. At one time, Carol would have considered it funny, but now it irritated her, almost as much as did Eileen's inane chatter. However, there was a brighter side. Their only other close neighbour was the Seton family who occupied the old manor house just below Mrs. Marshall's property. Mrs. Seton was a tiny lady with greying blonde hair, a lovely smile and a sweet motherly disposition. She paid a visit to the cottage as soon as she thought they were settled.

Jocelyn greeted her warmly and showed her into the living room where, after a half hour of fanning and coaxing with paraffin, Carol had persuaded the soggy wood they had gathered to burn in the fireplace.

"What a beautiful kitten," Jocelyn said, admiring the ginger ball of fluff that Mrs. Seton had brought in and which was now purring contentedly in her lap.

"Isn't he a beauty?" Mrs. Seton replied in her soft Irish lilt. "I really brought him because I hoped you might take a liking to him and keep him. He needs a home."

Jocelyn turned to Carol. "What do you think? Could we keep him?"

Carol, like her father, adored cats, so there was no doubt about her response. "Absolutely, we need a cat around here to discipline the cheeky mice we share the cottage with." She took the kitten from Mrs. Seton and it snuggled into her arms.

"Look, he's feeling at home already."

"He'll be company for Boo," Jocelyn suggested in jest. "Thanks so much, Mrs. Seton, we'll be glad to give him a home."

"That's settled then," Mrs. Seton said. "Now, how do you like living here in the valley of Sharnden?"

"It's very beautiful," Jocelyn replied. She didn't want to give any hint of their difficulties with Eileen.

"One thing to be thankful for is that those wretched doodle bugs have given us a wide berth so far. Have many fallen in the area?" Carol asked.

"Yes, we've had our share. In fact, one fell not far from here just the week before you arrived. Fortunately no one was injured or killed. Have you been into the village?"

"Not yet. It's too far to carry Boo. We have to depend on Mr. Honeybone's Saturday deliveries."

Mrs. Seton smiled. "I'm sure you find that rather costly."

"It is. He's an old fraud," Jocelyn admitted. "But we haven't much choice, even though our cupboards are already bursting with dry dog biscuits for which we have no dog, junket powders for which we have no milk, waterglass in which we have no eggs to preserve, and candles—well, we have enough of those to light our way to China."

"I know only too well that game he plays," Mrs. Seton agreed. "He used to practise it on me when I first moved here, but I finally put my foot down. I go into the village now to shop."

Carol returned from the kitchen, having given the kitten a saucer of milk, and made tea which she placed on the trolley by the fire. "These biscuits are pretty awful," she apologized, "But we're at Mr. Honeybone's mercy I'm afraid."

"Well, you shall be no longer," Mrs. Seton said firmly. "In future, when I go into the village, I'll stop by and pick you up."

She was as good as her word, never passing by in her car without offering them a lift. While it was a great boon, it posed a very serious problem for them. Eileen was usually peeping out of her window when they walked past on their way to the car, and the phenomenal change in her countenance from a smile and a wave, to the murderous expression that crossed her face as they climbed into the Seton's Daimler and drove away was worthy of a Dr. Jekyll and Mr. Hyde performance.

From then on, she launched a propaganda campaign to disparage the kindly Mrs. Seton. The only effect was to increase Jocelyn and Carol's appreciation of that dear lady, and lessen their respect for Eileen. In fact, all of the misgivings Carol had sensed on her introduction to that woman were rapidly being justified.

Eileen became less and less subtle in her spite. If they were going to be friends with the Setons, then she wasn't going to allow them to have any butter or eggs. The butter they wouldn't miss, because what she sold them was usually rancid. However, Carol was certain that she deliberately let the generator run down so that they had no electricity in the evenings.

At first, Eileen had reiterated often enough to make it seem genuine, "You may use my telephone as often as you wish. It's there, and you may as well take advantage of it. Especially when you're so far from a kiosk." However, each time they had occasion to use the telephone, they were forestalled by the excuse that she was expecting a call from her cousin Roger. He was, she told them with much fluttering of eyelids and stroking of bosom, 'a man of the woods'. Whatever he was, he telephoned her at all hours of the day and night, and awaiting his ringing summons constituted Eileen's complete monopoly of the line. The only time it was available for any other purpose was just after Roger had had his shilling's worth of billing and cooing, or from that time until he stumbled out of the woods and into another kiosk. Roger was indefinite, irregular, and yet damnably constant.

Not long after Mrs. Seton's first visit, they experienced their first doodle bug attack. It was late evening and they were settled before the fire in the living room reading when they were conscious of an increasingly loud noise. It sounded like the engine of a huge tractor. They got up, went outside and searched the night sky.

"There it is," Jocelyn said, pointing to the west just over the Seton's property. "Look, it's coming towards us!"

They dashed back inside, grabbed Boo's basket and put her under the bed for safety. The kitten, sensing danger, jumped from his chair and fell into the coal scuttle. Carol picked him up and cuddled him. She joined Jocelyn at the window and they watched anxiously as the bomb approached.

They knew that as long as they could hear it and could see the lights on the tail it would not fall. They watched it on its deadly path until it passed right over the cottage beyond Eileen's property. Suddenly, the noise stopped. There was an ominous silence, and then the tail lights went out. Within seconds they heard an enormous bang. It had landed somewhere nearby, but exactly where they couldn't be sure.

Visibly shaken, but relieved it had not fallen on the cottage or the big house, or on the Seton's, they put Boo back into her room, made themselves a cup of tea to soothe their tattered nerves and then went to bed.

The next day they were relieved to learn from the postman that the missile had landed on an empty field where it did no damage to anyone; nor did it destroy any buildings.

CHAPTER 36

By the middle of October, Dennis had completed his first tour of operations. Carol simply wept with relief.

"Oh, Joc," she sniffled, tears splattering the letter in her hand. "I can't believe it. Thirty wonderful days of freedom—no flying, no operations, no worrying. I think I'll even be able to smile at the 'broken record' when next she arrives with one of her epic tales, without feeling as though I have lock jaw."

"And who knows, maybe the war will end before he's due for a second tour," Jocelyn said.

"Now who's being a loony optimist?" Carol asked, sounding more like her old self. "But what I am hoping is that he may not have to do a second tour."

Jocelyn was absent from Sharnden when Dennis arrived home to start his leave. Derek Stewart had paid one of his now rare visits to the cottage and he offered to drive Jocelyn as far as Burton-on-Trent so that she could go and visit the Fords and let them see their granddaughter.

After she left, Dennis and Carol had the cottage to themselves for a few days. He quickly dispelled her hopes about no more operations.

"I had to make a choice, darling. Either I take a month's leave now and then go back on ops. or have a week's leave before going to a station for instructional duty."

"And you chose to go back after a month?" Carol's voice was flatly incredulous, and she turned tear-filled eyes away from him.

He had not been with her enough lately to appreciate the change that had come over her, and he expected that she would take this news just as she had always accepted his decisions—with a smile, and a 'well I guess you know best'. He was perplexed when this decision upset her so. She didn't often cry. He put his arms around her.

"I'm sorry, darling. But really it was a kind of Hobson's choice. The squadron needs experienced crews so badly right now when the war is at such a critical stage. I couldn't walk out just when I can be of the most use. Please try to understand."

Carol turned to him, tears still welling in her eyes. "I do understand," she said, unhappily conscious that she was somehow letting him down. "I hadn't thought of it in any other light except having you home, and safe. Maybe on a training station where we could relax for a little."

Dennis tried to make light of it. He gave a small laugh of protest and demanded, "What's safe about putting my life in the hands of some of those nit-wit, wet-behind-the-ears pupils?"

Try as she would, Carol could not laugh it off. Her heart was a solid lump in her breast, and she wondered if she would ever be rid of the dread that had put it there.

"Well," she suggested, drying her eyes with a small sodden handkerchief, "I suppose we'll just have to make the best of what we have then. But a month isn't very long."

Dennis gave her his own clean handkerchief and studied her tear-stained face. "Carol, what has come over you? I remember when you thought a month was interminable."

She tugged at a stray auburn curl over her ear. "That was a long time ago. A very long time ago...when time was cheap and plentiful."

"I can see you need me around for awhile," he said, lines of concern furrowing his high forehead and belying the smile on his lips. The ginger kitten jumped up on his lap and he stroked it gently. "Where did this come from?"

"Mrs. Seton gave it to us. Since he arrived, the mice have almost decided that the cottage isn't such a choice hotel after all."

Dennis laughed. "What's his name?"

"We just call him puss. I knew that if we christened him, you'd just change it to suit yourself."

"Good. I'll call him Taf," he said. "He can be the new mascot for the Second Tactical Air Force. Tim befriended a stray puss on the station, but when it turned out to be female, he found other quarters for it on the double."

Tim Rothney was Dennis's navigator. They had teamed up in Greenwood, when they discovered that they came from the same part of Lancashire in the north of England.

"How is Tim?" Carol asked.

"Just fine. I've invited him to come and visit us on the last week of our leave. He's been a bit jumpy lately. I think it will do him good to be here in this faraway spot for a bit. Do you think Jocelyn will mind?"

"No, I'm sure she won't. But there isn't much for him to do here."

"Oh, I don't know. We can go out in the woods and shoot a few rabbits. And he's a keen bridge player, so we should be able to get in a few games in the evenings.

"You'll have to send some strong hints to our dear landlady to remind her to fuel the generator, or we'll be playing in the dark."

As though she had heard her name being taken in vain, Eileen suddenly appeared at the door. She was laden with eggs, butter, and milk. Rudely, she pushed her way in past Carol and gushed into the living room.

"So you are Dennis. I've heard so much about you, and have been so anxious to meet you."

Dennis rose and took the large freckled hand she had extended. "How do you do, Mrs. Marshall. I also have heard a great deal about you."

Eileen sat down, fluttering her eyelids and stroking her bosom. "All good, I trust. I do so enjoy having your wife and her sister, and of course the dear sweet baby. It's a rather lonely place when I have no tenants. Of course, I have my stepson, Indroo, but he's not very good company really. In any case, I know how badly the girls needed a home, and I was just glad that I could help. There's nothing like doing someone a good turn, don't you agree?''

Dennis nodded, and Eileen prattled on.

"You know, Dennis, you don't mind if I call you Dennis, do you? It's so much more friendly. Let me see, what was I saying? Oh, yes, I felt so sorry for those poor children and was only too happy to offer them my cosy little nest here. And I do think they're very comfortable in it. Purchase, my former chauffeur, used to tell me that I was the kindest person he'd ever known. He was so loyal, and I miss him so.''

Heaven preserve us, Carol thought, and went off into the kitchen, returning shortly having fortified herself with a glass of water.

"Oh, there you are, Carol dear. I was so sorry about the telephone this morning. You did manage to get a taxi for Dennis, didn't you? I saw you going down to Setons. You naughty girl.'' She wagged a rough stained finger accusingly at Carol. "You could have used my telephone, had you just waited. Roger's call came as soon as you left.''

Carol hoped that a baring of teeth would pass for a smile. "That was quite all right, Eileen. I had to go down to the Setons anyway. Mrs. Seton hasn't been well.''

"Is that so? It's probably her nerves again. She's always feigning some illness or other.''

"This is not feigned. She has a bad case of lumbago.''

"Well, that's her husband's fault. He shouldn't allow her to work so hard in the garden.'' She turned to Dennis. "She's a very frail little woman. But they are an odd couple. I've tried my best to be friendly, but they spurn my overtures. Now they are trying their best to embarrass me by being overly friendly with my tenants.''

Fortunately, at that moment Andrew appeared at the door and summoned her to the telephone.

"It's likely my cousin, Roger,'' she simpered, and hurried out of the cottage, with a promise to see more of Dennis later.

"Not if we see you first, you magpie," Carol muttered under her breath. She looked at Dennis questioningly. "Well?"

"She just needs a man," was his typically masculine assessment.

"What about cousin Roger?"

Dennis hooted. "After all, darling. Not much can be gained by carrying on a love tryst over a telephone line."

***

Except for the intrusion of the persistent Eileen who, with the fluttering of eyelids and stroking of bosom, repeated the story of her life for Dennis, they completely enjoyed the respite from war and worry. During the days, they strolled through the thick carpet of leaves in the woods, often with a gentle rain falling from the grey October skies, and the evenings they spent before the fire.

Dennis seemed to have magic powers over it for it blazed merrily until bedtime. And Eileen, no doubt in order to impress Dennis, made sure that the generator was working so they had the lamps to read by. Once the fire died down and they were in bed, they loved, they dreamed, they planned, and they wished for an end to this seemingly unending war.

According to the news reports, during the month of October, the Canadians had taken Calais, and were desperately trying to destroy the German flying bomb sites located in the Channel ports. The first Canadian Army was on the point of opening the port of Antwerp to Allied shipping, and the Americans were pushing their offensive towards the infamous Siegfried line. The Russians had penetrated far into Yugoslavia and were about to take Belgrade, and they had moved into Hungary. But Stalin had decided not to give aid to the Polish patriots who had been trying valiantly to oust the Germans from Warsaw. These brave starving people, having fought heroically for two months against tremendous odds and with victory almost in their grasp, had finally had to admit defeat and surrender once more to the Germans. The British had landed in Greece, and the Americans had invaded the Phillipines and were about to gain victory over the Japanese fleet in the Battle of Leyte Gulf.

The tide was turning in favour of the Allies, but still the final battle was far from being staged. In fact, the Americans were about to receive a serious set-back in the fierce German offensive in the Ardennes, having fatally misjudged the strength of the enemy forces there.

No, there would be no respite for some time yet. The kind of support provided by the Second Tactical Airforce in which Dennis was serving would be sorely needed over the next critical period of the war and, unfortunately, many more precious lives would be lost. Carol could only pray with all her heart that Dennis would not be among them.

Jocelyn returned from Repton at the end of the week. It had not been a successful venture by any measure. She was glad to have it behind her. As she related sadly to Carol, the loss of her only son had not softened Violet Ford's peculiar nature. She was still preoccupied with the opinion of her neighbours, and she totally shocked Jocelyn by saying, "Jocelyn, my dear, I've told the village people that Kit's plane was shot down by a German fighter plane. I do hope you won't make me sound foolish by repeating the exact details. After all, what does it matter now? And it does sound better to say he was shot down."

Carol couldn't find words to express her horror at this piece of callousness. She squeezed Jocelyn's hand and said, "Don't think about it, hon. The woman is obviously demented." She quickly changed the subject. "How did you get along with Derek?"

"That's another story. I decided I had to tell him that I couldn't see him any more."

"Why?"

"He was getting too serious. And I'm in no position to cope with someone who wants to move into my life just now. It's all I can do to face what I cannot avoid facing, without worrying about hurting someone who doesn't deserve it."

"So, how did you leave it with him?"

"I simply said that this was good-bye. He took it very well, I think. And it was better to cut it off quickly, rather than letting him think there was any hope."

"You're probably right," Carol admitted. "But he is an awfully nice fellow, and he certainly adores Boo, to say nothing of her mother."

Jocelyn changed the subject. "What about you and Dennis? How have you coped with the babbling brook next door?"

"Oh, Dennis has her number. Actually, she hasn't bothered us too much. Incidentally, he wants to take me up to the Lake District for the next couple of weeks. Can you manage here on your own?"

"I won't be alone," Jocelyn reminded her. "Ellen is coming down to stay for awhile."

"But that's perfect. I'll feel happier if you have some company to help water down that harpy."

Dennis and Carol left the next day for their holiday in the north, and Jocelyn eagerly anticipated Ellen's visit. On the day she arrived, she was immediately treated to Eileen's favourite sermon on her war effort.

With a glint of amusement in her large olive green eyes, Ellen said, "What's with this war effort? What does she do out here in the back of beyond?"

"That's a deep dark secret. Even the government doesn't know about it. At least, she hopes they don't. She just uses her farm produce for a neat bit of bribery and corruption. You know, eggs and butter for petrol coupons, or other hard-to-obtain goods. It's not really illegal, she maintains, but then it's not exactly legal either."

"How peculiar," Ellen said. "By the way, how is your progress towards getting a passage home coming along?"

"It's just a matter of waiting. I'm actually hoping that it won't happen for awhile."

"Why?" Ellen was surprised.

"I think Carol needs me at the moment. She thought that Dennis was going to be through with ops. after this tour, but he has signed on for a second tour."

"I know how Carol must feel about that. Don was so close to the end of operational flying, having almost completed two tours of ops. I begged him to stop before it was too late, but...." She gazed into the empty fireplace, her face filled with sadness.

"You've heard nothing more about Don?" Jocelyn asked.

"No, they found some wreckage near where he went down but there was no proof that it belonged to his plane. I'm through hoping he might turn up." Her pretty mouth twisted into a determined smile. "Let's not be morbid. How did you enjoy your trip to Repton? I gather Derek Stewart drove you part of the way."

"There's nothing cheerful about either of those two subjects. Repton was a total disaster, and I had to tell Derek that I couldn't see him any more." She got up and went over to the window and gazed out over the lovely valley of Sharnden. The blue sky was dotted with fleecy white clouds, a bright sun spread its warm golden glow everywhere, and she turned to Ellen. "Why don't we go out for a walk? It's so nice out. We could have our first visit to Mr. Honeybone's establishment. Carol and I haven't ventured that far yet."

"What about Boo?"

"She'll be okay. She doesn't usually waken from her nap until noon, and I've put her near where Andrew is chopping wood. He'll keep an eye on her for me."

She found Carol's Wellingtons for Ellen, donned her own and they took off across the verdant fields in the direction of Mr. Honeybone's general store.

CHAPTER 37

Ellen returned to her home in Swindon the same day that Carol and Dennis were due back from their holiday in the Lake District. Jocelyn had a hot meal ready for them. After they had eaten, they sat by the fire in the living room, Carol describing the highlights of her holiday in the Lake District.

"I saw Wordsworth's cottage, Joc, an enchanting little gem of a house. It's one of the main tourist attractions of the Lake District. And you should have seen me mountain climbing with Dennis and Tim giving me instructions as I slithered and slid up and down the hills. You can't really call them mountains, not when you compare them with the Rockies. Dennis and Tim were like mountain goats scampering over the rocks, but I was pretty hopeless. Still I tried, didn't I darling?"

Dennis gave her an encouraging smile. "Indeed you did, my love. You were somewhat handicapped not having the proper hiking boots." He turned to Jocelyn then and said, "By the way, Jocelyn, I've invited my navigator, Tim Rothney, to spend the last week of our leave here. He's been a bit edgy lately, and I think that coming here might just get him back in shape to return to the squadron. I do hope you won't mind. He's a splendid fellow."

"Not at all. In fact, I'm anxious to meet Tim. I've heard such glowing reports about him."

"Well, he plays bridge, so that should be a mark in his favour. We'll be able to get in a few rubbers during the week."

The next day they went into Mayfield to meet Tim's train which was due in at one o'clock. Eileen had played her childish game of refusing them the use of the telephone, so they went down to Setons and rang for a taxi from there.

At the station, Jocelyn, with Boo in her arms, lagged behind purposefully while Tim, Carol, and Dennis greeted one another warmly. Then Tim glanced behind Carol at the young girl holding the pink-cheeked baby.

Jocelyn looked directly into his keen blue eyes widely set in a cherubic face. His blond, slightly wavy hair, so like Kit's, gave her an instant's pain which had the dual effect of reminding her of her manners and releasing her voice. "Hello, Tim. How nice that you could join us."

Tim seemed to have suddenly been struck dumb. Dennis had told him often enough what a stunning girl his sister-in-law was, but he had formed his own mental image of what she would be like. The pretty young girl now standing in front of him bore no resemblance to the dowdy widow saddled with an infant that he had envisioned, Dennis's sales pitch notwithstanding.

Carol and Dennis watched in amused silence, but finally Dennis said, "Aren't you going to say hello to Jocelyn, Tim?"

Tim flushed with embarrassment. "Oh, I am sorry. Of course. Glad to meet you, Jocelyn." And then he looked at Boo. "And you too, Boo." She gave him a big smile, showing off her two new pearly white teeth.

With the ice broken and the introductions over, they climbed into the taxi which took them back to the farm.

On the way, Tim was sitting in the back seat beside Jocelyn. He kept stealing furtive glances at her and thinking to himself how pretty she was. Suddenly, all of the misgivings that he harboured after agreeing to come to the cottage faded away and he felt absurdly happy.

***

Much to Carol's relief, Eileen came over only once that week, presumably to satisfy her curiosity about Tim and to acquaint him with her good deeds, especially her war effort, which amused him immensely when told what it consisted of.

On one occasion, Dennis went over to the big house to ask to borrow an axe, but Eileen refused him, saying that Andrew was using it. Then, she turned very coy and lured him into the house on the pretext that her Aga cooker had gone wrong. While he examined it, she went off, returning shortly wearing a provocative negligee in which she proceeded to flirt quite shamelessly with him. He ignored her, until she leaned over the stove pretending to see what he was doing and allowed her sagging breast to fall on his shoulder.

At that, he stood up quickly and announced, "There's nothing wrong with the stove, Mrs. Marshall, and I must be getting back to my wife." He put on his jacket, slowly eyeing her in his direct way with his head slightly cocked and a wry smile on his lips. He watched the freckled face turn crimson and the bosoms heave with anger. Then he left abruptly, without stopping to close the door behind him.

In that moment the seeds of revenge were sown on fertile ground. Eileen didn't bother them any more that week. In fact, she hardly left her house. Roger had not called her for two weeks, and she was afraid to go out lest she miss him.

Heaven smiled down upon Sharnden Brooks throughout the week and there were sunny days in which the two men went out hunting for rabbits, after which Carol expertly skinned them and Jocelyn used her culinary skills to fashion them into a gourmet dinner. And the four of them hiked through the naked woods, taking turns carrying Boo in a makeshift canvas seat.

Thanks to Tim and Dennis's efforts, there was a well stacked pile of dry wood for the cheerful fires in front of which they played bridge most evenings. When it was time for Boo's last feeding, they passed her and her bottle around the table to whoever was dummy. Even Tim took his turn. She was such a placid, happy baby and made no fuss when finally put back in her cot for the night. Nothing more was heard from her until eight the next morning.

Tim seemed to be enjoying himself, just pottering about and helping with any household chores. He even hung the diapers out on the line for Jocelyn. He was no longer jumpy and moody, so Dennis concluded that the change and rest here were acting as the panacea he had hoped for. They were a team, these two. As Arthur Steel, Kit's navigator, had told Jocleyn, the relationship between pilot and navigator was a closer bond even than between brothers, because on each did the other's very life depend. What affected one invariably affected the other.

But Dennis was no longer worried about Tim, and he was able to concentrate wholeheartedly on making the most of his remaining time with Carol. She, too, seemed to have benefitted immensely from their sojourn in the Lake District and had become once again the smiling, good-natured girl he had married.

On a particularly gorgeous autumn day in the middle of the week, Tim accompanied Jocelyn over the valley to get some supplies from Mr. Honeybone. As they strolled leisurely back to the cottage, Tim carrying the bags of groceries, he said casually, "What made you and Carol pick such an isolated place to live?"

Jocelyn sighed. "We didn't have any choice, really. It was a case of either remaining in a cold damp, spooky place which we couldn't afford without Sheila's contribution, or coming here."

Tim said, "Well, I can't quite figure out what made you abandon the comforts and safety of life in Canada to come over here and endure the hardships and uncertainty which are about all England has to offer just now. It must have taken a great deal of courage."

Jocelyn shrugged. "Courage didn't enter into it. Although we certainly had plenty of people telling us we were mad to make the dangerous crossing."

"Why did you come, then?" Tim persisted.

"I simply wanted to be wherever Kit was. It couldn't have mattered less where it happened to be, or how uncomfortable the prospects of living there were. The safety and comfort of home were totally eclipsed by being so far away from Kit."

For some reason that Tim himself could not define, he suddenly envied Kit Ford. He had yet to meet any woman for whom he felt more than a passing fancy. Some had shown a great deal of interest in him, but they had either quickly bored him, or irritated him, or were too transparent in their wiles for his taste. Coming to Sharnden, however, had had a disturbing effect on him, making him conscious for the first time in his twenty-two years of having missed out on something.

The independence he had always prized so highly, suddenly didn't seem so satisfying after all. He began to feel vaguely unsettled and dissatisfied with his lot. Yet he didn't know just why. Any more than he knew for sure why he had accepted the invitation to spend this week here. But he knew he wasn't sorry he had come.

Just as they approached the last stile before reaching the cottage, he said, "What do you plan to do with your life now, Jocelyn?"

"I don't have much choice. I'll be returning home as soon as Air Ministry can secure a passage for us. After that, who knows?"

Deep inside, Tim felt a small jolt of concern. "Do you mean you will leave Carol here, alone?" He liked Carol immensely, but he knew that it was not really only her welfare that he was concerned about. "Won't she miss you?" he asked.

"Yes, she will, and I'll miss her, but I am sort of a third thumb when Dennis comes home, and when he gets off ops. I'll become even more so."

Tim found himself arguing the point. "That may be so, but in the meantime, she will need you, and, if anything should happen to Dennis...."

She interrupted. "We mustn't even think about that," she said sharply.

"Of course not," he apologized. "It's just that we live with the possibility daily and we get hardened to it."

"Well, one thing is certain," Jocelyn replied, thinking back to Simon's lucky escape, "you never know who will be lucky and who won't, so one may as well live for today, and just hope for tomorrow."

"That sounds very fatalistic," Tim said.

"I suppose it does. But I only know that I wasted too much time borrowing trouble, and I wish I hadn't. It didn't buy me anything. I still lost Kit."

"But it's a common complaint, to borrow trouble," Tim replied. "I certainly suffer from it."

"Well, cure yourself of it right away," Jocelyn ordered, laughing lightly.

"Easier said than done," Tim answered, helping her over the stile and moving on towards the cottage. Suddenly he stopped and looked down at her. "Look here, Jocelyn, don't rush off home too soon...I mean... don't leave Carol too soon." Then he felt as though he had been presumptuous and silently cursed himself.

He was genuinely relieved when he heard Jocelyn say, "Again, I have no choice. Air Ministry has told me that it will be some time before I get a passage."

"That's good," Tim said, with more satisfaction than he meant to reveal.

On the last evening of the leave, the electricity failed, and the bridge game came to an abrupt end almost before it began. Carol put out a saucer containing the stub of a red candle. "The bohemian touch," she said.

"We can't play cards in candlelight," Dennis complained. "It's a lovely night, Carol. Why don't we go out for a short stroll before turning in."

"Would you two mind?" Carol asked, glancing at Tim and Jocelyn.

"Of course not," Jocelyn said.

Tim was already putting the card table away and pushing the chairs in front of the fire. "Sure, you two, go ahead. Jocelyn and I will chew the fat in front of the fire. But don't get lost in the woods," he needled Dennis. "Remember you have no navigator along."

"I think we'll manage," Dennis said haughtily, but with a wide grin. He helped Carol into her fur coat, put on his battle dress jacket and they went out into the crisp moonlit night.

Tim finished clearing away the bridge paraphenalia and then sat down on the floor opposite Jocelyn. She was gazing into the dancing flames. The room was diffused with the warm glow of the firelight and her cheeks were flushed by the heat from the fire and her long dark lashes cast their shadows on them.

Tim sat quietly and unobtrusively admiring her. He felt strangely at peace with himself. Sometime, he wasn't sure exactly when, he had finally accepted a fact that he had been vainly striving to deny ever since he first laid eyes on Jocelyn at Mayfield station. He knew now why he had envied Kit, why during this whole week he had contrived to spend as much time with Jocelyn as possible, even if it meant hanging diapers on the line. It would always be that way from now on, and he knew there was nothing he could do about it. He didn't know where it would lead, or how he would deal with the many obstacles in his path, but for the moment at least, it was a great relief to admit to himself that he was completely hooked on Jocelyn, and for that matter on that funny cute little baby, Boo. Somehow he must find a way not to lose them.

Jocelyn suddenly sensed his steady gaze. She looked up and their eyes locked in one of those rare and mystical moments of mutual affinity, which, although fleeting as a shadow, seem to last an eternity.

She turned away first and released her breath slowly. She hadn't realized that she'd been holding it. She was confused and alarmed by what she had seen in Tim's eyes. She tried vainly to think of something trivial to say, but he spoke first.

"What were you thinking about so profoundly just now?"

"Oh, a host of things," she said, surprised to find her voice quite controlled. "How nice this interlude has been, and I was wondering what Carol will do now it's over. Our lives here are pretty humdrum. We don't have the company we had at Susan Plum, and we miss Sheila in an odd way. She's a total dingaling sometimes, but could be fun."

Tim had heard about Squadron Leader Derek Stewart from Dennis and was anxious to sound out Jocelyn on that subject. But he hesitated to ask at this point. Perhaps he could ask Dennis later what the situation was. Finally, he said, "You know, I'm not much good at judging people. For instance, I wasn't one bit keen on meeting you, despite all the rave notices I had about you from Dennis. I figured he was biased. I had met Kit. Did you know that?"

"Yes, I remember when we made that quick visit to Greenwood when we left Charlottetown, Dennis took Kit out to the station and let him have a flip in a Mossy. He told me he had met you and that Dennis was delighted to have you as his navigator."

"I didn't have much time with Kit, but I thought him a hell of a nice fellow. Then, when Dennis told me he he'd bought it over the North Sea, well, naturally I felt sorry for you. I conjured up a picture of you in my mind. You know the sort of thing—the sad, lonely widow with a child—doleful, pathetic, and probably frumpish into the bargain. God alone knows why I dredged up that image. Whatever the reason, it was so firmly entrenched in my stupid head that I was reluctant to come here. Then when I first saw you, I got quite a jolt." The corners of his lips turned up in a half smile and he looked at Jocelyn shyly. "I expect you noticed that I acted rather dumb at the station."

She chuckled. "As a matter of fact I wondered if you'd lost your tongue in battle."

"I'd lost it alright, but not in that way. I was just thunderstruck at how young, and beautiful, and vulnerable you looked, just as you do now in the glow of the fire."

Jocelyn turned away from his intent gaze, but not before he saw the doubt, the hurt, the confusion in her eyes.

"I'm a clumsy idiot!" he said. "I had no right to come on to you like that. Forgive me, please. God knows you've had enough to bear without me adding to your burden."

She got up and went over to the window, her eyes blindly searching the fields which were silver with frost and moonlight. Her heart was pounding and her mind was churning with mixed emotions. Now that she had wakened to reality, and recovered her sense of discernment, she wondered how she could have been so blind.

Yet, in truth, Tim had said and done nothing to make her so disturbed. Even as a teenager, she'd never lacked boyfriends. Derek Stewart had been attracted to her, and yet he didn't affect her this way. She thought that she had accepted Tim in the same spirit she had Derek, just as a very nice person to be with and with whom she shared many common interests—a mutual love of classical music, books, and bridge.

What was so upsetting then that Tim found her attractive? Nothing at all, except that it followed a pattern that she had experienced before, even to the look that had passed between them a moment ago. It was as though...as though she were re-living her first meeting with Kit. But surely that couldn't happen to a person twice in one lifetime. She was overwhelmed by a heavy feeling of guilt and disloyalty to Kit, and she despised herself.

Tim rose and joined her at the window, putting out his hand to touch her shoulder, then withdrawing it.

"I'm so sorry if I've upset you. I won't do it again, I promise. It's just that I've enjoyed being with you so much. You can't imagine how wonderful it has been for me. And, now I've messed it all up."

"No, you haven't, Tim. I've enjoyed your company too. And I'll always treasure the memory of this week. It's just that I've been in a daze these past few months." She knew it sounded lame, but she couldn't think of anything else to say.

"Would you rather that I didn't come back again?" He sounded so desolate at that prospect that her heart ached for him.

"Yes...I mean, no. Carol and Dennis would think it odd, and in any case I'll be going home eventually, and you're going back on ops. So let's leave it at that for now."

"Whatever you say," he said quietly.

At least she hadn't completely turned him away, he thought hopefully.

Just then Dennis and Carol tapped on the window to let them know they were back.

"Let's go into the kitchen and make them some hot chocolate," Jocelyn suggested. "They'll be chilled after their walk."

"I could do with some myself," Tim said, and followed her into the kitchen.

CHAPTER 38

Tim and Dennis left early the next morning to return to their station. Carol's natural gaiety had returned while Dennis was home, but it disappeared the moment she saw his blue uniform disappear into the taxi. She went back to lapsing into the long silences that had disturbed Jocelyn previously. Each day she waited for the postman, and if he brought no letter from Dennis, she scarcely smiled the entire day.

Eileen's annoying early morning visits had ceased, but her animosity and spite asserted itself in dozens of little meannesses. She wished they wouldn't keep a cat on the premises—it worried her dog, Sugar Pie; she took away the baskets they used to gather wood—she needed them herself; she accused them of clearing the woods of kindling—all ten acres of them; she couldn't let them have any more eggs—yet took dozens into town for barter.

Jocelyn tried to act as a buffer between her and Carol, endeavouring at the same time to keep her own temper in check. It was important for them to keep this roof over their heads. The time came, however, when she had to leave Carol alone at the cottage for a while. Her friend, Frances Saunders, whose husband had been reported killed while Jocelyn was at Susan Plum, had pleaded with her to come to Bath for a visit. She was having her baby girl baptised and wanted Jocelyn to be there.

Carol was reasonably certain that she would be all right by herself, but her heart sank when she saw the taxi bearing Jocelyn and Boo to the station disappear down the road.

After one long day with only Taf for company, she wondered how she would endure a whole week in the atmosphere of veiled hostility with its thin veneer of pseudo friendliness that existed between the cottage and the big house. She was overjoyed when, the following day, who should show up on the doorstep but Eddy Johnston, full of news and chatter.

Carol greeted him with undisguised joy.

"What's the matter, Carol?" he drawled. "I know you folks always make me welcome, but this time I feel like I was royalty or something."

"Oh, Eddy, you've probably saved my life. I swear I wouldn't have survived the week without some help."

"Where's Jocelyn? She hasn't left for Canada, has she?"

"No, she's visiting a friend in Bath."

"Oh, that's a relief. I would've hated to have her go home without saying good bye to her. How's that cute little girl?"

"Just fine. Growing like a weed. Come into the kitchen while I make us some lunch."

After they had eaten, they sat in the living room and Carol admired the latest pictures of little Fredel.

"She's going to be christened after Christmas," Eddy said. "I wondered if you could do me a favour."

"I'll do anything I can," Carol said.

"Well, I know you are pretty handy with a needle, and I have some parachute silk that I think would make a swell christening robe. Do you think you could make it?"

"You overestimate my capabilities, Eddy. However, I'll look at the material and see what can be done."

Eileen was looking out of her window when Eddy's taxi drove up to the cottage, and her warped mind jumped to warped conclusions. She knew that Jocelyn was away, that Carol was alone in the cottage, and she was sure that an American soldier could be up to no good. She half gloated, half raged all night, and in the morning made a special visit to the cottage to speak her mind.

Eddy tossed her a grin and a 'hi' as he wandered through the kitchen in his dressing gown, carrying his shaving kit and disappearing into the bathroom.

When the door closed behind him, Eileen turned to Carol with beady eyes in a prim face. "Is Jocelyn back?" she asked pointedly.

"No, she isn't. Did you want to see her?"

"No, I didn't. I want to know what you are going to do about this man who is staying here."

Carol hung her dish towel slowly and neatly on the rod. "What do you mean, what am I going to about Eddy?"

Eileen bristled. "He slept here last night, did he not?"

"Yes, he did."

"Well?" Eileen demanded indignantly.

."Oh, he didn't sleep with me, Eileen," Carol said, eyeing her solemnly.

Eileen's head jerked upward and her face and neck turned crimson. "Well, I didn't think....I didn't mean...." she sputtered.

"Yes? What **did** you mean?" Carol spoke quietly holding Eileen with unwavering eyes.

"Well, really, my dear. You know perfectly well what I meant. You're being purposely obtuse. You know what people will think."

Carol didn't move or flicker an eyelash. "Oh, what people will think what?" she asked icily.

Eileen merely shrugged her shoulders and went to the door.

"Well, we'll see about this," she warned, her small eyes ablaze with anger.

Carol followed her to the door. Until Eileen implied that Eddy's friendship was anything but platonic, it had never entered her head. Honi soit qui mal y pense, she thought, remembering the number of times that cousin Roger had left the big house at a suspiciously late hour. She looked at Eileen now and said sweetly, but with well-aimed irony, "If anyone asks about Eddy, Eileen, just tell him that he's my cousin."

Eileen coloured, opened her mouth to speak, changed her mind and turned and strode down the path.

Carol shut the door firmly behind her.

Eddy emerged from the bathroom, clean-shaven, a wide grin on his cherubic face. "Your landlady doesn't approve of my being here, I gather," he said.

"How did you guess?"

"I didn't guess. I eavesdropped. I kinda suspected you were in for it when I saw her marching up the path. She looked as though she was ready to go into battle. I could see the sparks shooting from her eyes."

Carol perched on the edge of the table. She was quiet for a moment, then she said thoughtfully, "You know, I believe she was glad to have something to make trouble about. She really was. She pretended to be so self-righteous, but she was really enjoying herself."

"Well, don't worry," Eddy said, clumsily trying to be cheerful. "You don't want to let an old bag like that get you down. But if you'd rather I leave...."

"I certainly would not rather you leave. You're my guest, and I can entertain anyone I like. Besides, if I let you go, Dennis and Jocelyn would be furious with me."

"That's the spirit. Let's trot off to the village and mail those letters we wrote to our loved ones last night."

"All right. I'll pick up some groceries while we're there. The Setons who usually drive me are away at the moment, and if I don't go to the store myself, old Honeybone will load us up with more junk we don't need. So we can kill two birds with one stone."

It had rained heavily during the night and the fields were transformed into a soft spongy bog. Carol wore her wellingtons and loaned Eddy a pair of Dennis's. It was a half hour's hike to Mr. Honeybone's store, even allowing for the shortcut they took through the woods.

He greeted them jovially. He was a tall corpulent Dickensian figure with masses of curly reddish grey hair, a ruddy complexion, and a beaming smile. The thin gold-rimmed glasses perched on the end of his bulbous crimson nose, he apparently wore more from habit than necessity, because he always peered over the top of the rims.

He was delighted to see Carol, and grasped Eddy's hand firmly across the counter, shaking it vigorously. Then, while he chatted and joked with them, right under Carol's nose he loaded the basket with the usual off-ration junk. Carol only realized it when he presented her with the inflated bill.

On the way home, she was preoccupied with her thoughts, still fuming at Eileen's nasty insinuations. As a result of her lack of attention, she missed the turn and led them off the right path. They wandered on anyway in the general direction of the cottage, crawling under barbed wire fences, climbing over stiles, nonchalantly skirting grazing cows and munching sheep, leaping over small streams, until they reached Sharnden Brook where it meandered through the valley in a wide deep gorge. It was bridged by a slippery plank which would have presented a challenge to anyone, but to someone with an armful of groceries it was truly formidable.

"I'll go first," Eddy volunteered. "Then I can help you."

So saying, he placed a muddy boot on the perilous plank and made an unsteady dash for the far bank. He grinned triumphantly and shouted, "I made it; now it's your turn."

He leaned over as far as he dared and stretched out his arm. He was about to suggest that she give him her parcel first, when something went awry. She lost her balance, and made a swan-like descent into the brook.

"Hang on while I get a stick," Eddy said.

"Hang on to what?" she gasped. The icy water had taken her breath away.

Eddy finally found a long branch which he offered to her. She grasped it and he pulled and tugged, trying to give her a foothold on the greasy bank. Her boots were filled with the murky cold water, and were very slippery but she finally managed to reach the top of the bank. She stood dripping and shivering, and gazing forlornly at the soggy contents of her basket of groceries.

"There goes a whole week's supply of rations," she said sadly.

"Never mind that," Eddy said. "Let's get you home and into some dry clothes before you catch pneumonia."

***

In spite of Eileen's displeasure, Eddy stayed another night, leaving the cottage the next morning. Jocelyn was due to arrive on the five o'clock train that afternoon. To ensure she would not have a long wait in the cold station with a tired hungry baby, Carol went early over to the big house to telephone for a taxi to meet her.

Eileen was sharp and abrupt. "You'll have to come back later," she said. "I'm expecting a very important call."

The Setons were not yet home from their trip, so Carol had no choice. "May I come back in twenty minutes?"

"I suppose so," Eileen replied grudgingly.

Carol allowed an hour to pass before returning. Eileen answered her knock and said, "I still haven't received my call. It could come at any moment, so you'll have to wait."

Carol knew that if she was to get one of the first bookings for a taxi, she could not let too much time elapse before calling. But there was no use arguing. "I'll be back in half an hour," she said.

But when she returned Eileen pursed her thin lips in a gesture of helplessness and simpered, "Isn't he a naughty boy? He hasn't called yet. But he will at any moment, I'm sure. You may come in and wait if you like."

"Eileen," Carol pleaded. "It will take only a matter of seconds to ring for a taxi. You know how scarce they are at that time of day with everyone returning from work."

"I'm sorry, my dear, but it is **my** telephone, after all."

Carol felt a wave of hot blood racing up her neck and a throbbing in her temples. She was weak and jittery anyway from the wretched cold she had developed after her dunking in Sharnden Brook.

Without looking at Eileen, she said in a low voice, "Of course, I'm sorry. I won't bother you again." She walked towards the door.

Eileen intercepted her. "Now, you needn't get huffy. I merely asked you to wait few minutes. Surely, that's my privilege. It is **my** telephone, after all."

Carol's knees suddenly went all wobbly and her head throbbed as though it had been hit with a sledge hammer.

"You needn't remind me again, Mrs. Marshall. I'm sorry to have troubled you at all. Good-bye."

She stepped on to the porch, and Eileen followed her, frantically trying to justify herself. "You seem to think you can use my telephone whenever you like. I've been kindness itself to you and your sister and you repay me with this...this highhandedness. You don't appreciate anything....I've tried to be...."

Carol was half way down the path by this time and Eileen shrieked after her. "You're just a silly girl, and it will be your own fault if you're too late to get a cab."

Carol walked on. She had caught sight of the Seton's Daimler coming down the hill, and she gathered all her strength, and hurried as fast as her weakened legs would carry her to the Manor house.

Mrs. Seton ordered a taxi for her and gave her a hot cup of tea, which soothed her aching head and gave her the strength to get back to the cottage.

"Are you sure you are all right now," the kindly Mrs. Seton asked. She couldn't help noticing how pale and distraught Carol was.

"Yes, I'm okay now, thanks. That hot tea just perked me up. I can't thank you enough for getting the taxi for me. I must get back now and put some supper on for Jocelyn."

Outside, the heavy downpour of the early morning had turned to a soft drizzle which was refreshing to her hot face and stinging eyes. She turned her face to it gratefully and walked slowly along the muddy path, keeping her eyes straight ahead as she passed Eileen's kitchen window. She let herself into the cottage and almost immediately was summoned to the window by Eileen's imperious rapping. She opened the casement.

Eileen looked reproachfully at her. "Carol Carter, you are the most foolish girl I have ever met. I feel that you owe me an apology for the way you have behaved. You can't do me any harm by going to the Setons. It was silly and childish."

"Is that all?" Carol asked wearily.

"No, it isn't all. While you were being so clever running off to the Setons, a telegram was called in for you."

Carol turned ashen and trembled inside. "A telegram? Dennis?" she said in a hoarse whisper.

"It was nothing to do with your husband, if that is what you are thinking, but it would have served you jolly right if it had been bad news," Eileen said viciously. "Actually, it was from Jocelyn, saying she would be here at five."

"Thank you for telling me. Now, will you please leave." She was shaking with repressed anger.

Eileen's face reddened with rage and her voice quavered. "You are a silly stupid girl. After all I've done for you. I demand an apology."

"Mrs. Marshall, you'd better leave now, before I lose my temper. From now on, the less we have to say to each other, the better." She shut the window with a bang.

Eileen charged in through the door. "I'd like you to know that this is **my** property, and I don't like your attitude." Her voice raged higher and shriller. "I've been a perfect lady to you, and all I've received in return is ingratitude and impertinence."

"**GO HOME**, Eileen, **NOW!**" Carol warned.

"Why, why anyone would think I didn't have the right to say when someone can use my telephone," she sputtered.

That did it!

"GET OUT OF THIS HOUSE!" Carol blazed. **"I DON'T GIVE TWO HOOTS ABOUT YOUR TELEPHONE. YOU CAN GO TO BLAZES AND TAKE THE DARNED THING WITH YOU. NOW LEAVE, BEFORE I REALLY LOSE MY TEMPER."**

Eileen's mouth fell open and it was a few seconds before she closed it to speak. "I'll leave," she croaked hoarsely. "But so will you. You will get your notice at the end of this month." With that she slammed the door shut behind her and strode down the path.

The moment Jocelyn laid eyes on Carol's feverish tear stained face, she knew that something was very wrong. And when she heard the whole story, she took Carol's temperature (it was 104) and put her right to bed.

For the next three days she hovered over her, anxiously watching and waiting for the fever to abate. Just when she decided to call in a doctor, Carol began to show encouraging signs of recovery. Her temperature gradually dropped to normal, and, in another three days, the patient was well enough to leave her sick bed.

"What a nuisance I've been to you, Joc," she said, her voice still thin and hoarse. "You must be fagged out from waiting on me hand and foot."

"It's just good to see you up and about. You had me scared for a while."

"I think I scared myself. At one point, I began to wonder if I really wanted to get better. It seemed so easy just to lie there and not think about anything. Eddy will rib me when he hears about it. He was so worried about me. He said I'd get pneumonia, and he fussed over me like an old mother hen."

"I should have returned sooner," Jocelyn said reproachfully. "I didn't feel right about leaving you alone at the mercy of that harpy next door. I'm glad she did give us notice. We'd never have had the gumption to leave if she hadn't."

"But where can we go?" Carol asked weakly.

"We'll find someplace. Don't worry!"

It was strange for her to be doing the comforting now, to be making brave, optimistic predictions. Unconsciously, their roles had been reversed.

Carol regained her physical strength fairly quickly and was doing some chores around the cottage.

"How was Frances?" she asked, as she dried the breakfast dishes.

"She was having a hard time to get the baby on a sensible routine, and Susan cried night and day. They insisted in the hospital that she breast feed the baby, despite the fact that it was then that she got the news that Dick was not coming back and possibly as a result of her distress her milk was worse than useless. But I told her about my giving Boo whole milk and Sister Laura's food, the milk modifier that Miss Hatherley put Boo on when she was always hungry right after her feed. So we tried that formula and after that, baby Susan perked up and started sleeping through the night, and most of the day as well. Frances got some rest and she perked up too. I think she was in pretty good shape when I left. She was treated rather shabbily by Dick's mother, but she has found some other very supportive friends in Bath."

"Shades of Mrs. Ford," Carol said.

Jocelyn preferred not to think about that subject and she busied herself getting Boo's bottle ready.

"Incidentally, we had a letter from Sheila," Carol said.

"What's new with her?"

"Oh, the usual. Simon has been fanning the flames of the affair with that nurse who looked after him when he was in hospital. He sees her all the time, according to Sheila. In fact, he spends more time with her than he does with Sheila and Christopher."

"That louse! Sometimes, I just wonder if there is any justice in this world," Jocelyn said bitterly. "What is Sheila doing about it?"

"She wanted our advice. She's thinking of leaving him"

"That's a bit drastic, isn't it?"

"I would say so. In any case, how can we advise her? We don't know what chance there is of patching things up."

"Did you answer the letter?"

"Yes. I just told her what you told her once before. If she thinks he's worth holding on to, then fight for him tooth and nail."

"Has she decided?"

"I haven't heard. But somehow I think that the theme of that marriage is always going to be Simon running off the rails and Sheila giving him one more chance to climb back on."

"Until she finally gets fed up," Jocelyn suggested. She still couldn't reconcile herself to the injustice of Kit's death and Simon's incredible good luck.

CHAPTER 39

They were now into December and Carol had completely recovered physically from her illness. Mentally and emotionally, however, she was still very much on edge. Dennis had not been able to scrounge any time off. His squadron was busier than ever. In what was to be known as the Battle of the Bulge, the German army had broken into Luxembourg and Belgium and were aiming to recapture Antwerp. It was one of the most crucial turning points of the war. The Germans would not be thwarted until late January.

The Second Tactical Air Force was kept very busy and the aircrews had little respite from their constant sorties over enemy territory—blowing up bridges, trains carrying munitions and supplies for the German troops, and other strategic targets. Carol knew that there was no chance of Dennis getting home.

Meanwhile, as she had threatened, Eileen gave them their notice. They had to move by the middle of January. Christmas was fast approaching and they decided that, even though Dennis could not come home, they would decorate the cottage as gaily as possible. They went into the woods and gathered armfuls of holly and pine boughs and draped them over doors and windows and even pictures. It lent an air of festivity, even though they didn't feel particularly festive themselves.

Finally, it was Christmas Eve, 1944. Their family had always gone to midnight Mass together. No matter where they might be that evening with friends, they always left the party in time to join their parents at Holy Trinity, the small Anglican parish church where they had been baptized, confirmed, and taken every Sunday. Carol suggested that she and Jocelyn follow tradition and go into Mayfield and attend the midnight service at the ancient church there. Andrew agreed to keep an eye on Boo.

St. Dunstan's dated back to the 12th century, and was sadly in need of sprucing up. The interior was dark and gloomy, lit only by candles which cast dark shadows over the grey stone walls. The priest in charge was a dour individual with slightly crossed eyes, and a sanctimonious air. The congregation was made up of a motley lot who barely greeted one another, never mind two strangers in their midst. The choir was dreadfully off key and gave a lugubrious rendition of mostly unfamiliar hymns. It was a sad disappointment and as soon as the service was over they hurried out of the church and into the frosty, brightly moonlit night.

Carol had arranged with Dennis that she would telephone him after the service. There was a kiosk just outside the church so they walked over to it and Carol went in to make the call.

Jocelyn stood outside looking up at the few bright stars shining in the cloudless sky and at the moon which seemed to be smiling down at her. She was remembering the Christmas Eve of just three years ago, the night before her wedding, and she had to force back the tears that welled in her eyes.

Suddenly, she heard Carol calling to her. "Jocelyn, come quickly, Tim is here and wants a word."

He just had time to wish her a happy Christmas and to say he hoped to see her soon when they were cut off.

Outside the kiosk, Carol looked up at the brightly moonlit sky studded with a few brilliant stars, and she shuddered. Dennis had made it obliquely but abundantly clear that she had caught him just before he and Tim had to go for a briefing for their nightly sortie over Germany. She prayed fervently that they would somehow be protected as they flew on their deadly mission through that totally cloudless sky.

She linked arms with Jocelyn and they walked briskly to the taxi that was waiting to take them back to Sharnden.

***

The nostalgic strains of "I'm Dreaming of a White Christmas" were being crooned constantly over the little battery radio that Dennis had brought for them, and it was a poignant reminder that Christmas day had come and gone. Jocelyn, with stubborn determination, put the whole sentimental theme on which that festive season rests, out of her mind. She refused to think about it even for a moment, and when a singer attempted to woo her back to reality with that poignant song, she immediately switched it off. It was either that, which brought immediate numb relief, or continuing to listen and submitting to tormenting despair. She must not, for Carol's sake as much as her own, allow herself to dwell on what Christmas had meant to her in the past, or what it might have meant now, had Kit been there to celebrate their third wedding anniversary.

Carol continued to live in constant dread for Dennis's safety and, added to her burden, was a feeling of intense shame and regret for her behaviour towards Eileen, and its disastrous consequences. Thanks to her, they were once again homeless.

It snowed the day after Christmas. In the pleasant living room, Carol rested her elbows on the window ledge and watched the huge star-shaped puffs sail in leisurely procession through the air, and she was filled with a wistful longing for the crisp virgin whiteness of a prairie winter. As the fluffy flakes settled, they dissolved instantly, like bubbles, leaving only a wet stain as evidence of having existed at all. It reminded her that England's winters were not white, crisp, and invigorating; they were grey, sodden, and depressing. A wanton breeze stole by and tossed the snow flakes this way and that. As her eyes followed them, she pictured them as ballerinas in frothy tutus, pirouetting before a grey backdrop. It was a relief to indulge in such flights of fancy, forgetting for a moment a heart's aching fear and a mind's turmoil. Ever since the eviction notice was shoved under the door, she had suffered the agonies of self-recrimination. If only she had kept a check on her tongue and temper. Where, oh where could they start looking for another home?

Dennis and Tim arrived quite unexpectedly on New Year's day, ready for a well-earned celebration. They were both wearing, under their wings, the purple and white diagonally striped ribbon of the Distinguished Flying Cross which they were awarded for their brave and successful sortie on Christmas Eve. They had had a very rough trip home. After flying over the battle area of Trier, Koblenz, and Bonn, their starboard tail plane was blown off by flak. They were extremely lucky to get home safely.

This good news was offset by the fact that the much loved Wing Commander Dale had lost his life on that fateful mission. Dennis picked up his Mayday message on his radio and had tried to relay the location where Daddy Dale's plane had gone down over the Channel, but neither he nor his navigator was never found.

It was certainly no time to announce more bad news, so Carol and Jocelyn decorated the table with holly and candles, and made a special effort to camouflage the rabbit which had to stand proxy for the customary turkey, and Eileen's name was never mentioned.

It was all such ridiculously good fun that day, with Dennis remarking grandly upon the cheap sherry with which they toasted absent family and friends, "That was the best champagne I've ever tasted."

Tim, not to be outdone, said, "And that was the best turkey I've ever tasted."

He was in a surprisingly good mood, partly because Jocelyn accepted with delight the pair of gold R.A.F. wings he had brought for her. He had feared that she might refuse the gift.

Needless to say, Dennis was very upset when Carol finally told him the bad news about their predicament.

"You might have been more diplomatic, darling," he chided, strain and frustration mirrored on his handsome face.

Carol shrugged her shoulders hopelessly, and he continued. "Really, Carol, have you any idea how awkward it will be moving in winter?"

She tried to justify her actions. "I know it will be hard and I'm truly sorry. But, at the time, I was fed up with that awful woman, and I didn't think this place was worth that much hypocrisy."

"You mean you didn't think!" he snapped, and then immediately apologized with a deep sigh. "It's just that we're busier than ever on the squadron. Not only that, but everything is being made ready to move us to France. And I don't know how I'll be able to help you."

"We've managed on our own before," she said defensively.

And that was the gloomy note on which he returned to the squadron. It was simply a reflection of the terrible strain they were both under. They rarely quarrelled. She had wanted to cling to him, to try to make him see that her silly quarrel with Eileen was only a safety valve that had released her pent up emotions—the accumulation of the past months of tension arising from her constant anxiety for his safety; the overall effect of their unsettled existence, the strain of creating an outward impression of serenity and normality which she could not possibly feel.

It had mounted up over the past weeks and months—their precipitous departure from the Fords; the anxiety of finding somewhere to live before Boo was born; Simon's narrow escape; another frantic house hunt; the tragic loss of Kit; then Don Rowe; to say nothing of the news of the loss of husbands of three of their Canadian friends. Fear was her constant companion every waking moment, and even her dreams were nightmares.

She had nothing to rely on to keep her from cracking under the strain, except her physical well being. And when that was debilitated by the near pneumonia, she was at the mercy of Eileen's pettiness. Small wonder that she had said the things she did.

***

Jocelyn had gone to the Setons to borrow a current copy of <u>The Lady</u>, so they could look at the house rentals. On her return she hung up her coat and scarf and then went into the living room.

"Did you get the magazine?" Carol asked.

"Yes, but there's nothing in it. Mrs. Seton is going to keep her eyes and ears open for us though."

"That's good of her. But I was so hoping...."

"I know. So was I. But let's not get downhearted. We have some time yet to look."

Carol coaxed the fire into a healthier blaze and now leaned back in her chair. After a moment's silence, she said, "I wouldn't be half so concerned if Dennis hadn't taken it so hard. I think he imagines us camped out in the fields somewhere with not even a tent over our heads, while he will be stuck on the continent miles beyond our reach."

Jocelyn gave a small laugh of protest. "That doesn't give us much credit, does it? Is he coming home this weekend?"

"I think so, if nothing comes up to intervene. He had the idea that we should go into Brighton to look for something. It's a big city and there ought to be plenty of estate agents there."

"Sounds like a good idea. We did find Susan Plum that way."

"True. Incidentally, he's bringing Tim home with him again. I hope you don't mind. We're so fond of Tim ourselves that it doesn't occur to Dennis that you might not be so anxious to have him around."

"Quite the contrary. It makes me feel less like an intruder on yours and Dennis's precious time together."

"I had the feeling that you liked him," Carol said.

"I do, very much. How could one not like Tim? He's by far the nicest person I've met in a long time."

"Nicer than Derek?" Carol asked slyly. Dennis had told her that Tim was showing all the signs of being smitten, and she herself hoped that Jocelyn would be at least a little receptive. She received no reply to her question about Derek.

As she lay in bed that night, tossing restlessly and unable to sleep, Jocelyn's thoughts were centred on Tim and his forthcoming visit. The anticipation of seeing him afforded her a glow of pleasure mixed with guilt, which made her again question the wisdom of continuing their friendship. Where would it lead, she asked herself. And, was it being disloyal to find herself enjoying another man's company so soon after losing Kit? She wondered whether she should have been so ready to accept his delightful gift. But it was Christmas, after all, and he had gone to a great deal of trouble choosing it. She wondered also why she really had not had these misgivings about Derek. She only knew for sure that Kit's memory was as dear and clear to her as ever, and she felt sure it always would be. But, she had suddenly realized that, in making such a determined effort to be cheerful in front of others, and to submerge her grief, it had lost much of its grip over her.

In a sense, it might be said that she had been too successful, for the initial bitter agony of grief tormented her less and less. Only the happy memories

of all Kit's endearing qualities and the unselfish love and companionship
which had been theirs remained uppermost in her memory. Just as, in the
depth of bleakest winter, one can recapture in the scent of a lavender sachet
the serene beauty of a summer garden, and in its poignant freshness, one
can forget the icy winds and blanket of snow that have combined to destroy
the once lovely plot. Perhaps, having known that serenity of mind and
oneness of spirit, when suddenly deprived of it, the soul involuntarily goes
in search of it. Maybe it was just another strange quirk of fate that her soul
should have found a kindred spirit so quickly, when it might so easily have
continued the quest for years, covering the whole world over, and never
succeeding in finding it. Whatever the answer, if indeed there was one, it
was beyond her grasp.

CHAPTER 40

Dennis and Tim arrived at the cottage late Friday evening. They enjoyed a pleasant hour of bridge and then went to bed early. Jocelyn had no time alone with Tim, and she was glad. She hadn't made up her mind how to deal with his disturbing presence.

The following morning, early, Dennis and Carol left for Brighton to call on estate agents. This was his last opportunity to help in the house hunting. His squadron was moving in the near future, and he didn't want to waste this last chance to be of use.

Whether it was due to their early departure, or simply because she was overly anxious to find out how they had made out, Jocelyn wasn't certain. But the day did seem interminably long. Neither she nor Tim was able to concentrate on any subject for long without suddenly changing it abruptly to remark, "I do hope Dennis and Carol have some luck," or words to that effect.

By five-thirty, when there was still no sign of their return, Jocelyn served a light supper before the fire in the living room. When they had finished, Tim carried the tray into the kitchen and brought back the coffee which they drank in silence—a companionable, rather than a heavy or awkward silence.

Tim put his cup down and sank back in his chair. His broad shoulders spread the width of it and he stretched out lazily with his feet resting on a footstool. His mouth crinkled in a contented grin. "You'd better start talking," he warned, "or I'll be sound asleep."

He and Dennis had been flying night and day, with very little rest, for the past fortnight and they were both extremely tired.

"My mind's working like a broken record," Jocelyn said. "I can't get it past the groove of wondering how they made out. I wish they'd come back."

Tim looked directly at her. "Don't let it get you down, Jocelyn. Things will work out. They're bound to."

"Oh, I know. It's just how they'll work out that bothers me. Anyway, it's silly of me to worry about it. I apologize for being such rotten company all day. You must have wished yourself back in camp."

"God forbid! I've had a very pleasant day. Apart from the odd spot of wondering myself how the search was going. They should be home soon. I do hope they had some luck."

Jocelyn laughed. "Our worries are contagious evidently."

"Well, shouldn't I be worried?" He looked at her quizzically, a meaningful gleam in his blue eyes.

"I expect that Dennis has made it difficult for you not to be. He's such a fidget, when he can find something to worry about."

"His main concern is that we'll be shipped over to the continent and you two will be stranded without a home."

"We're not exactly helpless," Jocelyn protested. "And we're not as scatterbrained as Dennis makes out."

Tim changed the subject to one that had been on his mind all day, but he hadn't had the courage to bring it up until now. "Have you heard anything about your passage?" he asked, trying to sound casual.

His relief was clearly visible when he saw Jocelyn shake her head negatively, and replied, "No, I don't really expect to hear much before spring."

"I'm glad," he admitted, fixing his eyes on the smoke ring that hovered between them. "For two reasons...."

"And what may they be?"

"I think you know the first one. But the second isn't quite so selfish. You said a moment ago that you and Carol could always manage without

Dennis's help. But when Dennis goes to France, which he will do fairly soon, and you return to Canada, what about Carol? Will she be able to manage by herself?''

"I must confess that thought had occurred to me but I didn't know that the squadron would be leaving England so soon."

Tim's concern for Carol was certainly genuine, because he was very fond of her, and also he knew how worried Dennis was about her being left alone when he was no longer in the country. However, his reason for bringing up the subject was, in reality, a means to an end. He knew of nothing else that might keep Jocelyn in England a bit longer, and never in his life before had he hoped for anything so wholeheartedly. He needed time, needed it desperately. He was only too aware of the formidable number of obstacles that stood in his way. One of these had been eliminated by Dennis's assurance that Jocelyn had severed contact with Derek Stewart. But, having at long last found a girl who measured up to his ideal, in looks, brains, common sense, compassion and imagination, he didn't intend to stand idly by and allow her to slip out of his life. Not without making every effort to prevent it, anyway. Where there's a will there's a way, he told himself. And he was driven by that inexplicable power, inadequately termed 'being in love', to find it.

Darkness had settled over the valley long before the crunching of car wheels on the gravel, and the bright gleam of headlights shining through the window, announced the return of Dennis and Carol.

Carol's gay laughter and Dennis's loud 'hyah' were sufficient evidence that they brought good news.

Carol hugged Jocelyn. "We're in luck," she exclaimed happily. "We've found a home—four walls, a chimney, electricity that isn't apt to fade out, a gas stove to cook on and a landlady who adores both cats and babies."

They settled around the fire for the rest of the evening while Carol and Dennis described their day, and the house they had found. It was situated in the tiny hamlet of Telscombe Cliffs, seven miles east of Brighton and it was called Cliff Cottage, and it appeared to fit all their requirements.

***

The move from Sharnden Brooks cottage was made in two stages. Carol and Dennis went first with most of their belongings, and Tim and Jocelyn followed with Boo and Taf who proved to be a poor traveller. When they got on the train for Brighton, he slipped out of Tim's hands, dashed under the seat, and no amount of persuasion could tempt him to come out. After burning his hands on the scalding hot steam pipes under the seat, Tim finally gave up trying to retrieve him. But when the train drew into the station, Taf nonchalantly crawled out from under the seat and jumped up on Tim's lap. The rest of journey they made by taxi, a mode of transport apparently more in keeping with Taf's idea of how to travel.

***

Two months later, Carol and Jocelyn were settled in Cliff Cottage, a small square bungalow perched at the mercy of the elements on top of the cliffs overlooking the English Channel. The white paint on the house was badly weathered, and the green trim on the windows and front door was also peeling off. However, the house itself was comfortably furnished and their landlady, Miss Thompson, and her companion, Miss Knaggs, who was bedridden with arthritis, were happily congenial. As Carol had said, they liked both cats and babies.

The elderly ladies occupied a suite that had been added to the roof of the cottage and which lent a ramshackle air to the property. Their ancient car was stored in the garage, which also housed the electric meter. A midget-sized door, one of seven that opened off the small kitchen, gave entry to the garage, and to reach the meter it was necessary to climb over the top of the car and balance on some boxes while endeavouring to slip a coin in a small inch wide slit. Since it was usually pitch dark when the lights gave out and the meter required feeding, this was a dicey and challenging feat. Nonetheless, Jocelyn and Carol were well pleased with their new haven, and very well pleased to have escaped Eileen Marshall's overweening and petty presence.

It was a wet, blustery grey day, as had been almost every day since they moved in. A fire was burning steadily in the grate, but it had little beneficial effect on the draughty room whose ill-fitting windows were no match for either the strong winds or beating rain. In the kitchen, the Ideal Boiler glowed a dull red on top, and intensely hot coals crackled and spit inside it. But, for all that, the warmth was more of sight and sound than of feeling. Carol and Jocelyn made no mention of it, but each put on an extra sweater.

As Jocelyn mopped up the water from the window ledges, she said with more conviction than she felt, "It's supposed to be fine tomorrow."

Carol's attention was fastened on a colourful conglomeration of strands of wool, wound about plastic holders, with which she was knitting a pair of diamond socks for Dennis. At last, having reached a point where she could take her eyes away from her work, she looked up and remarked laconically, "When Dennis and I came to look at this place, Miss Thompson impressed upon us how **perfectly glorious** it was when the sun shines. I just wonder how she knew."

The rain did not let up all day, and by bedtime it was still pelting savagely on the slate roof. But by morning the weather forecast justified itself. When Jocelyn flung open her bedroom window which overlooked the Channel, she breathed deeply of the salty tang of the sea air, and felt as though she had wakened into a new world.

Just as Miss Thompson said, it was perfectly glorious: the balmy air, the golden cliffs rising so straight and imposing from the sandy beach far below, the quiescent sea, as blue as the sky reflected on its shimmering surface. It might have been the quintessence of peace had it not been for the occasional black specks floating menacingly close to the cliff bottom, a grim reminder that the tranquil water was charged with explosive mines. Having caught one's eye, they seemed to compel one to follow their unplotted course as they shook gently from side to side with the swell of the sea, as if in silent mocking laughter, until they disappeared from view.

Jocelyn made up her mind in an instant to skip her daily chores, and, after breakfast when Boo was sleeping soundly in her pram in the front garden, she joined Carol on the sunporch where she planned to write her letters while absorbing the warm rays of the sun. It was not long, however, before that same warmth, intensified as it shone through the glass, made her too drowsy to concentrate on letters. Finally, she tossed aside a long complicated form sent to her by the British income tax department, and, smothering an insistent yawn, complained to Carol, "I'm going to need a secretary if my official file numbers keep piling up at the present rate. I'll bet I occupy a cubby hole in every Government office filing cabinet by now."

Carol looked up and smiled briefly, which was about all she ever managed these days. She, too, had her writing case out but she had progressed no further than putting an address and date at the top of the page. There had been no letters from Dennis for nearly three weeks. She knew that there was some simple explanation for it, but every so often the morbid implication it could have struck her with terrible intensity. If there were nothing wrong, why hadn't he written? He's probably missing, and they've just made some awful blunder and haven't informed me. She had heard of such mistakes being made, and the thought that it might be so in her case sapped her energy and took away her appetite.

Jocelyn was becoming very concerned. She, herself, wondered what was preventing him from writing. It was not like him. She didn't expect to hear from Tim, although he had taken to dropping her a note occasionally, as he put it just to make certain she didn't forget his existence. At one point, she had decided that this might be a good idea. But, as time went on, and she saw him so seldom anyway, it was hardly necessary. Upon the odd occasion, when he and Dennis were able to spend a few hours at Cliff Cottage, she was very grateful to have his company while Dennis and Carol wandered off together, making all of their precious moments count. In fact, she hardly realized how much she had come to depend on his pleasant company, it had happened so gradually and so naturally.

Carol was gazing pensively out of the window, as she did so often lately, with the sad distant look in her eyes that tore at Jocelyn's heart, and caused her now to throw down her pen, clear away her correspondence, and say brightly, "Why on earth are we wasting this heavenly day inside? Come and get your coat and we'll take Boo for a bouncing buggy ride along the cliffs."

"All right," Carol agreed without enthusiasm. "I suppose we could use the air and exercise. But let's wait for the postman. Surely I'll hear from Dennis today. It's three weeks since he and Tim were last home, and nearly as long since I've had even a note from him."

"I'm certain that he hasn't been able to write because they've moved the squadron to France. They've been expecting the move since before we left Mayfield. It can't be anything else."

"I know you're right. I just seem addicted to worrying lately."

"Look, there's the postman now," Jocelyn said. "I'll get our coats while you take in the mail."

She disappeared into the house, and Carol greeted the postman. He gave her a cheery, "Good morning," and then went off down the path whistling while she searched rapidly through the letters. But the handwriting she longed to see was not on any of the envelopes. Despondently, she put the mail on the table, almost choking with disappointment.

Jocelyn returned with their coats and knew by her expression that there was no letter from Dennis. Picking up an official looking brown envelope bearing her name, she said lightly, "Hmm, I wonder what this is. It looks rather promising." She tore it open quickly. As her eyes assimilated the contents of the letter she gave a small gasp.

"What is it?" Carol asked anxiously.

Jocelyn looked up. "It's my passage. I can sail for home at the end of March."

Carol was unable to force out a single word. This was something she had been dreading, and the realization that soon she would not have Jocelyn's company was a crushing blow.

Jocelyn understood. She took her arm and said, "Come on. The walk in the fresh air and sunshine will do us both good."

She followed Carol outside, then walked over to where Boo's pram was parked and pushed it across the grass. They followed the well worn trail which twisted along the cliff edge. Boo wakened and sat up in her pram gurling happily, her enormous blue eyes twinkling with delight at the bumpy ride she was enjoying.

Suddenly, the deafening roar of an aircraft, approaching from behind startled them, and so frightened Boo that she began to howl. Jocelyn picked her up and held her close.

The plane swooped below the level of the cliffs, and when Carol recognized the familiar fin-like tail of a mosquito bomber, she exclaimed, "It's Dennis and Tim! I know it is. Look, they're turning round and coming back."

The wings dipped crazily as the aircraft circled the sky above Cliff cottage. So low did it come that they could clearly see the two helmeted heads and the waving arms. Then the plane turned, headed west and was soon out of sight.

CHAPTER 41

Dennis and Tim arrived at the cottage in time for supper that evening. They had forty-eight precious hours before they had to return to the village of Rosieres in France where the squadron had been moved from Thorney Island on February 6, 1945. That, and increased censorship restrictions were the simple reasons for there having been no letters. Carol could not imagine now why she had been so foolish to think the things she did.

They talked exhaustively for hours, and played bridge in the evening. Finally, when Carol and Dennis went to bed, Tim put more coals on the dying fire and said, "That coffee has given me renewed energy. Would you mind staying up a while with me?"

"Would you like another cup?" Jocelyn asked. "I can warm it up in a second."

"No, thanks. I never will want to go to bed if I drink any more. Just sit and listen to me natter for a while, unless you're too tired."

"No, it was so nice today that I didn't do a stroke of work. And I have too much on my mind to want to go to bed just yet."

Tim settled comfortably in his chair. "That makes two of us. This move to France really has put the wind up me."

Jocelyn squatted on the floor at his feet. "But you'd been expecting it since January," she reminded him.

"Yes, but until it really happened I didn't realize what it would mean. I didn't know how cut off we'd be. It's not far in miles, but that stretch of water between us and England is a greater barrier than mere mileage. It started me thinking. And when we're not flying over there, there isn't much else to do but think. And, with no mail coming in, I began to wonder what was going on on the other side of the Channel. After all, a lot can happen in two weeks." He paused for a moment, choosing his words carefully. "For instance, you might have received your passage and have returned to Canada without me even having had a chance to say bon voyage."

"Yes, that could have happened, I suppose. As a matter of fact, I had a letter from Air Ministry about it today."

Tim looked up quickly and leaned forward, a worried frown creasing his forehead. "What did they say?"

"That I have a passage at the end of March."

Tim felt a sickening jolt in the pit of his stomach. After a long pause, he said, "Then, this really is good-bye. We haven't a hope of getting home again before then."

"It would be," she said, "if I were going."

A glint of hope sprung into Tim's eyes and he asked eagerly, "What do you mean?"

"I mean that I'm asking for a postponement. I realized this morning when the letter came and I saw how the news affected Carol that I can't leave her alone while Dennis is still on ops. Especially now that he's on the Continent."

"Will they allow that?"

"I can only ask."

There was a broad smile now on Tim's handsome clean-cut features. "With so many people hoping, I don't see how we can lose," he said. He settled back in his chair and lit a cigarette. "Now there's one more thing I want to get off my chest before I return to France. I hope you won't consider it a breach of the promise I made at Sharnden Brooks. I've tried my damnedest to live up to that, and I don't think I've let you down, have I?"

"No, you haven't, Tim. And I'm grateful."

"It's been a struggle at times, and I don't say that looking for sympathy. I just want to be honest with you. I know you will be with me. Things are a bit different now that we're over there. I hardly ever see you, but that doesn't mean that I don't think about you. In fact, I've thought about you so much lately that it's driving me to drink. I've just got to know, Jocelyn. Do I stand a chance, at all, or am I just fooling myself?" His eyes were tender and pleading, and Jocelyn had to turn hers away.

"I don't know, Tim. I really don't know. I'm so mixed up inside. All I can say with any honesty is that when I lost Kit all the sunshine seemed to disappear from my life. And I really thought it would always be that way. Then, you came along and, ever since then, the black clouds have been slowly rolling away, and the horizon seems to be getting brighter all the time. I still feel that I have a long way to go before the clouds lift completely. I suppose I'm talking in riddles, and it doesn't make much sense to you."

"It makes a lot of sense, Jocelyn, and I can wait. Now that I know you won't be putting that great stretch of ocean between us, at least for a while."

The forty-eight hour leave was over too quickly and Dennis and Tim had to leave England and return to France. They both promised to write now that things had settled down a bit over there.

***

The end of March and the beginning of April 1945 saw the inevitable rebirth of an English spring with all of its freshness and beauty, but it also brought a rebirth of optimism to the war-weary world. The turning point in the long struggle against Hitler's once mighty war machine was in sight and hopes for an end to the senseless conflict surged in people's hearts everywhere.

The cloudless skies over Cliff Cottage were host to an endless stream of fighter planes, bombers, gliders, flying in precise formation, night and day, their ceaseless drone bringing the end nearer and nearer.

Jocelyn was successful in postponing her passage and, as the month of May approached, the prospects for peace were clearly visible. On May 2, 1945, Berlin fell to the Russians, and the Germans surrendered in Italy. The next day their armies in the north laid down their arms.

The toll of death and destruction was horrific. Just between June 6th (D-day) and August 31, 1944, the Allied Air Forces flew nearly half a million sorties. Of these, the four Royal Air Force commands concerned—the Air Defense of Great Britain (Battle of Britain), the Second Tactical Air Force, Bomber Command, and Coastal

Command—accounted for 224,889. Second Tactical Air Force and Air Defence of Great Britain flew 151,370 sorties, lost 829 aircraft and 1,035 aircrew killed and missing; Bomber Command flew 54,687 sorties, lost 983 aircraft and 6,761 aircrew killed and missing; Coastal Command flew 18,832 sorties and lost 224 aircraft and 383 aircrew. In total, the R.A.F. lost 8,178 men; the Americans lost 8,536. And these figures did not include the army or navy casualities in all the forces.

***

On an unsettled morning of that first week in May, on May 7th, to be exact, a sudden squall blew up over the Channel, and the rain and wind played a damp dirge on the glass panes of the sunporch where Carol was seated reading. Jocelyn had been smitten with spring cleaning fever, and had pulled down all the curtains and washed them. She hung them on a clothes horse which she placed in front of the fireplace, then joined Carol on the porch.

She curled up on the window seat opposite Carol. "Isn't it tragically incongruous," she mused, "that in the very country where the industrial revolution was born, women still have to do their washing by the old back-breaking methods, when in countries like Canada, which were in their infancy at that time, one can wash clothes with the maximum of speed and minimum of effort."

Her words were no sooner uttered when a peculiar swooshing sound sent her racing back into the house.

"Oh, Carol," she moaned. "just come and look at my beautiful clean curtains. Confound these antiquated coal grates!"

"What happened?" Carol asked, viewing Jocelyn and the bedraggled wash, both generously sprinkled with black greasy soot.

"I guess the chimney should have been swept. How will I ever get these things clean now?"

"Send them to the laundry, as I suggested in the first place," Carol said, most unsympathetically.

She went back to the porch and looked out of the window for a moment, noticing that the wind had dropped and the rain had stopped.

"There's a break in the sky now, Joc," she called. "We can probably hang them outside to dry." Suddenly, her face lit up. "You'd better nip into the bathroom and wipe that soot off your face," she called excitedly. "We've got company."

Jocelyn dashed into the bathroom just as the two blue uniforms strode in the front door.

Carol flung her arms tightly around Dennis.

"Hey!" he said laughing. "After coming through this war unscathed, must I die by strangulation at the hands of my beloved wife?"

"Darling, I'm just so relieved to see you."

"Well, you need worry no longer, my sweet. The war's over!"

"What do you mean?" Carol said, feeling sure she hadn't heard him correctly.

"Just what I said. On this seventh day of May, 1945, in the city of Rheims, France, the Germans officially surrendered. The European war at least is over."

"Oh, my darling," she could only breathe with a relief so intense that she could hardly contain it.

Jocelyn rushed out of the bathroom when she heard the news and bumped squarely into Tim, who happened to be standing in the doorway of the living room. She looked up at him and smiled apologetically. As their eyes met, time suddenly stood still and, for a second that for them seemed more like an eternity, two hearts involuntarily beat as one.

Finally, Tim broke the spell. Smiling broadly, and lightly touching the tip of her nose, he said, "You have a black smudge on your pretty nose."

"Oh, dear, do I? I thought I'd washed it all off." She pointed to the soot-covered curtains. "Look what happened."

"Never mind that now," he commanded gently. "Get your coat and come for a walk along the cliffs." Then he added softly, "I don't know if you have noticed, but there isn't a cloud in the sky."

Other Military Titles Available are :

THE MEMORY OF ALL THAT *$14.95*

TO THE GREEN FIELDS BEYOND *$14.95*

THE RIDGE $14.95

THE CANADIAN PEACEKEEPER $12.95

ORDINARY HEROES $14.95

FIFTY YEARS AFTER $14.95

ONE OF THE MANY $14.95

THE SURLY BONDS OF EARTH $12.95

NO TIME OFF FOR GOOD BEHAVIOUR $14.95